feelgood

feelgood

a trip in time and out

Peter de Lissovoy

Houghton Mifflin Company Boston

1970

First Printing w

For Sue

"In these pages I offer only my story. You may suggest that the historian is also the diligent spinner of a tale."

feelgood

one

WHEN I REMEMBER HARVARD, it's not the ivy. It's the morning glories. I loved to get high, I studied drugs. My solitude never craved a nostalgia. When I was stoned I was in a league of my own. It was the early sixties. There was talk of the New World, and luminaries were getting their thing together. But I didn't know the hip off-Harvard scenes. I didn't think of my friends as so hip, even the little Cambridge hipsters, I liked them better. Employing my ability to listen, I nurtured acquaintanceships with dealers. But I didn't really care about the origins of the drugs, and that helped my high. Naturally they would want to speak of their wares and name them, but it never felt like I was being sold something. "This is Panama Red!" — How do you do? — Whatever the label — even the morning glories that I discovered came from a local garden store — I'd imagine the stuff was gathered in midwestern fields by kids with a sense of humor. And if I was wrong, who was right? I understood that I preferred to float in myself. I might like to get high and lay back and look at the sky of the ceiling, speechless. And the hip ones judge your high! By what you said or didn't say, they might laugh, "Hey this man's way out there," hip scowl. — Let me walk on . . .

Books I loved, and when I stole one from the library I believed I was rescuing it. After me a friend would get it, and it'd be on a new train, thought with different dues. The days of silence were a joy. I liked to get high and look at my calculus text which was beyond me. The intricate scripts and formulae and fine pictures of moving relationships were so far from my grasp they shone like stars. And I could laugh at the dilemma I was going to be in come exam time, and the riddle itself of my connection to the advanced course which I'd somehow wound up taking only because I had credit from high school. Any symbol in the book made my mind go away and up, and the feeling of life came closer, that I wanted to leave school to go into. I wasn't figuring to graduate, except in my own slim ceremony on the morning that I'd split. I never could think of myself as a Harvard student and didn't respond to those vibrations, perhaps because my drift to the place was inconceivable and planned by others. Only one subject at the place turned me on, and that was the civil rights struggle making beautiful news down South.

Maybe people fighting elsewhere for their rights got my sympathy because I was having trouble locating my own rights, which I wanted to fight for. Maybe the automatic education to which I'd been subjected — and I'd never complained — the learning process itself that stepped on by the numbers to a graduation into apparently curved space had never taken into consideration the rights or likes of me, and when I began to discover this, my mind shot off to the outside, in search of a context in which I might find myself. The idea of people nobly fighting for their freedom was the one by which I freed myself from school, just as the student struggle that began to rage later in the decade right inside the university would also create dropouts. If I had any liking for myself at this moment, it was in my reverence for those engaged down South. I felt like all of life existed outside the place I was in, and the ease with which I could just leave must have demanded a fight to go to. Meantime I joined the Socialists — and gave some of them the mind-expanding chemicals. I told them the address of the garden store! In those days I wanted to put up the barricades and break them down too. The New Culture was on its way — it'd soon be in the shops, boom. On the printed page, the everyday world, the same old fantastic setup I'd seen too little of, was lighting up and beckoning. Yet — when the glow in the distance was most attractive — I was in no hurry to leave; maybe I was in love with listening . . .

The world which at Harvard seems so far away was peeling up the ivy and shouting questions at the walls. Sometimes a voice would sound through a window. Very few people heard. I noticed a few heads looking up as I looked up, and then all attention was again focused on the professor, and inwards, on notes and cartoons in the notebooks. I didn't know what I was hearing when I heard the world; it defied my experience, and all I could hear was like a little brook, needing somebody to sit by it maybe, a fisherman who could hear it like it was. I didn't notice that it was a roaring indivisible ocean that was going to go on making waves without my help. When I was angry at being where I was, I was ready to leave and go find it. And really I didn't know why I was here at Harvard since I'd thought of quitting school altogether since my sophomore year in high school. There was no category to fill out like that on the applications: Have you ever thought of quitting school altogether? Perhaps school was too easy, although it was too hard. Maybe I just liked to read. I always liked to read, even the required books, though suddenly for periods I would be unable. Then I would refuse to hand in all work, all exercises would be handed in real blank. My record was so good I could slide, and such lapses were acceptable. Maybe the high school had something to gain sending a certain number on to Harvard? Well I'm glad, though it was a short experience. Harvard took me in, they had their reasons too. What are the reasons for going to Harvard? The truth of it is I had no reasons for going there, if not that it was the next and easiest thing to do. I didn't think of it. And I didn't think of anything when I considered leaving because I was too angry at the meaning or meaninglessness of my even being here. I had no issue with Harvard itself. I remember the good teachers more than the bad ones. I remember my friends — to the rest I was indifferent. In my head — I thought I was beginning to be able to hear the world . . .

Sometimes, late at night, walking the streets of Boston or Cambridge, I would find myself pounding a wall, like I was the world crying questions. It might be the wall of the old burlies in Scollay Square: "Hey kid! What the fuck you doin? Hey don't do that, the place might collapse!"

Or it was the wall of that old club where Joan Baez used to sing. Sometimes the world sounded like her voice, as if this was the nature of it, what got in here: haunting, pure, bright world sound . . .

"Hey look at that dumb kid," shouted a hippy. "Breaking his hand on that wall!"

On the off energyless days when I couldn't walk far, it would be the side of a lost, gutted furniture store on a street whose name I never did notice that would receive my numb rage. In

East Cambridge someplace, a little knuckle blood for a block of old crumbling wall that I had a chance against in the middle of a vacant lot.

It was the conviction of my body below my brain that if I could just break through I'd be somewhere, not in the library anymore. Ah the black and silver anguish of that many-branched library, maze of knowledge scattered about the campus, all the walls of books! I ran through the stacks gasping book-cover air; I grabbed a book at random, on principle, and slipped it under my overcoat. When I got out I noticed it was a book on archery. And I ran faster and faster, as if the wall, which I'd naively identified as the one surrounding Harvard Yard, was now in the air itself, an invisible wall, a spiritual barrier I could penetrate if only I could run that far and fast. I knew I was going to quit. And it didn't do much good to bring a girl to my room, even at a time forbidden by the rules. If I didn't tell her right away there was no future with me — and I usually didn't — the satisfaction might leave me feeling more imprisoned, like I was inside a woman now as well as a college, to say nothing of an infraction of the rules. And I felt kind of dim, and lost, like a book in the library; and I felt angry to have been stuck in there, and left out of life. I was ready to go . . . and I didn't yet . . .

The world was a flickering image in my head like the sound of the sea in a shell. Other heads may've been glimmering with this notion, the world. A few were joined together in organizations, and there must have been many others. Soon the universities would start to crack a little bit, like eggs under a fine pressure, but I'd be long gone by then. I'd read about it in the newspapers . . . I wanted to go down South and join a Good Fight. I was amusing myself writing leaflets for the Socialists and helping pass them out at the dining rooms in the evenings: Cuba, South Africa, Harvard's holdings in Mississippi. I was delving into all that and handing it to the hungry students, the pamphlets that looked like naked lunch bags, like vomit bags naked of airplanes with lists of U.S. holdings in the cruel dictatorships of the world mimeographed on them.

"When's the revolution?! Hey angryyoungman, when's the revolution!" taunted a Hasty Pudding.

"Up your father's factory!" screamed a Socialist.

The arguments! The tedious bitter arguments that never quite got to blows. And I hardly participated because I couldn't remember the pertinent facts. I could write that shit down, missiles deployed here, dollars flowing there, but I could never remember it. I grew weary of the pompous discussions that were always won by whoever could master the best facts. I would walk in the dining room and at every table the wordsters were warring. The Socialists were no different from anyone else; they had another idea. But everyone had another idea and the batteries of opinion stoked themselves up nightly. I lost my appetite. Hell, guys would argue about the classics over their morning eggs. Argument seemed to be the style of life around here, and all I had were my feelings, which weren't too clear. Damn, if the Socialists meant it, why didn't they do something? Why didn't I? I remembered my high school days, the nights when we cruised through the neighborhoods with our new driver's licenses, looking for windows to break, water mains to wrench open, institutions and other weird buildings to vandalize.

Halloween! Once when we were messing with a warehouse on the edge of town, a watchman jumped out of nowhere and caught all the others, for I ran. They stopped when he threatened. They were already in the car, and they could've just driven away. Why didn't they? Afterward, they never could explain it to me. I was a little late in getting back to our "getaway car" and I ran when I saw what was happening. The threats of the watchman didn't slow me down! Like the cries of spectators at a track meet, they helped me go faster. And I was hearing the coach saying, "Slack your jaw, even your shoulders!" like he used to shout during practice. And I laughed, like this was just the mile run or something. I had a mind that was endlessly joking and tricking me, and at this moment, the old urge to quit in the middle of the course came over me. There was this sort of a devil that used to afflict me, and during a race it'd be strong, telling me to run off at an angle through the broad jump and high jump pits, maybe leap a few out-of-the-way hurdles on my way out the fieldhouse — but only after I threw a roadblock on the other runners near me! And now my mind was toying with the idea that this was only track *practice* and I could stop and risk only some hard words from the coach. And I had to tell myself, Wait a second, quitting? *Quitting?* But I was running for life, so it seemed. I was in this unclocked dash away from the cops who would be called, I had no doubt — trouble, parents, teachers, the works. I ran like hell. I was gasping and laughing at something, looking for a place to hide . . . Now I wonder if I was ever more than an adventurer, but I thought I understood what I was hearing. I could almost hear the state of Georgia!

I was going to leave Harvard, and all I had to go on was my vague sense of life outside the institution that I seemed to have inhabited for decades. I got high and thought about it all. I was sure that the world was a mystery never to be revealed from the lecterns or caught in notebooks, and I wanted to try

8

my own luck. To the South a fine struggle was calling me, and my response was not pure, only real. It was to be a journey that'd last many seasons.

Of course it's not fair for me to write anything about Harvard. When I left Cambridge and hitchhiked to the South, I was really trying to quit a state of mind. My main experience at Harvard was that I had no use for the place and, therefore, I never could make any sense out of it. Anyone who enrolls there soon develops some idea of the use he's going to put it to, even if it's a facet of the culture against which he's going to rebel. So leaving the school is only the starting place for this story — it's not a turning point, it's only a drifting off. At Harvard, the subtle cliques form quickly. The big scholarly one was beckoning me, and I suppose I could have found some comfortable spot inside it, except that I was drifting uncontrollably. I was on my way out. It's no use trying to make sense of my tale with a traditional ivy setting as the foundation. Harvard meant drugs to me, and in that sense, it could have been any other university in the country. It performed its function, as far as I'm concerned; it fulfilled its classical purpose of connecting me with the possibility of truth. And I soon left for the American countryside.

two

ONE NIGHT word reached me that a Winthrop House dealer had mescaline. Of course I wanted some, and I knew friends would. I wonder what it's like at the university today: any drug, any book, like New York, Saigon, or ancient Rome . . . It was spring, there had been rain and the air was fresh. I took a walk through the electric academic maze to see the dealer. All afternoon I'd been smoking and playing my thumb piano, an African instrument composed of a small wooden sound box and metal keys. You can find such musical instruments in America, but rarely one beautiful as mine. I took it with me on my walk so that I'd have some chimes to listen to in case anything about the business should start to bring me down. I was stepping along, hitting some notes, forgetful of my aim — a method that usually improved a business trip. The streets I knew so well would lead me where I needed to go. — I almost walked into a cop. He held out his arm which I suddenly noticed. With a scowl on his face he demanded to see my bursar's card. But I didn't have any identification with me. My instrument was not enough — but it was all I had. I told him that; I

asked him, Wasn't the instrument and the music enough? I
went back to playing the little piano. I tried a slow, idle
rhythm; I eased down into it, and he stomped away. I continued to a certain suite at Winthrop House. There was a poker
game going, and the man was in it. But when he saw it was me,
he announced the next hand would be his last. He said he had
to quit anyway; he'd talk to me then. I stood to one side and
went on playing my music. The streams of it were almost anti-
thetical to the round of the game, but nobody seemed to mind.
Yes, I was stoned! There was a musician present and he admired the instrument, and I was glad to show it off, it was such
a beautiful thing. I thought I sensed some amusement among
the players, mixed with respect. Some held serious expressions
when they looked my way. I didn't consider the possibility
they were putting me on. I was just a bigheaded freshman. I
don't know, I guess my impressions depended more on my state
of mind, which was pleasant just then.

The dealer and I walked out together. He said he was on his
way to a yoga class — it helped his card playing. I mentioned
the mescaline and gave him an idea what size of purchase I
would want to make — I'd be more specific after I'd talked to
some people. He responded that nothing was happening yet,
but the arrival of the drug was imminent. He named a date. I
said I'd be in touch. He said I'd take a trip naturally and see
that everything was right. We parted, to the sound of my
thumb piano. He was a gentle businessman, and when the day
came I was shocked to see not the white crystals I'd been expecting but a gray vegetable powder I didn't recognize. He
explained it was not mescaline before I could get the look out of
my eyes into words. It was something better, he said, *Yage.*
Now the look wasn't in my eyes, which were almost shut.

"*Yage?*" I said. I didn't have the piano with me this time, and I needed it at this moment. He must've been reading Burroughs' letters — I could hardly believe this was the mythical vine. Was the dealer trying to con me? But he kept saying good trip, beautiful trip, and he had a trip there on the table, one portion of the stuff to take a look on. Well there was nothing to do but try it and see. While the dealer was getting some water to mix up an edible paste of it, I slipped a tiny bit into a paper and into my pocket. I knew a chemistry student, and that's how I finally found out what it was — morning glory seeds. It didn't take him a moment to tell me. He was into drugs himself and he recognized the stuff, Heavenly Blue or Pearly Gates variety morning glories, containing LSD-principle and a convulsant. It got me high all right. It tasted awful, like eating mud, a godly mud! I had expected a nice easy mescaline capsule, and swallowing this gunk was like work. When I started to go up, I thought I wanted to take a walk.

The dealer was walking along with me because he didn't mind, he would listen to me riff and raff and try to word my thoughts, and he'd catch what far-out shit I happened to say, and laugh. And naturally he had his business to tend, and he didn't want me to float wildly, or mess with anybody, or run afoul of the law. The streets were starting to glow in *that way*. The late afternoon sun was red, and the buildings were giving off the light that they'd been storing up all day. A student passed us reading a book lolled open on his hands, in his world . . . Every now and then he looked up to see if he was still headed right. I identified with his absorption, just walking along unable to stop reading; it could've been me. Out of a gateway in front of him appeared a professor whom I recognized. His sparkling eyes were far-fixed, for a moment he just hesitated there. The student, passing him, made a motion out of his loose stride like to say something to him, as if his voice, gathering up to speak to the important figure, was propelling him headfirst toward his target. I thought I sensed the man's attention focusing. To my amazement they passed without speaking. Then I felt sadness as the eyes of the professor wavered, as if the beauty of some intent were wavering. Had they actually wanted to speak? I stepped on quickly and grabbed the professor's arm, and I called to the student who at first didn't seem to hear. Immediately the dealer separated me from the man, who was smiling incredulously, and we were walking on at a brisk pace, passing the student who gazed at us with an abstract emotion I couldn't quite grasp. My friend walked faster; I was content to be led along. The concern I sensed in him was laughable and I laughed; I wasn't brought down by the failure of my effort, I was glad to have made it. I knew it didn't matter, spirits parted by a wind. It made me extremely glad to be bringing them together. When I was no longer doing that but walking away, the gladness didn't diminish. This cat was feeling danger close around, but my stoned joy was keeping it beyond my horizons. Hey this Yage, whatever it was, had got me out of sight! I had to compliment the dealer, who smiled. We walked up onto Harvard Bridge and gazed down at the rippling surface of the river that at sundown was black, white, light red, purple, lavender, and dark silver. There was a shingled movement to it, like a snake with scales made of colored water. And in the motion I saw beautiful couples dancing, strippers gracefully stripping, little children twirling hoops, boxers sparring, Zen swordmasters that I'd only read about courting death with fast sharp love. "Charles River Arthur Murray!" I shouted. I remember I shouted that nonsense again and again. I was laughing and pointing, and my friend was digging it too. He was cool; this was an okay place to stop and admire. There are subtle gradations along the walks of man. Up on the twilit bridge other people were resting and accepting some beauty over the wall; nobody minded a fool pointing and exclaiming in the vision that's as far beyond words now as it was then, the only difference being now I've got a few more words for the time past. What I noticed most of all was the *light* itself, and I couldn't even mention that. At first I might not have the stomach for the certain deceit.

Some people had trouble holding down the glories because of the strychnine — I think that's the poison to be found in them. I offed some at a party in East Cambridge and came back later to find almost everybody sick, wan, cast about the floor, strung out on the beds with a bad look for me out of their partly open eyes. I tried to talk, to ask them how it was, what was wrong — then I fell silent. Silence. A slow curse rang forth, and sighs of disgust followed. Most of them hadn't held anything down long enough to take in anything but the convulsant. I walked around the rooms of the place. Well I just couldn't help it. But in the back room there was one chick, I dug her, she was high, smiling out a back window in a stony way. She was an acquaintance whom I felt very friendly toward and I was glad she had made it. When I tapped her, she looked at me and grinned, with her hand up over her mouth. She was missing some front teeth, which was involved in her whole beauty. She'd got high and didn't even know the others hadn't. She said she wanted to go out and breathe the air but she wasn't sure she could walk. I assured her she could, and helped her take a few steps till she saw she was able. We were headed for the front door when her old man came out of someplace talking to her like he'd never been interrupted. Then he broke off — he told her to mend his knapsack which he had in his hands. He was wearing an Indian headband and was stoned as he could be. When he saw me — and it took a few seconds though I was standing right next to her — he asked me did I have a car, because he needed some air. I was ready to get out of this disappointing recovery room, and so we all left. I didn't dare a general goodbye, so far nobody had asked for their money back anyway. They had paid three fifty each for the trip, and I was sad it was bad. When I had found out it was morning glories, the price began dropping. The Winthrop House dealer must've thought me a sucker — it's not the first or last time that mistake has been made. I didn't care about that; I cared about my friends and I cared about the price, which dropped quick. But I couldn't get him down any further than two and a half. It was more than it was worth, but after all he had gone to the trouble of grinding it up to a powder. You'd have to invest in a blender or something. In those days you could buy some seed packets at the garden store and get high for a dollar or two, but I bet you can't anymore, I bet the law has seen to that.

The cat with the headband was telling his chick she could mend his knapsack later. He put it on a chair in a corner of the hallway and had her take notice of where it was. When we got in the car, they wanted to go over to the Charles River and dig the bit of nature to be found there, and I could well understand that. I had this car, you see, that I'd borrowed from my roommate. It was night and green along the river. It was such a pleasure to get out of the car into the deep air under the trees. But right away this cat wanted to jump into the water. Unbelievably he was stating that he could walk across the river. I told him yes, across the bridge, he wasn't even into a good joke.

I told him that, harshly as I could, but he wouldn't hear it. He was joking and serious in the strange way of people who believe in their own antic spirit, and he got very wild, and I couldn't hang on to him myself, but the chick grabbed him too, and for dear life she tackled him and held on with loving hands and prevented him from testing out his pathetic certainty that anyone stoned as he was would be supported on the river's surface according to some old inverse law of the cosmic imagination. It was a cool night in April and I was sure he'd catch pneumonia if he fell in the Cambridge creek. But the chick put his hand between her legs where he wouldn't want to leave, and kissed him and talked to him stuff and good nonsense about her and the sky, and when he noticed the sky overhead through the leaves he put his other hand on her breasts and relaxed. Every now and then her hand would go up to hide the gap in her mouth that was sexy, even classy to my mind. He was looking from her to the sky like maybe the two of them would go swimming in the warm up there. I walked along the river. I thought about it near its pouring into the sea: somewhere off the coast a colorful snake entered the eye of a storm and there rested. I glanced up at the sky, and it was clear and full of stars and comets. I had a joint in my pocket, and I got it out and lit up. I walked back to the car — I was wondering if I'd taken care of all my business, which is the problem of people who mess with drugs but don't accept the vision entirely. I had a little money riding on all this, but now I was stoned and I couldn't rightly remember who I was supposed to see when. Out of the glove compartment I got my thumb piano. I held it in my hands under the starlight. The beauty of the instrument humbled me. I approached it as I walked with it through the dark park like a man who is all thumbs approaching a grand piano. But soon as

16

I began to play, the instrument and I remembered each other. We remembered the river and the sky and the grass. Tunings and rhythms developed and hung in bright curved growths in the black air. There are some good African thumb pianos around; people are building them and selling them in places like Chicago, New York. Beautiful! But I've never seen one to compare with mine from the banks of the Nile in the southern Sudan. I still have it, I stored it away with some friends before I went South.

three

I HAD A GOOD TIME on the morning glory seeds, I took many trips that spring. There were some bad times too though, when night fell and somebody came by my room to transact some business, lesser emotions including fear colored the high. One night I left the dealer's with a bag of a few dozen trips for friends and some Harvard students I knew. The dealer walked me partway. In fact he walked me to the corner where he could see the door of my dormitory, and I was resenting his continued presence. Not wanting me to get hung up at all, I suppose, he waited there while I walked on. When I stopped for a moment in the doorway, I glanced back and saw him there, waiting still. He waved. I was stoned as I could be but I didn't wave back. I was starting to resent his doubts that I could stay out of trouble. Perhaps it was this resentment that contained the seed of some loneliness and fear that began to plague me in my empty room. I stared out at the darkening city, thinking that I would like to be out there myself, away from these doubts that I was safe to get high. I thought about turning some music on, and then I forgot about it. I sat down there awhile, I just sat there stoned. A girl came by to see me, to talk about some money and some drugs. These were subjects which could easily make me fearful and uptight, and besides that she seemed to feel that I had stolen something from her. And she had her dog with her. I didn't remember having stolen anything from her, and I was sure all my recent dealings had been honest, if clever. But the dog seemed to sense something. Maybe it knew better than I, or at least it well understood its mistress' suspicion. It tried to bite me on the leg. I grabbed a handy wooden shelf and took a swipe at it. What was the trouble? She towed in the dog. I was perfectly clean. She said, "Hey you must be high or something, we oughta talk about something else."

That was the truth — she took the words right of my mouth. The books that had been on the shelf were strewn about the floor. I didn't think about picking them up, I sat down in a chair by the window. My feet, which I had actually taken hold of, seemed made of clay. I could stretch them, I pulled on them, I envisioned the bite of the dog like a chomp out of some clay with short strings of it trailing out between the clamped teeth. Good substance of my body seemed to be draining away with the adrenaline pumped up by the dog's attack or the girl's bad feeling. With these thoughts I was not bringing myself back to life . . . And she was joking, she was on a riff that was a favorite of hers since she'd found out about my ambition to go to the South and work in the civil rights movement: "Whata you think you're going to do down there? Whata you think, man! Those people gonna have you washing their windows! Are you listening to me? You know what you are? You're what the spades call an A-number-one sucker! You got a nice scene here, stupid!"

I just couldn't follow that. I accepted her sentiment, but I could never connect it with the people in the South who were marching, and could always use some more marchers, the people getting desperate and ready to try anything, sabotage — who after a time of testing would let me join them. Some such vision of an embattled people facing great odds, with a use therefore for any extra hand, was what I dreamed in these days when I was making up my mind to quit school and hitchhike to the South. To her, who thought I had a nice scene here in the regulated dormitory with its loopholes, I had no way of speaking. Certainly not then, so damn stoned! I felt like if she stayed in the room with her dog another minute, the windows would fall out — then the dog too, he'd go. Maybe me and her too — damn! These imaginings were useless and worse, I knew I'd feel better when I got them out of here, especially Fido. When I'd summoned the strength and pushed them out, saying so long, later, and her saying okay, okay, okay, and hauling on her dog who did want to stay and chew on my foot some, then I relaxed, my head came together again, I remembered that I wanted to play some music. I put on Bobby Timmons: "This Here" . . . In the piano sounds I began to feel the pleasance of presence, reality, the here and now. This is a simple emotion but not an easy one to express, for it might be confused with contentment in the situation. I knew I'd forgotten where I had come from and I was highly uncertain about where I was going, but it was getting mellow just to sit here. I didn't know anything, though the music was affecting me, and I was experiencing the room, and my being in it — plus my keen desire to leave this place at some future unknown date, all this with ease. "Moanin" was the next band . . . Over the piano the words sang through my imagination, "Every day I'm always moanin, every day I'm always cryin the blues —" With everything a kid could want, right? A scholarship at Harvard, what else? But I was blue as the night, I was blue as if I was in *jail*, I thought, never having been in jail but romanticizing my predicament just the same. The drugs, the lysergic, the morning flowers were revealing to me an essential characteristic of the place I was in as a glimpse of a place I'd not yet been to. A few days later I left Cambridge, but by then the revelation had slipped my mind.

I put the needle back to "This Here," but before "Moanin" came up again I was already hearing it. I'd been talking about splitting for weeks. It was mellow hanging around, getting high, enjoying the freedom that came from having already quit. There were a lot of drugs around . . . but now I was messed up behind this not leaving, and taking more drugs . . . How long will this go on? For days. And now I thought I was late, I should've split already: what was I doing still in this room? In answer to that, I must've gone into a fog; when my friend the dealer showed up the record was still spinning. He shut it off and the dull clicking stopped. I remembered him vaguely, I hardly noticed him, I kept looking out the window. He said I didn't look too good, I said I felt worse. I didn't mind him sitting over there in the chair, but my attention was elsewhere. He started asking questions about my state of mind, and I couldn't answer them. A word or two might've escaped. I remembered how good I felt that evening by the river, but now I felt bad and cold; I didn't know why I was there, because I kept intending to leave this room and the university for good. Every day I meant to leave on the next, but I didn't, it had been too much fun hanging out. But it was catching up on me, a certain cold meaninglessness was setting in, and I could've handled it but my head and identity were far away as Georgia. It was like a devil with a bad smell of death on it had entered the room, and there was hardly a memory of me around to put the kill on it. Its sound was a bad reptilian shrilling, very light, you almost couldn't hear it. I glanced around viciously, uselessly. I saw I was going to have to suffer its presence. I asked my friend did he notice the weird effluvium penetrating all corners of the room by a strange devil method. This caused him to kindly start in reassuring me, explaining something about the drugs, heaven and hell, something like that. The word "devil" on his lips had the condescending sound of a grown person trying to humor a child, with the kindest and most responsible air coming off him, so ineffective against the devil that was flickering and threatening like a cold flame. He suggested I could climb out of the sadness if I wanted to, I could use my mind to chase the devil — yes, I could move a mountain with a teaspoon too! I laughed — the laugh made the devil jump back. I laughed again loudly, and apologized to the dealer, explained what I was doing. But it wasn't necessary. When I laughed a third time, the devil crept forward slightly. I couldn't see my friend but it was okay for him to go on sitting there. I sensed the clumsy good spirit, and he meant well, if that didn't mean anything. He didn't notice the bad influence in the room, but that didn't mean anything either. Occasionally his face appeared out of the fog. Fangs were growing out of the corners of his mouth like weird curved cigarettes. I shook my head violently and turned away from both friend and devil and stared out the window at the dark streets abstractly lighted. Tomorrow — or whenever I got together again and got the bad spirit out that had climbed into the vacant stretches of my absent mind — tomorrow, I thought wryly, I could decide whether to go on promot-

ing myself in the drug business or make my break from this
drug dream, this low-pressure area that I'd created at the college. The South was pulling on me — but I hardly had the
power of my legs. Drugs every day, morning glories at night!
For a moment I regretted letting my courses drop; I felt lost, as
if my connection to reality had been through the theories of
Max Weber and Karl Marx after all. But when I remembered
the immense amount of work waiting for me if I ever decided to
pick up the scholastic threads again, I recognized that there
was no satisfaction for me there, in the concepts and precision
tales. I got up and put another record on the machine. It was
Eric Dolphy, I forget which record. The flying reed sounds
filled the room; directly they were searching it out and beginning to kill the smell of the devil, that was trying to hide in
front of the far window, being almost transparent. I wondered
which record this was: "Last Date" or "Outward Bound"? I
didn't care that much to think any further, the names left my
mind as the music gave me ease. The devil didn't move, it was
scrunched down trying to hide. As if concentrating all energies
inward, only its tongue was flicking, reverberating cold waves
back into the room off the iron ball in its stomach. Its breathing was what gave it away, in front of the window there; deep
down in its chest, it was like the sound of frost amplified, or like
a hacksaw being idly drawn by some mad artist through a city
skyscraper. Eric Dolphy's music went straight for the devil:
that is, in its startling new territories, the intricate burning pre-
figured the sly leaps of the devil, who wasn't deaf; and I rushed
to the support of the Dolphy group. Suddenly I was feeling
quite well and contented: the devil was external now, not so the
music. I noticed the devil being routed while my glance fell
musically around the room, through the glass (it was of little

matter to me), traveling the lights and the streets in my near-at-hand journey away from this room. In the lightness of emotion I grabbed my books and began throwing them at the retreating demon. To my surprise I noticed the window was now open, the books went sailing out, and so did the bad spirit. But I didn't stop heaving out my books, and then my writings too. As they sailed through the air, I could imagine they were beautiful as songs. That seemed to clear something up. A constellation of printed matter was being formed on the ground below. In some bushes to one side I noticed two clowns sitting. They were laughing and doffing their caps and smiling at me, and shaking themselves so all the leaves of the bushes danced. Their costumes were covered with small white letters, like sequins, that sparkled. The whole alphabet many times over was winking and grinning at me from down there.

When I reentered the room from my active reverie, I noticed that the dealer was gone. Possibly when he heard the music he knew everything was all right, or something. Eventually — beautifully to my drugged amaze — there was nothing anymore in the room but the music and the mellow night vacation from decision. In a dream I was standing on a diving board looking down into a pool in southern Illinois. In my mind, I was waiting for the moment of perfect concentration, over the rectangle of water that was the diving pool in a municipal park containing two other swimming pools, a zoo, wide green lands for walking and horseback riding — a nice suburban setup. That wasn't all I could imagine, not just the geography of the place to keep me hesitating over the long flight down to the water. I wanted to enjoy it, and be fully conscious of that pointed drop, and the loud penetration of the water, the poignant touch off the bottom and the exhilarating burst upward toward the air. Simultaneous with this picture, another was forming in my mind and coloring the time: I was waiting for the starting gun that would signal the beginning of that long mile. The pressure was building up as before the gun, and the pack was bunching and shifting its spiked feet, and the moment before the start seemed endless and so charged with the hopes of this little multitude tensing under the sun at the line of lye on the black cinders. And finally the moment came, and the blank charge is sounded — we're off! Immediately I'm beside myself with the desire to tackle other runners and ruin the spectacle which at this early moment I might throw totally asunder, but I run, yes I run, and turn in my time . . . Or the moment comes to dive. Off the board, I remember many things, including my short future at Harvard, flying through the air . . .

I wished I hadn't said goodbye to my girl! One night recently she'd called me up on the phone to say, "What's wrong with you anyway? You were supposed to come by today! You don't care anything about me do you? All you want to do is fuck and then you don't care if I go or stay! Why don't you ever talk to me?!"

Well she often said something like this to me, and sometimes it almost made me feel bad. But right now, over the phone? It wasn't appropriate. So I knew she had something else to say, so I didn't say anything, I waited.

"Why don't you say something?" she said.

"Something," I said. But after a short silence I went on, "Hey what's wrong with you? Why don't you come over so we can talk?"

A little sob over the wires. "What would you say if I told you there's somebody else?"

"Nothing," I said, with a surprised effort.

"I thought so," she sobbed.

What did she want? She wanted me to fight it, to stand my ground. What ground? Truth be told, I didn't feel like I had any and never thought about trying to get some. The other guy had made a string of promises and probably they were true. Very soon I was going to depart from this little room I'd been allowed under the ivy and I wasn't coming back. I ought to plant a million morning glory seeds around here first, I thought, along the walls. "You're taking care of yourself like you ought to," I told her. "I may leave tomorrow."

"You've been saying that for months," she sighed.

"Months!" I laughed.

I guess it was my pride let her go. The way I thought about it, a girl could stay with me as long as she wanted, but I wasn't going to ask for or fight for anything. And I didn't much like to talk, but I could listen. And if I knew that I was leaving, and if she was telling me something like this — and she bent my ear for a while, and told me about him, that he loved her, and I listened. Then out of the feeling I did have for her I cut her off . . . And now in the early morning hours of another day — today I should be gone! — coming down from the strange fears and far joys of a trip on the flower seeds, I desired her. And I could have kept her till I'd finally actually split. And right now I could've made a call. But I didn't. I didn't want to talk.

I got out my African piano and worked out on it for a long while. In the streams of sound I made, I nodded and dreamed. As the sky lightened, I was floating in the chimes. I forgot I was playing but the music didn't stop, it flew by like multicolored birds, beyond my fingers. I no longer cared about the past, the present, or even what the future might bring: no thoughts pleased or troubled me. All I knew was the light currents of the music that I was in, an image of flowing water, of warm flames dancing out of my hands on the instrument whose wooden lines were disappearing into the air with the sound.

The longest race that we ran back in high school was the eight mile. Perhaps it was the considerable effort involved, perhaps the time span of the run — there was something special that used to happen to my head during the course of it. It may have had something to do with the solitude I always enjoyed, well behind the string of leaders, and well ahead of the slow pack, the half-milers and basketball players in training who usually had a card game going amongst them, and who ran (and walked) only to finish. Somewhere in the middle, when I was well into the run and the machine of myself had been pumping and breathing at a steady rhythm for a few miles, a change in my perception of the scenery would begin to occur. Hills of the golf course on which we ran got *so green,* the sky popped out so it seemed *very close,* the air was another texture and each breath tasted sweet as a drink of cool water. I began to think I was never so happy and real as during this run, when the pace was just right and the exhaustion of the last distance (with its own rewards) had not yet set in. I began to run just for this effect, I didn't try to place. It was what went on in my mind, or perhaps the loss of my mind, that I cared about. The feeling of it was like I was *inventing* the landscape through which I was passing, even my body that was doing the running, while I floated somewhere else. After a few trips on the morning glories, I started getting the same sensation about Harvard, that I was dreaming its streets, its rooms. And now I have to wonder, did I invent this whole picture? I don't know, but as for historical certainties, I offer this reservation. And later, in the South . . . In these pages, I offer only my story. You may suggest that the historian is also the diligent spinner of a tale . . .

But this wonder that moved me was getting me nowhere. The drugs were delaying me, in the nicest way. And summer vacation might start, and I could still be here, getting high and not worrying about any exams or classes of summer school either. Knowing little enough about my own head, I guessed that I would leave when I was angry about something, and I was right. At such a time I was in motion. I was waiting for that special angry power to light my way to the road. Instead of looking for walls, I'd break on through and be on my way. And I could keep my anger for the South and perhaps it'd be some use to the civil rights struggle. For my own reasons that I couldn't examine much I'd be ready to sit-in, march, disrupt — anything. When I got down South and came to know people, I'd care about what they cared about. The beauty and nobility of the people in the movement existed independent of my ideas. But my growing awareness of the issues didn't hide from me the fact of my own motivations, which I wasn't clear about: it was going to feel like drifting, like always, I couldn't help that. I read the papers, I went to SNCC meetings and listened carefully. Tales told by the field workers of pursuit by southern sheriffs, escape, jail, deeply stirred my imagination. Perhaps the goals of the movement were even secondary in my naive mind to the excitement of the conditions. I was in favor of the goals, but they were the goals of the black people in the South, and my goal was to leave Harvard *for* something. These were heroes to me, these people recently come up North to talk on the campuses. They were fighting for the good against tremendous evil. I was sure a lot of right-hearted people would soon be in motion toward the South.

After a meeting I was walking along, my head on fire and my mind far away. I was flashing, Hey man what are you doing on the streets of Cambridge? What are you doing at Harvard University! My pleasure self answered, Getting to some college girls and smoking some boss Harvard gold down by the river; reading books the likes of which you never thought existed back in that required reading desert at high school, which goes on, no doubt, but you have hit the oasis. Learning to write — but what more can be learned here? Watching TV — is there a whole lot more to it? — Though I didn't know it, I was going to travel far, and one day I'd smoke some flowers from the swamp. I walked back to the dorm and up to my room, which was like a girl to me sometimes. First thing I did was put on a record — Eric Dolphy and Booker Little, who was to die soon after digging his ax so, in the red light of the cover photo. Soon I was hearing them blow beautiful "Aggression" —

While I bounded a tennis ball off the wall hundreds of throws, I considered the natures of the pulls of the university. All the beauty and terror in the world was what was available here in print in the vast libraries: all the books and stories, including mine someday, and the intricate avenues are always deeper, concealing astounding lights that are always brighter, that you only discover in time. You could spend all your life here, forgetting the Dewey decimal system. Surely it's a peace to get back to! On my shelves were many-colored paper books, reflections of the world, treasures. Forego them! They'll always be here, or in another life. Ride!

four

AND I DID. I left the next morning, before sunrise. (I had some dope money, I had a few dollars together.) I was saying good-bye to drugs and leisure but I didn't mind. I woke a girl I knew and she gave me a ride out to the highway on her motor scooter. I caught good rides all the way into the South, and till I hit the border states I talked about where I was going for the sake of conversation. Somewhere in North Carolina, a sailor in a new T-bird stopped for me. He asked if I could drive, he wanted to sleep. That was a relief — we could ride in silence. He was going straight to Atlanta. What a joy to slide behind the wheel and know my travel worries were over!

In Atlanta, I settled down with SNCC for a while. On orders from that organization, I threw my body into the guarded door-way of a segregated restaurant in the downtown area and received for that effort a cut on the head from some cracker's shoe. I also gained entrance, as between me and my partners we broke through the guards. There we were standing in the middle of the place. Outside the TV cameras had caught our act, but inside we were at a loss as to what to do. There was nothing else to break really. We were all recent dropouts from the universities and the insides of a fancy restaurant were still sacrosanct to us as a library. I think our common impulse was to bolt when they fell back and let us in. Nothing else to do, we went limp, and lay about in the entranceway and under the tables laughing at the fat legs of Dixie matrons and hoping they wouldn't break out the Maddox ax handles. There we stayed, the day wore on; orders came in: stay where you are. We were sent food to eat, and momentarily we sat up to eat it. Late in the afternoon, the cops finally arrested us. They had to carry us out. I was ready for anything.

After a short night in the Atlanta prison I was free to return to the SNCC office. It was hardly enough to get a taste of jail — the romance was still strong on the tongue — but I was tired. I got a rest of some days in the house of a girl in the movement. It was just a pure rest. Then I received orders to continue on to a little town in Georgia, town called Meansville. When I got there, they had the voter registration drive on. This was my assignment — work on the vote drive. I wasn't even old enough to vote, and what's more I didn't care a thing about it. It wasn't the adventure I was looking for. But what did I know about these people's scene? It was all new to me. The people were new. They definitely wanted to vote . . .

Besides me there was at least one other crazy kid around town who had a relation to the movement as tenuous as my own, though he was black, and who cared as little as I for the vote drive. Like me, he had a vague sense of his own freedom; because of a tragedy we became friends. His name was Knight Collins and he held a disdain for nonviolence. Soon enough we had all the trouble we wanted. A young girl was raped by a white man, driver for the Sunbeam Bread Co. It happened in a nearby town, not Meansville, but the whole region was affected. I hate to think how perfectly it suited my mood, and his. We were so ready to be angry and bitter. I saw her picture — she was beautiful. We never met her (Knight had never heard of her), but we decided to avenge her; that was in our nature. I hung around the movement office as usual. In the confusion there were meetings, out of town officials came in to advise, friends and church people, and people from the town where it had happened stopped in for long hushed conferences. The girl's life was insecure for days. All advice was to wait. It had happened so many times! folks said, not in so many words. Everybody had a sad and weary look in their anger that made me cast my eyes down. I did a lot of looking down among these people, the nonviolent and committed good people. And what right had I? They wanted their share of the vote and things which I had no right even to think about too much, being just an outsider.

When the little girl died, we quit taking names for the vote drive. We got on the phone to announce the bad news and fanned out across Meansville in our old cars. I rode with Sam, a dropout from a black college in the South. We talked to preachers, barbers, influential old ladies, and other good talkers, and he explained it softly in a few words, so they could amplify it themselves in their neighborhood or circle. He spent the most breath urging mass meetings for as soon as possible. But between times he lost control and cursed the killer and pounded the steering wheel and drove dangerously.

"Sick? *Killer!* He hate black people an hate chicks! Tol her kid brother: 'Please don't make me hafta kill more a y'all family!' He free right now — in his Sunbeam truck!"

Sweat was pouring off his face. I was a junior staff member, but he was the right-hand man of the Director of the Meansville movement. I'd never seen cool Sam like this before! Between stops he let some of it out. But he wasn't going back on his commitment to nonviolence, no.

"Like she hit by lightnin or some *natural* shit — her poor ol family can't think a nothin but pray."

In his conversations, he didn't emphasize this note, but it struck me hardest. Nothing but old hands and young kids in her family I knew — why didn't somebody waste the bread man for them? There's no doubt, except about the future, though the present keeps pushing it out of sight. The bread man's openly laughing. In the bar where the cops hang out, he's drinking his beer same as always. A bullet could finish this. I dreamed it. He was my color or race, and I'd often been told: cherish America. While Sam and the others worked to organize the anger momentarily kindled by another mad attack, and even hoped to make a legal case against him, I dreamed of shooting the ugly dude. I had nothing to lose — except our world of beautiful rivers and women. If I'm going to play for such low stakes as a white bread rapo, I'd have to be sure. — In my dream, I'm very sure, I make my escape —

But sensations of the beauty of the pastel clay roads and weather-softened gray wood houses kept interrupting my mood of solemnity and anger. I enjoyed so much just being present in this small Georgia city, in many ways like a country town. But there was no possibility or reason for expressing my joy in being near beauty. For Sam, poverty was poverty. I kept quiet.

We were in a sprawling semirural area bordered by industry, cut up and distinctly cut off by railroad tracks: a vista of thousands of clapboard dwellings, liquor stores on almost every corner, a few more substantial houses and some apartment projects around the churches. Sam said it was a landing stage for almost all newcomers to Meansville from the country. We went to visit the minister of the CME Church, which was the biggest church in the neighborhood. But he was very hostile, he was so hostile you would hardly know a little girl had just been killed. For him something else was at stake, it seemed. Emerging from the cool basement of the church, Sam laughed bitterly. "We should've had suits and ties on for that one!" To that portly gent behind gleaming specs and straight suspenders and a starched white shirt, *we* weren't the movement, *he'd* been the movement for forty years! Sam said the kids would have to carry the word for us here, and there was one who'd make the difference. There was one who might get them to do something. That was Knight Collins, former warlord of a gang that was now defunct. We went looking for him and found him asleep in the shade under the brilliant tin roof of the porch of his mother's house. Seeing him lazed back there so comfortably, heels propped up on the railing between decorative figurines and flowerpots, I thought I'd have let him be and come back later. But Sam called his name. His eyes opened already fixed on us. He jumped down, bare feet puffing up the dust noiselessly. "What's happenin, Sam?" he said.

"Hard at work, Knight!"

"Yeah, over on Easter Street hard at work on em little gals don know no better."

"No better than me!" Sam laughed, and then frowned with a vengeance. "C'mon ride with us, Knight. You know, that little girl across the river died this morning. We schemin how to shake up whitey!"

"Sheeit!" In the sharp midday sun his skin was black as wet

carbon. His untended process bristled up from his scalp in tall spines. "Shit," he said, softer and disgusted, as he turned to go back on the porch.

"What's wrong with you?"

"You talkin about y'all nonviolent."

"Man if you a leader roun here you sposeta show some imagination!" Sam shouted.

"I show some dynamite!" The angles of his face were merry and sly. He stood on the steps and stretched. Hey this was talking something, I thought; now this is the people I've been looking for. Dynamite!

"Knight, you ever seen a thousand people in the street headed one direction?" asked Sam.

"Yeah, they was followin Martin Luther one direction to the jailhouse," Knight laughed. But he was full awake now. He looked out at Sam, who said nothing more. "Okay Sam." He stretched once again, "lemme get my shoes."

"Man I'd like to see that dynamite," I said, after he'd gone inside. I didn't know for what. The image of walls flying through the air was pleasing me, though I hadn't thought it through.

"Don't even mention it," said Sam, impatient with me. "We got to bring this man aroun." He stuck his hands in the pockets of the blue overalls he wore as a symbol.

"You think he's really got some?" I couldn't help asking, as he turned his back toward me. But I was going to shut up. I didn't open my mouth much, because when I did, what I said was usually out of place. It was easiest to be silent. I was here to help. I would act when required and try to be dependable . . .

The screen door creaked open and out came Knight wearing

old tennis shoes with holes snipped out for the comfort of his little toes. "Mama say, 'Hey who that white boy out front a my house?' I tol her, 'Oh that nothin but my frien, the mayor son.' She peepin at you right now!" He howled with laughter at that one, and I grew embarrassed, aware of her eyes as we walked to the car.

"You know where you are?" Knight asked me after Sam gunned the engine. "CME!"

"The only place in town named after a church," remarked Sam.

"No it ain't! Those letters stand for Crime, Murder, an the Electric Chair — that CME!"

"That's what the cops call it! Electric chair is the truth!"

"Didn *no* police come in CME when the Stars was together! The brothers had a thing! White folks ran stop signs don even slow down! Ain no white man gon stop in CME! It ain like it useta be. *Movemen* cool things down till cats is scared —"

"Don't be ignorant," said Sam.

"Don *you* be ignoran, Sambo!"

"Listen motherfucker, the movement the one thing stay hot! Without the movement where is the action? Today I say, not in the past. The movement tryin to do somethin!" Sam pulled over at the bottom of a hill in front of a little cafe with a blue roof and new shiny gutters. A sign on it said "The Raindrop." On its single board step a lanky young man sat whittling on a thick length of yellow wood held between his knees. We got out of the car and approached him. His hat made of a white porous material hid his eyes. All his attention he centered on the exacting work of his hands.

"Hello OD," said Sam. "What you makin?"

"A club," he said. He looked up, blinked, and moved over to

the end of the step so that we could enter the cafe or sit down beside him, whatever we were going to do. He went on cutting.

"I'm shapin the handle," he said, when we stood there. Knight grabbed the stick and feigned a blow at Sam's ass.

"Mighty hot under this sun," said Sam, starting through the door. "C'mon an talk, OD."

Knight handed it back to him. Good-naturedly he closed his knife and followed us inside to one of four blue tables arranged at the sides of the room. The windows were blinded against the heat. A weak light hung from the ceiling, reaching only a bulb-shaped portion of the room about ten feet in diameter. Nobody was here but us and, behind a short bar, a fat woman standing in shadow. Knight called out for Black Label beer, and she uncapped the bottles and set them down in front of us.

"Sam, I thought the movemen say we can go to the swimmin pool," said OD, fingering the sweaty bottle and staring at his fingers.

"Yeah," said Knight, "I like to blow that motherfucker clean out the park!"

OD chuckled and spun his long curved knife on the tabletop. Against the wood wetted by the bottles the handle empaneled with mother-of-pearl made an oily whir. Sam leaned across the table and pointed his forefinger at Knight — "Yeah? What you gonna swim in then?"

"Same as always — mudhole by the river."

"In the *end* they gotta open up that pool if you keep up the pressure."

"No they ain't! I like to blow them peoples sky high!"

OD chuckled louder. He stopped spinning the knife and opened it with a flick of his wrist. "I'm gon break me some heads with this ol club —"

"Don't you mess my floor, boy!"

Behind the bar the fat woman was up on the tips of her toes. Her face was blank, like before a storm. "You mess up, you clean up!"

"Sheeit!" said OD very softly, dropping it next to his chair. "Ain nothin but a little shavins . . ." He began sipping his beer.

"Look here, OD," persisted Sam, "you think we can get the kids to march on the pool, man?"

"Nope. Unless it gonna be a picnic at the end. Camp out in the park an watch the animals in the zoo — free sanwiches an beer — play baseball in the white kids' diamond — "

"Swim in the pool!" cried Knight. "Climb the fuckin fence an swim! That the trouble with you all nonviolent — you wanna stan in front in a march like a fool an really you lettin em turn you back cuz you ain gettin *in!*"

"You don't know what it'll do if you ain't tried."

"*Sheeit!*"

"It builds up! Time! You think they gonna give up a good thing overnight they have for three hundred years?"

"Fuse burn down in fifteen seconds."

"*Light it then!* Better than talk an don't *do* shit!" Sam was mad. He put money on the table for the beers, stood up, slapped my shoulder, and took a couple steps toward the door.

As I rose, with disappointment that we were leaving the craziest and most interesting person I'd met since I came to Georgia, Sam paused to say, "You bad CME boys look lame to me. You talk bad! Here is *something* — here is a little girl dead an the movement tryin to do *something* — I guess your gang was strong, but you pitiful now!"

But at this moment a very heavyset young man walked into

The Raindrop with a scowl on his face. He wasn't much older than Knight, I'd guess, but in his expression there was something infinitely older. Knight took my arm and pulled me back in my seat. "Hey Sam, sit down an finish your beer." His voice was sincere, and Sam did a kind of double take and sat back down, saying nothing.

"Hey Jack!" Knight called real gruff to the cat who was standing at the bar getting a shot of something from under the counter. "Bossman give you time off?"

"Boy, you know I go an come when I please," said Jack, and downed the taste. He sighed and wiped his mouth and glanced over our way. "Hey, you gone with the movemen these days?" he sneered.

Knight might be at odds with Sam, but between him and this man the enmity was crackling. A second of hostile silence passed. "You said it, Jack, an you can tell the sheriff! Collins with the movement! You go tell your boss I come out a retire an I'm gonna fuck with him. You tell him, pimp!"

Sam was having trouble holding down a smile.

"Knight you ain shit," said Jack, and got another finger of what looked like whiskey in his glass.

"Jack a pimp for the sheriff," Knight said to me. "I ain even gonna argue with him no more."

"One day we take care a cats who forgot their people," said Sam.

Jack got a good belly laugh over that one. He finished his glass of beer he had for a chaser. "Ain none a you all shit," he said, with a slow look at all of us. With plenty of cool he walked to the door where he hesitated, squinting into the sun that streamed past him into the cafe. Then out he went, leaving us in a very different mood for his five minutes in the place.

"It too hot to go to jail," said OD, with a worried frown.

"Man, that ain no reason," drawled Sam.

"You gonna march?" OD asked me.

"Sure," I said, "if you do. I can't march unless you march."

"I don wanna go to no jail by myself," he said.

"You won't!" grinned Knight. "We all goin!" With a step and a jump he was standing on top of the bar. "It ain gon be no *good* march!" The transformation was amazing. The fat woman behind the bar couldn't believe it. She began banging a beer bottle against his legs. The laugh he laughed brought a smile to Sam's face that must've been love. And OD was waving his unfinished club around in the air, slashing out at imaginary assailants. "Gon be a *bad* march!" yelled Knight, "march *a CME!*"

five

AT FIVE O'CLOCK we were on our way across the river to have dinner with Deacon Stock and his wife. It was not the last stop we were going to make before sleep. After we crossed over the bridge we soon turned off the main road onto a pleasant street of solid cottages and nice shade trees. The street was not surfaced, the neighborhood was poor but very tidy, and most of the houses were painted. We passed a big red-brick church on a corner. Opposite it was a grocery store covered with posters and signs, tiny as a concession stand at a fair. In the middle of this block, we pulled up in front of a green house with a stout brick chimney. The porch was nearly hidden by tall cedar bushes that lined the paved walk from the road. In the second square of cement was stamped: J. P. STOCK 1939. I stopped to admire it. Once strips of wet cement had been peeled up with a sharp tool drawn along at equal angles, in a V-shape incision. But now the letters were softened in the way of a stamp on a day-old bar of soap or a centuries-old marble tombstone. I might have remained there studying it minutes longer if Sam hadn't hurried me on. The porch was painted white, and around the front windows of the house were neat white frames and sills. A long-tailed dog woke up on the doormat, sniffed the air around our cuffs, and went to sleep again. Sam rapped on the door, and after a moment a thin, dark, beautiful young girl appeared behind the screen and lifted the hook and pushed it open.

"Evenin. C'mon in," she said. "I'm Beverly." Leading the way into the front room, she called, "Mama!"

Immediately a small woman wearing wire-rimmed spectacles and a little white cap appeared out of the kitchen, at the back. Wiping her hands on a cloth, taking short quick steps toward us, she looked about sixty, but her stride had tremendous spring.

"You the movement boys."

"Yes ma'am," said Sam, "we're happy to make your acquaintance."

"Well I'm mighty pleased to meet *you*. My husband has spoken of you. Take you a seat here an I be right back. My fish bout to burn up."

She disappeared into the kitchen. I sat in a brown upholstered rocking chair. The wood of the sills, ceiling, and floor was brown, and all the furnishings of the room were dark green or cool brown. The blinds were drawn. Behind my back was a pillow stuffed with Spanish moss. Over a fat gas heater next to one wall was a mantelpiece, and above it was an arc of photographs — weddings, children, the topmost a portrait of a very old man with a gray beard wide as a spade. Right above him was a large wooden cross with green plastic ivy twining around it. On top of the television Beverly was tuning up was a statue of the Virgin Mary holding little baby Jesus on a pile of yellow hay in her lap.

"What he say about the march they had up in New York yesterday?" asked Sam, sitting on the sofa.

"Who?" asked Beverly.

"Him." Pointing to the screen.

"How I know? You see me turn it on."

"*We* be on there next! The North done took away the spotlight but we're gonna take it back."

"Who that?"

"Us! Me. Him. *You!*"

"Me?" asked Beverly, coaxing up the volume.

A little boy was begging his mother for his own phone. All the kids had their own phone, they didn't have to tie up Mommy's and Daddy's with calls to their friends. In the end, she saw the light — it would be a convenience and even a saving somehow naturally — and, yes, agreed to have the new phone installed that very day by Southern Telephone. The little boy's beaming face with freckles, "My mom's with it! How about yours?" It embarrassed me. I laughed, and my laughter set off a little trill from Beverly who looked perfectly contented and entertained however, seated on a stool about ten inches from the set. We were into a whiter brighter wash routine when Mrs. Stock came back into the room carrying a chair. Sam jumped up to assist her, then I did too, but she shrugged us off.

"I ain't that old lookin, is I? This chair fit my back so natural I jus tote it roun with me wherever I go." Sitting down in it, she said very softly, "Well tell me bout the movement."

"Ma'am," said Sam, choosing a determined bright tone, "we gonna march on Means Park pool!"

"No!"

"Yes ma'am! From all parts a town, a march on the swimmin pool!"

At this Beverly looked away from the television. Sam said, "You wanna go swimmin?" She smiled but dropped her eyes and turned back.

"Turn that noise down, girl," said Mrs. Stock. "You done your homework or you wastin time?"

"Yes ma'am, I'm all done," she said, and obediently turned the sound down to almost nothing.

"You talkin about *Means pool* right yonder in the park?" asked the old woman. She looked at me and to my discomfort I realized I had no idea where it actually was.

"Yes ma'am," said Sam, "right in the park with the zoo."

"Scuse me for askin all these questions but I wanna know. Do Mr. Maddon really own that pool or do he jus say he do? What is the truth?"

"Well, you see it's not too clear." Sam cleared his throat and wrinkled his forehead thoughtfully. "Movement got this order from the federal court say no public property can be segregated — that's the city theater, the parks, an the pool. So the mayor an his boys, they sell the pool to Maddon — that makes it private an he can let in who he wants to. My view — probably he ain't really bought it! They give him a fake deed or forge his name on the old one — or maybe they ain't done nothin, jus say he own it. Whatever it is," he looked at Beverly, "our young people ain't got no place to swim on a hot summer day!"

"Ain't it a shame! When the march?" asked Mrs. Stock.

"Well that depend on the people," said Sam, crossing his legs and leaning back. "That depend on *you*, ma'am."

"Oh!" said Mrs. Stock, letting her eyes linger on the TV for the first time.

"It's just a matter of days in CME," I said, to get her off the spot.

"CME, huh? I got a niece stay in CME. On Gordon by the

school. I give you her address, you stop by tell her I sent you. She ain exackly with the movement, but you can't never tell — maybe she march with you!" The image tickled her and she chuckled — a beautiful sound, a watery clucking.

"You ever hear of Knight Collins?" I asked on a whim.

"Collins? He kin to Collins run the grocery on Valley? . . . Seem to me I remember a boy . . ." She frowned. "Course it a right smart a years ago . . . but seems to me I remember that man say his nephew done turn out bad — got the *devil* in him . . ."

Sam was regarding me very sourly. But in a way he was the cause of my curiosity, because he had assigned me to CME, to be the movement man with Knight. Mrs. Stock looked puzzled. Sure she had the memory right, I said, "Maybe it's somebody else. This Collins works with the movement. He's the head a the march in CME."

"Oh yes," she said. "I'll ask JP. But no tellin when he be home. I reckon we go ahead an eat."

"No ma'am! We ain't in no hurry!" said Sam, glancing sharply at me.

"Yes ma'am, we'll wait for Mr. Stock," I said.

"JP always late on a Thursday. No sense lettin the food get cold. You know what he do?" More than a touch of pride came in her voice. "He run the thread machine over to Meansville Welding, the onliest man in that outfit can make a bolt! Ain no other can do it, black or white! It a delicate operation an he kep overtime quite a lot. C'mon now!"

There didn't seem to be any way to change her mind. Anyway, sooner or later Sam would speak with the deacon. As Beverly set the table with plates and silverware, the old woman had us sit down. The dining room was between the kitchen and the front room. The two of them brought in bowls of fish, grits, black-eyed peas and potatoes, and a pitcher of ice water. We bent our heads and Sam said a grace. I opened my mouth to cap it with an *amen* — but Mrs. Stock was started on a second prayer. I had a moment of intense panic, thinking we were all expected to say one. And I didn't remember any except some jokes (Good Bread, Good Meat, Good God, let's eat!). After the tiniest testing hesitation, she kindly finished hers up with an *amen* that I managed to echo.

"Help yaself, help yaself," said Mrs. Stock, showing her hands palms up above the table. "It ain nothin too much but what they is, you welcome to it."

"Thank you, ma'am," said Sam, nudging me for the potatoes. "You're very charitable."

"Yes ma'am, you're really generous," I said, passing him the bowl.

"Pshaw! It ain nothin to what you deserve! I declare! You all doin some wonderful work."

"Yes, it is wonderful," said Sam with his mouth full. "You right. But it ain't us. It's everybody who participates. It's *you!*"

"Oh yes, that the truth . . . They plenty fish in the kitchen. Go on take some more."

"Believe I will," said Sam, "mighty fine bream. Come from the river?"

"No, these fish is a present." She toyed with a piece of one with her fork and gazed down at her plate. "You wanna know, they was give me by my white folks." She looked up into my eyes and gave a laugh. "That how we say ain't it! My white folks! This a lil hushyamouth for that nice nigger lady. They be surprise to see who eatin it!"

I laughed with her. This old lady was wonderful. I was just happy to listen.

Outside, a huge crash — followed by a series of smaller crashes. The ice in the pitcher rattled and on the walls the pictures crept sideways. The old woman softly laughed. "Them trains! We jus about out in the east freight yards!"

Like an echo, a door creaked in the kitchen, heavy feet shuffled.

"That you, JP?"

Sounds of water running — washing.

"Us waitin on ya, JP!"

At last a barrel-chested man stepped ponderously into the room. He was wearing a brown cotton work shirt spattered with grease, sturdy striped trousers rolled up above the ankles, high-topped black work shoes reinforced at the toes. In his right hand, held out from his body like a tool, was clenched a blue engineer's cap, on his face was a look of expectation so earnest and confident that it could not possibly have changed to surprise and would instantly have masked displeasure. In the moment after he entered, it relaxed, became warm and friendly — he seemed to fill with new energy.

Sam got up, and I rose —

"Keep ya seats," said Deacon Stock, smiling. "Hello Sam!" Sam introduced me, and we all shook hands. "I'm mighty proud," said the Deacon.

"You want your dinner now, JP?"

"No, I'm a little tired jus yet, honey. Some grits all I want this minute."

"Put JP some grits, baby," she directed Beverly.

He stirred salt into them and mashed them thoroughly with the back of his spoon.

"How your day, hon?"

"Well, you wanna know it?" She barely laughed. "Not so good. I wen to work this mornin, JP — I'm gonna tell you what happen this mornin! — That lady, seem like it right difficult for her to talk *to* me. Words go off funny, an kina circle where she wanna go, her eyes lookin off out the window, say, 'Here for the chillern breakfas. Milk and cereal an this here bacon here' — an she pointin at it in the icebox. Okay, I understan — but she say it again, '*Here* for the chillern breakfas.' What she *don* say — they a plate a ol fat white meat on the other side — that mine! I don ast to eat in her house! She pay me more, I be glad to eat right here at home before I go. But if she gonna knock offa my money cuz she gimme to eat, then the Lord know that what I'm gonna do! Somehow. *Some* kina way! Well, everybody know niggers steal. Whitefolks say, 'They all do it. This nigger he good an trustworthy otherwise, I gotta overlook a little theft.' But me — I ain the stealin kind. I don know why — it the fool in me I guess — only this mornin, she don even have the gumption to say it — 'This ol white meat for you, girl' — even though it plain as day! I got mad! Yep — I ate my fill a good lean meat! I just about ate till I got sick on that red bacon!"

"Why honey! You did that?" chuckled the deacon. "I declare! I'm still learnin about you!"

"That right! You don believe that, do you?"

"Well I don think I do — "

"Yessir! It gonna be remembered, I know . . ." She began to laugh. "I had me a good breakfast *this* mornin!"

After a little pause, the deacon looked at Sam. "Tell me somethin! Gimme some news!"

"Well like they say," Sam said, turning over his fork on his plate with nervous fingers, "it's gonna be a mighty hot summer. We're on the edge a some marchin, to start with."

A code of propriety seemed to be operating, with nobody wanting to bring up the subject I could sense was in everybody's mind. That it was a concern, I admired. Against all natural odds that it could be anything but a terrible concern, I still felt this reverence.

"Well listen to you!" The deacon almost smiled. "Say it so easy. I admire you boys!" He took a bite of grits and chewed them quite a while before he got another. A pause in the conversation became a silence that began to echo so strangely Beverly began looking from one of her elders to the other. "I'm gonna put on some clothes, Daddy," she said, rising. He gently excused her, and she withdrew to a side room and shut the door. He watched her go with something like satisfaction in his eyes. For another few moments he ate thoughtfully, and nobody spoke before him. When he did, his voice was tight. "Sam, you know what the coroner rule? Cause a death a fall!"

"Fall from that cracker's truck!"

"Oh Lord!" cried the old woman.

"They gon do jus like they please: kill us like a fly!" He put down his spoon and pushed his plate away. "You know . . . I hate to say bad about anybody if they *anything* I can say good, but these folks that run this town they ain nothin but evil, so they but one way to speak of em. I sure do admire you nonviolent folks can get out an march an all like that. If a cracker mess with me or one a mine — " his brow shot up in fierce earnestness — "I got to kill him — *try* to — "

"JP — " said his wife, laying the tips of her fingers on his broad arm.

"Why that jus plain horse sense, baby!" His eyes widened

further in terrific sincerity. "I'm a Deacon of the Church. I follow the Lord jus so far as I am able. But can't all of us *be* nonviolent. The Lord know that! Why he sent Jesus."

This old man was right up and down! "Jesus whipped the moneychangers outa the temple," I said, remembering that from someplace.

"That God's Truth!" cried the deacon, gazing at me with recognition. "Lord know they need a lesson," he whispered.

The old woman had removed her hand from his arm and was drawing a little figure right next to it with her finger on the tabletop. "Well it ain nothin *new,*" she said with a little sigh, and inside her eyes she seemed to be weeping as she looked back on the past. "An they some misunderstandin all around." Now she looked up brightly, "JP, you know what Bessie tol me? She overhear some ladies down the block — church ladies, JP, say, 'Them movemen boys, they ain lookin for nothin but a free meal!' "

"No!" he cried.

"Yeah! I wish I'da been there. Say, 'They can get it when they want it in my home because they doin the Lord's work!' I like to shut them fools up!"

"Well . . ." said the deacon, rubbing the tops of his cheeks with his forefingers. "I know I don need to tell you boys we seen some bad times in this land. I don guess no mortal can ever tell it proper — all that sufferin past. But you got to take the long view . . . It ain easy for me, you young folks can't hardly manage I know. We a long ways from the goal, don see me wrong, but we done got through some hardships in this country an I'm thankful for what been change, and the Lord *know* I'm thankful for the movemen what been changin things!"

"Oh yes!" exclaimed the old lady in a voice so firm and bright a lump formed in my throat.

"I can't be out in it like y'all," he said, "but y'all boys welcome in my house *any*time. Hear? I don say that to many, an I wouldn' say it less I meant it. It ain gon be nothin fancy, but anytime you care to join us, you welcome to what we got."

His leathery hands with veins like pipes and long graceful fingers that could hoist tremendous weights and yet precisely and artfully thread a bolt lay loose and open on the table. "You may not believe in the Lord jus ezackly as I do, but I see you got belief. Gon be a meetin at the church tonight an our pastor gon be with us. I be mighty please to see the movemen represented. I sure wish you all come along."

Sam declined for himself, but I could stay if I wanted and he'd find me later. I thought, I'd be proud! I'd walk down the road with the deacon and his family, and maybe it'd do something for my soul which was somehow more bitter than theirs. I felt good in my vengeful dream, but Mrs. Stock's gentle spirit made me ask myself was I for real?

Before he left, Sam asked when a mass meeting could be held at the church. They agreed tomorrow night. As I waited for the family to get ready, I became self-conscious about my clothes, which were for the street, not church, and they were about all I had—

"Shoot!" said Mr. Stock, "you clean. I useta ten church in my overalls!"

Deacon Stock spoke before the preacher. He urged everyone to return tomorrow night to the mass meeting. He had me stand and identified me with the cause, and then he spoke for ten or fifteen minutes about the little girl who died this morn-

ing. His words found their way from anger to hope and from
grief to joy. He started to sing. His voice was heard in the
church like taut velvet seen through a sudden opening in bright
printed cloth. The cords in his neck stood out. He stood very
straight between the tall pulpit and the front pew, hands relaxed at his sides, his eyes solemn above his passionate lips. His
voice had a strong edge, almost harsh. It lifted and fell delicately, dividing and dividing the minor tones that stir awe and
wonder. The emotion of the congregation, responding, was
formal and restrained. Light or heavy, sliding, their song was
dependent on his. The pastor sat in an armchair on a little
raised stage with his legs crossed. In his hand was a thin rod
and on his fingers were gold rings. He was smiling and his eyes
were almost shut. Mrs. Stock and Beverly and I sat on the aisle
eight or nine rows back. Beverly wore a yellow dress and held
a small green pocketbook. Mrs. Stock wore a gray dress and
had a white cotton shawl about her shoulders. On her head
was a round straw hat with little pink cloth flowers wound into
the brim. She opened a songbook not much larger than the
palm of her hand and held it up so I could see, and even pretended to refer to it herself, so I would feel comfortable. The
voices of the flock splashed like waves into the hollows of the
deacon's hymn. They increased, as under a fast, clean wind,
and covered him over, continuing in his direction. When, after
a quarter of an hour, he took a seat on the deacons' bench at the
right hand of the preacher, there was a time of many voices,
many winds, scattered peaks and caps. And finally silence, into
which the pastor rose. I didn't listen closely to his words. I
didn't follow him carefully through and out of the wide circular
byways of evil up the narrow steep path to good. I couldn't
listen to sermons, but its sounds were joyful, and I was filled

with a diffuse love for the shining tops of the pews, the shoulders of the people sitting ahead of us, fluttering paper fans, the white plastered walls that enclosed the tiny cloud of belief like an eggshell, the red and blue stained glass in the windows, the black organ and the black hats on wall pegs, the choir of three boys in green, the deacons in brown and gray, the old ladies dressed like fading flowers in the amen corner at the side of their pastor who roamed near worlds of ecstasy and shouted back glimpses of the time beyond time. Afterwards he exuberantly gripped my hand and said how happy he was I had come and that he hoped he would see a lot of me in his church. I had many feelings. What did I understand? His happiness made me proud. Sensing my emotion, he smiled firmly and nodded assurance and assent. His spectacles glittered, his eyes twinkled making a dazzling flash. He extended his right hand to the deacon and his left to Mrs. Stock, standing on either side of me. They gazed into each other's eyes, and I wondered at the long flowing between them which now included me.

six

TODAY we walked through the streets of CME, through the
mean sun hours, losing a patrol car, drinking water in front
rooms, informing or reminding people at the right, or last, moment: mass meeting this evening on the grade school playground. We didn't bother with any printed notices, but every
kid we saw Knight sent off with the message. If nothing else,
we would have these dozens of child messengers. And if each
of them brought a few friends we'd have a good crowd.

In The Raindrop, speaking with some cats inside from the
twelve-thirty sun, he hinted of happenings that might develop.
I too had felt distinct interest when I had realized his hopes for
a "disturbance." Stretched out here together in the shade of a
few weathered boards, we gloated over the idea of hundreds of
kids charging the dozen blocks from CME to the city courthouse. What would we do there? Encircle it and sing curses?
Defile it? It wasn't spoken. Having a mob of kids, by night,
close to that citadelic shithouse was enough in its possibilities,
delicious to imagine. One thing, we were laughing — and we'd
be laughing tonight. The fate of this dream, and many others

like it, our contribution to the nonviolent movement, soon
convinced us to give up all pretense.

Today our precious star hovered way too close. I don't remember a hotter day in my life, the temperature had risen
above ninety-five degrees before ten in the morning. The
streets were white as winter, and the orange dust smoldered on
the corners. We found a few cats in the package stores and told
them to come around tonight. We met others in shuttered
rooms, playing cards, drinking wine, and relaxing.

"Fuck it, I wanna swim Jim!" cried Knight, changing his tune
since yesterday — and minute by minute. "Get cool in the pool
Jewel!"

"Shut the fuck up an sit down!" yelled the oldest cat, maybe
about twenty-five, looking at his cards. About ninety percent of
the illusion of it being cool in here came from nobody moving
except to flip some cards, but Knight was walking up and down
making gestures with his arm that took in his whole shoulder.

"I be floatin an divin if the black man weren a fool that's
happy with a piece a shade. I ain got no fuckin ice for my
juice!" he complained, peering into his warm glass.

"Listen boy, they twenty cats right here on this block who be
thankful for a taste a my wine *fuck the ice!*" He returned his
gaze studiously to his hand as Knight sat down on the edge of a
bed, but he looked up again after his play. "I want some
money! I ain got time to be fuckin with no lifeguards."

"I got somethin for them motherfuckers! I could blow them
peoples out a sight."

"I'm hot as a stone in a fire myself," said a player, throwing
down his cards and getting up to wipe his face and neck with a
rag by a window where he cracked the shutter for a peep. "I
wish we did have a pool to cool off. I like to hit some water,

shit!" Dazzled by the light outside, he turned away, rubbing his eyes and groping for the blind, to close it again.

"I don swim in no river," said somebody else. "My cousin got drowned in that sonofabitch!"

The irony of my scene was that I'd like to try that river, or that mudhole, that dangerous current. But I didn't say so. I was whole-hearted for the dream too: "We oughta just hit the fence like you say, Knight, and jump in!"

"All you gotta do is buy a ticket an walk in," he said, bringing me down for a moment.

"They won sell him no ticket!" laughed the chief cat. "They don sell no freedom rider no ticket!"

"You be our inside man for the lifeguards!" said Knight.

We hit the street again. After the dark of the room, waves of white and silver light rolled by my eyes, parting gradually to reveal a pale glazed world. In the distance the lumberyards gave up a yellowbrown haze. Every now and then we passed a little parched tree, its leaves dull and coated. Nobody was outside at high noon. We stopped at a few houses on every block, where Knight had friends or relations. Some didn't let us in, and we stood on the porch and talked through the screen. To all the elders, he talked about the little girl, and he played on the reputation of their neighborhood as rough and indifferent. "I know you think CME where you live by CME Church, but ain no preacher in CME care about that child! Crime, murder, an the electric chair — everybody bad'n scared, they don care bout no childern. Listen — if you can't come, let your kids come out a respect!"

"Oh oh," said the gray-hair, suddenly closing and latching the wood door behind the screen. When we turned around, two detectives were alighting from a brown Ford, adjusting

their hats. They wore short-sleeved white shirts, snub-nose re-
volvers sparkled at their fat waists. They came at us very quick
and had us raise our hands while one frisked us and the other
watched. "What you boys up to?" he asked.

"We're registering voters," I said, knowing the appropriate
response.

"I know you," the cop spoke to Knight, "an I been knowin yo
family fo years, Collins. What you wanna mess with this
trash?" He thumbed at me. "I'd be too proud a my race!"

"I wish I was proud a mine!" I said, and the other cop whirled
me around and sort of ran me to their unmarked car and threw
me against it. "But they're too many rats in it!" I shouted. Obviously I didn't know what I was up against, other than the side
of the car. If I felt any danger, I knew it only as excitement.
The adrenalin was flowing. "Voter registration workers are
covered by federal law, an we're also sellin Boy Scout candy," I
said real close to this fat man's red face.

"You better shut your mouth if you know what's good for
you," he retorted, moving even closer. I was surprised by his
accent, which I placed out of the Midwest, Gary or Chicago,
somewhere.

The other one was talking to Knight, who was looking kind of
grim and saying nothing. "What would yo uncle say, Collins?
Mess with this Communist!"

I must've read too many northern newspapers. Parodies of
redneck southern cops seemed to have come alive before my
eyes. Maybe it was this strange familiarity that made them
seem funny. But I dug Knight's silence and got back my cool.
Now we just stood there, looking around, and the cops stood
there glaring at us. Finally the senior called, "Okay let him go,"
and the other gave me a shove away from the car.

"Hear me, boys!" he said. "We got a nice peaceful town here an we aim to keep it that way. We don want no trouble but if you boys start any, we gonna finish it!"

In the car, they settled their elbows out the windows, and took off in a swirl of dust. Knight was sullen, and embarrassed. His lips were pressed together in a bitter line. "This shit didn useta happen. Black Stars didn put *up* with no shit! Man, it so hard when you ain together!"

We cut off the street into a brambly vacant lot. The high grass hid molehills, tires, tin cans. I stepped on something that honked: it was a child's pink rubber duck which I picked up to give to the next little kid I saw.

"We kidnap a police one time, you know that? It was famous back then, but you probly never heard it. Not from Sam!"

"How'd you do it?" I encouraged him.

A gleam entered his eye. "He come in alone one night on his bike. It was easy — bout ten of us hit him at once, got his gun — tie, gag, blinfold him. We took his horse apart, an stash the pieces. We took him out in the country, man, an chain him to a tree — out in the woods, man. Never did take that mask off his eyes, free his mouth to eat an, you know, jive a little after dinner. Like the Stars' pet, man, we fed him dog food stew!"

We were a hundred feet into the lot, almost to a stand of small trees, when suddenly, from the road we'd departed, came the roar of a motor and the squeal of brakes. It was a white and blue patrol car, and out jumped two uniformed cops shouting. Knight hesitated only a moment. "Run!" he cried, and took off. *Halt! Halt!* they were yelling as we sped into the rank of trees. Running, I was Knight's equal. I wasn't on the track team for nothing! I spoke to myself of the danger. Panting at the furious pace, I was very happy. We cut between houses, jumped a fence, and raced several blocks down an alley. Rounding a corner, he threw out his arms, and slowed, and trotted up to a little house on a cinderblock foundation. Green plants in red rubber tires packed in with black dirt marked the walk to the porch. Rose vines in full bloom climbed the railing. Knight didn't knock.

We entered a small room with square windows. In the center, on an oval mat, two babies looked up with surprise. I gave one the rubber duck to hang on to, that miraculously I hadn't discarded. On a billowy red sofa that took up most of the wall facing the doorway, two chicks were picking collard greens into a big tin pot.

"What this? Headquarters?!" cried one, sitting back with her legs spread apart, twirling a jeweled cross that hung around her neck on a gold-colored chain.

Knight stepped over the pot and flopped down between them. He threw an arm around each, and let out a sigh.

"Get off a me, you!" shouted the younger girl. She twisted away and sat at the very end of the sofa, and went on with her work.

"I declare!" exclaimed the older, giving him a hard scrutiny. "What you been at?" She got up though and got a chair for me, but Knight jumped up and took it and straddled it.

"Damn police stop us, wanna know, 'What you fixin to do?' Sheeit! How they know we was there? That what I wanna know! — Give us a damn speech — 'We got a peaceful town an we gon keep it that way! You boys better remember what we say!' — Uh-*uhh!* Noooo! They wanna know somethin else from this nigger, they gotta catch him!"

I sat on the couch, and began noticing what a good-looking chick I was next to, with big haughty eyes. This was Cara Lee.

The older woman kept standing. Her name was Mae Liza. "So what *are* you fixin to do, Knight Collins? I like to know that myself."

"How I know?!" he exclaimed. "How I know that? The kids know tonight!" That statement was worthy of the Director: The people will decide.

"What happenin tonight?"

"Mass meetin."

"Oh my," she said. She glanced at Cara Lee, and her face showed some pain. "I sense trouble."

"I *see* it!" said Cara Lee, flicking her eyes at Knight, but with a delicate snort that denied any connection to it.

"God's gonna trouble the waters," he said.

That cracked her up. I almost laughed myself. I never heard him say anything like that yet. He grinned. Mae was standing up over him looking at him with hostility, respect, love, and some puzzlement. "Just you leave it to God, boy, we all be a heap better off."

"He think *he* God!" laughed Cara Lee. He jumped up and feigned a slap at her, and she fell back in the sofa.

"I know one thing!" he shouted at Mae. "You believe one thing in church an another out in life!" He stuck his fist back at Cara Lee. "You can be against what I do but don you bad-mouth me, girl!" He moved his hand in close to her jaw.

"I ain afraid a you, Knight, cuz you goin back to jail," she said.

As she was seated to my left, I guess my attention had been constantly drawn in that direction, because chancing to turn the other way I caught sight of a man sitting in the extreme corner, with one stiff leg extended out in front of him. All this time he had not spoken a word and must not have moved. He held my gaze with a soft smile. "This Cousin Yellow," said Cara Lee quickly; there was something like defensive love in her speed. I got up and went to his corner, extending my hand, which he shook. He didn't say anything, and his sweet satisfied smile didn't change.

"Here have some ice water," said Mae, coming out of the kitchen with three glasses, then returning again with one for herself, and one for Cara Lee. There was a silence, spread in by good sounds of our drinking. Like a water ceremony, it seemed to tone things up. One of the babies was trying to climb in the pot of greens. At the last moment Cara Lee plucked him from the tin lip like an exactly ripe fruit from the limb. "Don fall in that, *bubba!*" She had the gentle firm motions of fruit pickers and mothers. She began feeling his thin hair with the tips of her fingers. Mae wanted to speak seriously with Knight. She was sipping her water and tasting it like somebody getting ready to deliver some words. But he didn't want to be messed with further. He rolled on the floor with the little girl baby. "Ladies, we different," he said, tickling her in the stomach. "Us new niggers comin up, we Mau Maus!"

"Get outa my child, Mau Mau!" cried Cara Lee, grabbing her away with one swift hand.

Knight shook his head and got up. Looking sad, he took his glass out on the porch. Mae sat down next to me and put her hand on my leg. "Hey, you ever pick greens?" she asked me. On one side of the pot was a pile of the fresh plants, on the other lay the discarded bare stalks. "Time you learned! Greens easy! Look here — dig in your nail . . . an peel. You in the *South* now, honey!" I set to work on the vegetables lovely as thick green feathers. I felt their strength and spring and experienced the sharp separation of leaves and stem. "Hey, what y'all fixin to start tonight?" she asked in a low voice.

"Well, uh, maybe there'll be a march. If the people at the meeting want to." I had to grin.

"Oh yeah?" She walked to the doorway and told Knight he'd better come inside if he'd been messing with the police. She sat down again and told me about the time the man came for him and took her away too because she'd been outside with him, trying to get the Buick started —

"Listen here," she said in a motherly tone, but loud enough so he could hear out on the porch, "Knight Collins gonna find some way to raise hell, with you or either without you, or the movement — "

"What's wrong with that?"

"What wrong? What wrong with botherin an troublin other *folks!*"

"White folks!" I objected.

"Boy, you don have no idea the number a folks that mad nigger has caused pain an vexation —"

She dismissed me wearily with a wave of both hands but I went on, "So what, if they're white?"

"Who!"

"The object of his hell-raising is *white* —"

"Am *I* white? The object a Knight is to raise hell *period!* He ain no genius. Who been able to separate the white from the black? If them powerful crackers got all the money ain't, you think one crazy fool nigger gonna make it? Believe me, listen to these words, there gon be five Negroes shakin they head with grief for every white man get hell-raised by Knight!"

"Well . . ."

"Well *shit!*" said Cara Lee. "You be sayin *well* in the jail or the hospital one before Knight get through with you!"

Mae regarded me with solemn eyes. Very slowly and sadly she shook her head.

There was something I wanted to express. "Knight's a great talker . . ."

"Now you catchin on!" cried Cara Lee.

"No — " Then an idea struck me. "Look, last night I went to church. I really liked it, you know, the singing, it was peaceful and made me feel a lot of things — it's the same with what me and Knight are into — "

"What!" said Cara Lee.

But Mae was looking at me in a new way. "You ten church? That fine. You jus go, or you go with some folks?"

"With Deacon J. P. Stock."

"He ask you to join yet?" asked Cara Lee. "You gon be in the choir — "

"Hush, girl! Don pay her no min —"

"I believe! I believe more'n a heap a folks out there in they Sunday hats!"

"He ain studyin you!" Mae told her. She looked at me seriously, hopefully. "I know Deacon Stock an his wife, I know all the family. You met up with some good folks —"

"It gonna look might funny you sing in the choir on Sunday, hang on the street with Knight the rest a the week. Maybe you get *him* to join." That thought made her laugh. "Practice up, you can sing a duet come Christmas. Wear shades, somebody help you on the stand. The Genuine Calvary Blind Boys. Milk an honey in that *land!* Folks come from miles! Bring the pastor down in The Raindrop for a beer after the show — drink it out a glass . . ."

"You come into the church very slow," said Mae. "If it don fit at first, you wait. Cara Lee gon joke you. Knight gon sure joke you. Christian folks done always had a hard way to go. But you listen at your own heart. The Lord take note . . ."

When Knight came back in he was laughing. "What that police say?" he laughed, pointing at me, " 'This here white trash! This here Commanist.' " It was funny all right, and I laughed too. He fell back on the bed by the window. "Sheeit! *I* may look for *him!* Fuckin with us like that!"

Mae picked up a collard and shook it at him before she stripped it — "Y'all playin with the laws! You playin with fire!"

They argued for a while. Cara Lee took no part in it. She held her two babies, one in each arm, and hummed and sang to them. I had the greens to enjoy, and her too. Under Yellow's grave smile, time seemed to have turned and slowed, and I was happy and at ease here, I forgot about the cops, and tonight. When she put down the babies on the floor again, her breasts were pressed into beautiful curved fields of subtle matter where I'd love to plunge my hands. But right after my desire came a tail of guilt, and an image of the Director's face, as he spoke to a few of us new civil rights workers: "One thing we don't need down here is any illegitimate babies, especially tan ones. Remember: There are people in this community who think of you as saints." So far I'd taken no chances. He was the type of man, if you messed up, he'd buy you a bus ticket out of town in a hurry. But I hadn't met Cara Lee!

I took a rest from the greens, and took the little girl baby on my knees and gave her a standing lesson, which she got into with eager legs and solemn eyes. She couldn't be but a few months. The little boy looked a year. He had crawled over to the side of the bed and was trying to pull Knight's shoe off.

"Take me to the show, Knight!" said Cara Lee.

"I would baby, but all I got is forty cent an I got to buy milk for *my* baby," he said.

"When the las time you bought milk for that baby!"

"An if it wasn for that, I'd buy me a half pint a somethin fore I waste no money on you."

"Will you take me?" she asked me.

I was almost not ready for that one, and I didn't have a cent. No, I wasn't thinking of taking her to the show. But I told her I wished I could, and I would, if I had anything.

"You movemen boys, ain ever got nothin," Knight cracked.

"All too damn true. What we get in the movement, we just barely stay alive. I wish I knew how to get somethin in between times!"

"Stick aroun here an see what you can't get into!" laughing and socking his elbows into the mattress.

"He's welcome anytime," she said. "He ain no tramp like you!"

"Long as he don be messin with no cops," said Mae. "I can't stan no heat!"

"Thank you," I said. "You're generous *and* beautiful," I told Cara Lee, feeling her waves, and feeling close to her, and less and less far, like it is on an old soft sofa — you sort of cleave together.

When we'd finished picking the greens, Mae took them into the kitchen and prepared some for eating. It was going to take a little while to cook them up. She gave us the price of a quart of beer, and we took a walk to get it. The sun was low, the cage had lifted off the land, old women lolled their hands over sills, and people were venturing out at last.

"Every time you get with that baby she start to howl!"

Out a door and across a porch a mother was chasing her small boy with a hairbrush. He leaped off and hit the dust that licked his elbows. Off down the curb he ran, with his mother hollering after him, "You better run! You little brown butt be blue!"

"When I was a little boy," said Knight, "I like to climb the talles tree an curse grown folks. Smoke cigarettes an drink ginger ale preten it gin. See somebody comin, start to talk about em. — 'Oh look at ol ugly black-ass Mrs. Jinks, I wonder who been fuckin her this mornin!' When they haul me down an whip me for it, I never cry. Time I got my belt buckled again, I be right back up there! — That why I understan young kids today. They trust me because I can think like they do."

A boyfriend of Mae's had shown up by the time we got back. He had a bottle of wine. We all had a plate of greens, and drank beer and wine. By the time we got high, we weren't thinking of a thing but getting higher, and then this cat brought up the rape, the murder. It brought the girls down, and they protested not now! But it didn't bring me down, he thought just like I did, that there wasn't but one thing really to do, anyone man enough. But Knight said, dig it, come by the meeting tonight an see if we don't raise some sand! The cat said okay, he would. Mae told him he was crazy. She said there was only one thing that *could* happen. A lot of fools go to jail. And then Yellow spoke for the first time: "I'll be there," he said. Just like that, no more. Knight charged up on that. He stood up and drank on it. He pulled my arm. We had a few plans to get straight yet. I thanked Mae for the dinner. And I told Cara Lee, see you later. At the meeting, said Knight. "Shit!" she said as we went out the door.

seven

THE DUSK was pink as an ax in rosewood — like a dawn, a beginning. There were a hundred people on the street for every one I'd seen all day. The alcohol was reminding me I'd caught a little sunburn lately, though it didn't interfere with how I felt: mellow and ready, and very excited.

"Hey! Damn if I ain still hungry," said Knight. "You got anything to eat over at the movement?"

At the office, nothing but grits, rice, beans, coffee, and charity canned goods that I wouldn't offer a starving man, they were that stale. I think some grocery chain sent them down for extra points, what's been sitting on their shelves long enough for the labels to fall off. There were the Stocks, however. I could take them up on their invitation, I explained, only it was going to be a long walk. Silently, I wondered about the old lady's reaction to the name "Knight Collins" last night. Out loud I emphasized the distance.

"Knight! Knight!"

A boy sped straight at us no-handed on his bicycle, with a

grin wide as his handlebars. Knight threw out his arms and maneuvered in front of him. He tried to swerve, but Knight caught the seat and yanked him to a stop. He shook him friendly till he laughed.

"Hey — how many friends you bringin by the school tonight?"

The kid began to number on his fingers. "Eight," he said.

"That all?"

"That *all?*"

"Are you sure?"

"Yeah," he grinned proudly.

"Try to make it ten. Hey — listen cat, I got important business in a hurry, borra me your bike till the meetin, okay? One hour, okay?"

Reluctantly the kid gave it up. "Hop on," said Knight, and I got up on the handlebars, and he kicked off. It didn't take us long at all. We got up some good speed.

"Look at that, man," I pointed out the deacon's pavement. "He laid that himself in thirty-nine." He looked appreciatively at it, and at the house too. He carried the bike up on the porch and laid it down in the corner. Beverly answered the door.

"Hi," she smiled at me, "you come back to see us!"

"I'm Knight," said Knight.

"How you do," said Beverly, leading the way.

"Who you, sugar?"

"Beverly." Smiling shyly and casting her eyes down, acutely conscious of Knight's eyes on her as she walked to the kitchen.

"Hey man! That is these people's granddaughter," I whispered. "Be cool with Beverly . . ."

Out of the kitchen strode the deacon. Into the kitchen walked Beverly.

"How you doin?" he clapped me on the back. "Stock's my name," he said to Knight.

"I'm glad to meet you, Mr. Stock. I'm Collins."

"Collins! I'm pleased to know you."

"Yes I been hearin some fine things about you, Deacon. Tell me, is that nice red church on the corner y'all church?"

"Yes it is! Mount Olive Baptist!" He motioned us to have a seat.

"Well it a fine lookin church, Deacon. I partikly like them red bricks."

"Why thank you. That the new church, built in nineteen fifty-seven. The ol church was all wood an mighty pretty, but not so sturdy."

"I can't think a no church prettier! I notice your chimney here made out a red bricks too. I like to build me a wall out a red bricks like that."

"Oh? Well, they some sturdy bricks all right . . . Well, so you work with the movement?"

"Yessir!"

"Where you stay, Collins?"

"CME."

The slightest tremor crossed the old man's face. I began to wonder how this would turn out.

"How the movement?" he asked me.

"Well — we got a meeting planned for tonight."

"Tonight?"

"Yessir! In CME."

"Let the folks speak what on they mind," said Knight. "Let em talk. What is the movement without folks speak free — ?"

"What you think on they mind?" asked the deacon suspiciously.

"They wanna march!"

"Yes?"

"That right!"

"Well . . . I think what you boys doin gonna count. One day you be known . . ."

"Yeah, that swimmin pool gotta get took care of one way or the other!"

"How you mean that?"

"Well sir, Deacon, the truth is I ain't altogether nonviolent. Times I can't help myself — I get way hotter'n a nonviolent ever be. Summer is hot an *somethin* gotta be done! But if I can't swim in it, what I care about it?"

"Jesus brought a sword! Sometimes you gotta show folks, you gotta spell it plain!"

"Yessir, I believe in the Golden Rule — but it work both ways! If they gonna be nasty, then so am I too!"

"To put a *finish* to the nastiness. — The Lord understan that!" The deacon was warming up. "Look here, back a long time ago, when I wasn much older than either one a you boys, *we* had a little movement. That was way out in the country an believe me movement was a *crime* in them days! We had a movement for votin, an votin was an *evil crime!* Ha ha! The NAACP voter convention, an the center of it were my brother church. Shady Grove Baptist! That is a pretty wooden church! They tried to burn it down but it standin today! The Klan come to set it afire in revenge for us votin. We shot em up. You shoulda seen em run! Got they sheets hutched up roun they knees, white sheets flappin. Folks don believe we was bad in them days! How we know they was gon burn down the church, cause they drop some buckets a gas when they run, gas spill on the ground. It killed almost a circle a grass. To this *day* that spot is bare! I seen it las year on a trip. Don no grass grow there!"

Knight had the good manners not to try to top the story with one of his own. "What kind a guns y'all have?" he asked.

"Me, I had my shotgun. Deacon Bradley had his army rifle . . ." The deacon's face was beaming pleasure in thinking back on it. "Elder Berry got one of em in the knee with his rabbit gun. A couple a handguns. They ain never come back since that night. How many churches been burnt aroun here the las fifty years? Shady Grove a fifty year ol pine board church. We had to be reckoned with back then. We were so bad we didn't have to mess with no ordinary everyday bad, cause they knew we were ready!" Carried away with his memory, the deacon was on the edge of his chair.

"Hoo! I bet they soun nice," cried Knight, "them guns poppin! I wonder why do them Klux wear sheets anyway? They a dead giveaway, see em for a mile. One time I threw a brick at one of them, hit him right in the point a the cap — bam! Bounced off! That his head in there no lie! Ha ha ha!"

Knight laughed and held himself. The deacon chuckled politely and leaned around in his chair and called to his wife in the kitchen, "How supper comin, honey?"

"It about to come right on the table. Go on set down!"

As soon as we had taken seats, Knight and I on one side, the deacon at the head of the table, Mrs. Stock and Beverly brought in plates of boiled potatoes, red beans, sunfish, corn bread. Just looking at the hard salty pie-shaped bread made my mouth water, and I thought it was only Knight that was still hungry. Each of us said a grace. Deacon Stock asked the Lord to bless our good work with the movement. Knight asked him to bless the house and its people from the oldest to the youn-

gest. I couldn't top that. I asked for peace and joy for us.
"That was back in depression days, that shootin," the deacon
went on, helping himself to beans. He seemed to have forgotten all about his first doubt of Knight, who'd turned out to be a
pretty good listener. I guess he guessed it — I was the best
listener he may ever have. "They was some *mean* ol times for
everybody. Meanes of all was white folks to white folks! You
believe that? I lef the country an come to Meansville an got me
a job at Dixie Bakeries. I was right lucky with thousan a folks
roamin every road lookin for scraps . . . I remember every
day how the poor stop outside the main bakeshop an beg a little
stale bread. White an Negro, don say nothin, beg with they
eyes. I seen that man turn his own kind away but I ain never
seen him turn away no black man without a crust at least!
Funny, huh? Like he too ashame a them sorry rednecks even
to help. An then they come trampin by *my* house — knowin
the niggers ain gonna let em starve! Say, 'I clean yo yard fo ya,
sweep yo drive, only lemme have a little leftovers what you gon
throw out.' I say, 'What I need your help? I'm able-bodied, I
got a strong wife.' I give em somethin, if only an ol heel I took
from work. But I don let em do nothin! . . .

"Hey, this ain no depression!" The deacon pointed at me.
"Where your appetite?"

I was chewing steadily, — but I'd eaten a lot of greens at
Mae's.

"I bet you nervous bout your meetin!"

I laughed — "No, I got plenty!"

"Ain got no room for some more potatoes?" He helped me to
some more. "You need your strength, you better *make* yourself
eat. Jail food mighty poor! Ha ha! Better get you some good
vittles while you can!"

"JP!" Mrs. Stock looked askance at her husband.

"Shoot! I ain tellin him nothin he don know. Am I, son?"

"Well we be prayin for ya," said Mrs. Stock. "The Lord ain gonna let nothin slide by He don notice it. We be prayin your meetin get good results . . . an don bring no more trouble than it naturally hafta."

Under cover of the conversation, Knight had been eyeing Beverly, who had been keeping her eyes on her plate. "Maybe Beverly like to march," he said.

A long silence.

"Well, that be up to Beverly," said Mrs. Stock.

"I like to march," said Beverly, smiling shyly —

Deep down in his throat, the deacon grumbled. "Well I hafta think about *that!* Huh! . . . If you march, honey, I *sure* hafta go along, an I don know if these ol bones ready for that."

Now I was ready for anything, but he was looking at us compassionately. He pushed his plate with only the skeletons of two sunfish and a bit of corn bread rind left on it to the center of the table.

"While I think of it, I got somethin for you two boys to study. Love, look in my big trunk under my bed, see can you see my blue box, bring it to me please."

Dutifully, Beverly found the blue box and brought it to the table. Before he took it, the deacon wiped his mouth and hands with a paper napkin and dropped it onto his plate. It was a big box, with a silver cord around it. There was something well-worn and private about its surfaces that strangely intimidated me. The small white peak of common tissue settled on the plate with snowflake force distracted my attention from him untying the silver string, and delving around in the piles of cards and papers inside the box, and finally pulling out a little pamphlet covered with black and white wavering stripes — "I wish I had one to give each of ya. I thought I had a whole stack but I see I only got one so you'll hafta share it. Take it home — here — study it in private."

It looked like a little square of zebra skin. I put it in my pocket.

Everybody was real nice the rest of the time. Nothing of substance was mentioned. My moment of discomfort I almost forgot. Knight was silent, as if contrite. We thanked them carefully and left.

We got the bike, and walked it down the street. In front of Mount Olive Baptist I pulled the little book out of my pocket. Its title was *Trapped* — in jagged terrifying letters across the black and white bars. I read —

Many young people find themselves *trapped* today. They are caught in a subtle trap laid by the devil, which is the trap of mistaking *lust* for *love*. The Bible speaks of love as the highest gift of God, not easily received by men. Lust is the pleasure snare set by Satan. It is the fool's gold of the heart . . .

"What is *this*? Why'd he give us *this*?"

Knight had walked over to the church and was running his fingers over its brick surface.

"He a deacon, ain he? They always givin out little books like that. Tear it up. C'mere look at this good brick. You know, I like to have me a ranch, with cows, sheep, an vegetable gardens, an a tall wall all aroun it made outa brick like this here keep out everybody but my friends. Sometimes I have a dream about it, like my own town, an the wall too high an slick to climb."

I hated a little religious pamphlet, but I didn't tear it up. I put it back in my pocket, and Knight took his hands off the brick wall of the church. It was his turn to ride, and suddenly I had energy to burn, I rode him back to CME faster than we'd come. The speed and the wind picked up my spirit. The action was about to start! There were a couple good hills on the way and he jumped off before the climb. I hadn't ridden a bicycle for years. I'd almost forgotten the pleasure of the swoop down-hill.

"Sometimes I dream about a *river*," he hollered back to me over his shoulder. "I'm driftin down in the sunshine, take it easy — here come a *waterfall!* The river explode. Bricks flyin like it was a dam. Noise make me deaf. It soun beautiful!"

eight

THE SOUND I heard up ahead was music. Maybe fifty kids had already arrived. Under the big tree in the middle of the yard, they were singing movement songs, clapping hands, popping fingers, and some of the girls were dancing. Half a dozen old women had put down newspapers out a ways from the kids. Boys on bikes with streamers flying from the handle grips circled round and round. Knight delegated one to ride and get a wooden box for the speaker's platform. It was deep twilight, and time to get started. I wondered how Knight was going to trigger it. Would the old ladies march too? He wasn't talking about his plans. He was sending all the boys on bikes out with word it was time. Porches across the street bordering the playground were filled with folks watching from a good safe distance to see what might develop. A little kid ran away from one and was halfway to us before his mother caught him and dragged him, howling and protesting, back to the house. But despite their parents, the kids were arriving. And young men were coming in from the bars and hip hangouts. I recognized many faces from our walk today. Knight got up on the box and waved his arms for quiet, and when the singing and talking had died down, he jumped down and let a boy wearing a medallion over his T-shirt stand up. He had a cardboard megaphone with the name of a high school on it. He was a cousin of the little girl who'd been killed. He said some nice things about her in a quiet, invulnerable voice, then he started winding up good into the pig, the killer, and the cracker race that didn't punish him. Yells, hoots, threats, laughter, and kids' curses filled the air. A movement car — the old Studebaker — pulled up at the corner. Knight told me to go over and tell them we had enough speakers, and if they had any other ideas, to cool them. I started over. I didn't know how I was going to put it to the Director whose form I could make out through the windshield. Before I got there Knight was up on the box.

"We gon have a march aroun the block!"

His arms were outstretched as if he meant to embrace the whole crew.

"Line up two by two — no shovin! Aroun the block show these Negroes can't get off they porch we together!"

He began walking toward the other side of the playground. The kids were with him. The girls started to sing, "Ain gonna le-et nobody turn me roun!" A long line was forming behind him. It stretched from the big tree to the curb, where he stopped, with his arms raised above his head.

Dragging kids by the arms, old women listed their hips like boats for the shoreline of porches.

"Jimmy! *Oh* Jimmy! Where you at?"

Knight was off, with a parade alive at his heels. I ran the rest of the way to the car as Sam got out to greet me. He looked excited and almost happy, but inside the Director had a skeptical frown on his face. He didn't like to see the kids and the old folks running away from each other. With nothing to say to each other, Sam and I watched the line of hundreds circle the school block. Man, they looked beautiful marching down the street toward us. Knight had got a wooden cane from someplace. It had a polished brass head, and he was flicking it high in the air with every other step. Songs! Laughter! Rhythms! Kids slipped away from their mothers and ran out of the cuts between houses to push into line. The grounds were clear but for a few newpapers fluttering under the meeting tree. On the porches astonished, outraged, fascinated old ladies and gents holding cardboard fans given out by Jones' Funeral Home eyed their children passing in unstoppable waves.

"Les go roun again!" cried Knight. "Les do it again!"

But when he reached the far corner the second time, he didn't turn, he took a straight course down the road. I took off. "Oh Jesus!" exulted Sam. "He's takin em downtown!" Only the Director, who was shaking his head sorrowfully, restrained him from running too.

I passed Cousin Yellow making good speed but with a bad limp. His brow was beaded with sweat, and he smiled at me.

A drunken wino was dancing and laughing — "Think Chief Pullet let a barefoot nigger in without any shoes?" kicking up his naked heels.

OD and a gang of boys were running alongside the lines. They disappeared up alleyways only to reappear again with their number strengthened. We were in a white neighborhood. The town was laid out like a checkerboard. And it was our move now! I was almost to the front when we passed a gas station with a bunch of whites gathering in its doorways. In the bright lights of the gas pumps shaped like coffins they looked more red than white. Out of the lines leapt OD. Three blows of his club and the red lights were smashed. Rocks and bottles followed, chasing our first opposition back in the garage.

Out in front — twenty feet ahead of the first of the marchers — Knight was strutting. He was swinging his cane like some hip baton. His eyes were glossy with triumph, though the courthouse was blocks away. It lasted another few minutes. My memory of the rest is confused. At a cross street, without a siren, squad cars and paddy wagons made a cordon. Forty or fifty cops advanced on us, and the lines buckled and broke. I don't know how many kids got away, or how many got caught in the crush. I don't know how or why the hundred of us in front kept marching into the strange pass. Everything was shining: fenders, windshields, buckles, gun barrels, badges, and eyes — giving out a white light. They grabbed Knight and pounced on me. All around us identical glittering lawmen were closing in on the kids.

"You can now disperse and you will not be arrested. This is your warning," somebody was calling over a bullhorn.

Upside down, as I was being carried to the wagon, I saw the smallness of the children. A celebration of children! — consumed by streaks of blue and red cops. Three were carrying me and a fourth was smacking me with his club. In my memory is a photograph of fifty white chins, crossed by long sticks working like windshield wipers.

"Only chance we got now is stay crazy!" whispered Knight, as the motor roared and the wagon lurched. They had packed about thirty of us inside. "Come in on the Lord's Prayer . . ."

In a loud grave voice:

"Our Father which art in heaven . . ."

A little behind him, we joined in, haltingly:

"Hallowed be thy name . . ."

The cop in the shotgun seat began to draw his club back and forth across the screen that separated the two sections of the wagon: it made a horrible grating noise. We prayed louder —

"Thy kingdom come. Thy will be done in earth as it is in heaven . . ."

A little girl was sobbing. My God! So little! They throw her in too?

The driver slammed on the gas and cut close to the curb at a corner, pitching us off the thin benches.

"Give us this day our daily bread . . ."

Shotgun switched hands and rattled his club faster.

"And forgive us our debts as we forgive our debtors . . ."

The driver took the next corner even more sharply, and though we were expecting it, we just barely held on.

"And lead us not into temptation, but deliver us from evil: For thine is the kingdom, and the power and the glory for ever! Amen!"

Knight whispered, "Nex corner, throw all our weight the way the truck leans!" And then he began to preach:

"We love our white brother! Ain nothin wrong with a white skin that a little thought won cure! My ol granmother herself — God rest her soul — she was pretty bright-skinned!"

He crouched under the screen at the front of our cage. He delivered right up into the faces of the cops in the front seat.

"Yes, oh yes, we love our white brother! An our white sister too! Our white brother think that *all* we love, but it ain so, I want me *thirty or forty* of them white sisters!"

When we hit it, the wagon rose onto two wheels, skipped, trilled on its tires, and wobbled for several very enjoyable moments, and finally, disappointingly, bounced upright again.

Both cops were clinging fast to the dashboard. The driver ground down to a slow crawl. "Boys," said the cop who'd been beating his stick on the screen, "you see that big tree yonder? Boys, I swear to God if I had my way, I'd see you every one a you hangin from the highest limbs!"

There was true light in his eyes. The littlest of the boys began to shiver and the girl who'd been crying was frozen in a corner with big eyes and no more tears.

"The Lord is my shepherd!" cried Knight, "I shall not want!"

A lot of the kids were let to walk out the van. Not me and Knight. By our heels we were dragged over the coarse gravel of the alley behind the jail and over a tall sharp doorstep into the walkway of the Negro cellblock. A cop for each heel, wearing inscripted shields with war wings a little above their cold hearts. "Ain't you somethin!" one licked his lip. He nudged me with his boot, not hard, as if to assure himself I was really there. "You ain't black — an you sho cain't be white!" He stood there looking down at me with disgust for what seemed a very long time. Then they all disappeared — maybe they were on their way back for another load. Like waking at gray dawn in a rainy ditch, I eased up on my elbows. There was something deceptively peaceful about the scene. Our bodies were cast down in a long circle, heads tilted up and knees were drawn up. The apparent peace of shock was echoing over the dank concrete. My thoughts floated uneasily at the sides of my mind, and couldn't be assembled toward any move. I seemed to see a mobile of metal and gray cloth sections turning above me, with red gaps between the shapes fanning into the pale air. Momentarily we were alone. Knight got up and began searching for something to destroy. On top of a tall steel locker lay boxes of blue prison uniforms, which he tipped onto the floor.

That was all there was in here. After the uniforms, nothing else. He vengefully laughed. He tore open the boxes and began ripping the cloth hand over hand. His anger was a matchflame in a hawk wind — yet leaping up. It flared defiantly against the darkness of the cage that towered into the night. My confusion was dispelled by a lucid bitter rage that didn't doubt he was my brother. Many joined us. Only a few minutes had elapsed before the law returned. Very beautiful strips of blue against the dirty gray cement. Around it we lay with our heads in our hands, laughing. Triumphant, fragile, a new star in Knight's fan of stars.

nine

I WAS NOT KEPT in this jail. In a squad car I was driven out into the country.

Now I was scared enough to know I was scared and to know that I knew. You ever been carried here and there in mystery and rode back and forth by men with guns under legal authority cryptic and for real as the pyramids? Any of you older (or younger) survivors, did this fear born of lost bearings take its cold grip on your throat as you got into the unknown automobile? Out the window I could see neat pecan groves, and later shining peach orchards. After only a night in jail, the countryside seemed fantastically fresh and moist. The cops in the front seat spoke only to each other. In about half an hour, we arrived at a modern new jailhouse inside a high barbed fence. A dirt road led off the highway to it. It was built in the functional flat style of public outhouses in a busy picnic area of a park, except for the locks and the wire. One of my captors had the keys. He unlocked the fence, and then the steel door set in the brick wall. We walked around the walkway past empty cell after cell, and he opened the door of one in the corner. There were windows in the outer walls with reinforced panes that let some light in. The small center pane was clear and you could actually get a view of the road. "You the property of Sheriff Dick now!" he told me, with a weird smile, and departed, locking all the doors behind him.

Through the window I watched the car go up the road. The dust settled, and I occupied myself with watching it. This was no single cell. It was on the order of a pen, recently constructed, with a metal table like a picnic table, and a toilet and shower in the open. Off the main area were half a dozen little two-man cells, with bunks. The walls were an even, new gray as yet undecorated with dates, names, messages, mottoes, or obscenities. I had a pen with me, left in my pocket since the vote drive. By bending it back and forth I succeeded in breaking the metal clip, and with the sharp end I began scratching my name. But I had hardly started when I heard music! I walked to the other end of the pen area, from which direction the sound seemed to come, and got a look out the window at that end. All I could see was sky. I climbed up on the upper bunk in the last cell — I couldn't believe it! I saw a swimming pool! Outbuildings — it looked like some recreation center, in a shallow valley, below the jailhouse. I could see white kids on the sides of the pool, and heads bobbing in the blue water. There goes a chick doing a fancy dive off the three-meter board! And when the song stopped, I heard their shouts and laughter, faint but clear. Then it started again —

> If you wanna be happy for the rest a your life,
> Never take a pretty woman for your wife!

I was glad to hear it. Man, some music was a relief from a minute ago. I laughed at the words, the weakness in the sentiment was somehow appropriate for a man in jail out in No-where. Though I didn't have a wife, I almost felt as if I'd been betrayed by a pretty woman. Who? Not Cara Lee, who had made her warning clear! If I had listened to her, I might be in her bed tonight! I remembered her neck and her breasts — I pictured her breasts and — oh man, stop killing yourself.

The kids played the song over and over, even at night. It became ridiculous. At first I thought, well they got only one song on their box, but then I began to think, no, they're playing it to torment me. Late at night, they shut it off, and I thanked my luck.

"Steak an porkchops this evenin, boy!"

At dusk the sheriff came in with his friendly greeting, "Hi boy!" and my dinner.

Chortling at his joke, he set my plate of grits and fatback down on the floor and gave it a little kick under the bars. I gave it a big kick back out again. Why should I eat this hog food always slid along to me on the floor? This time-torture was in-jecting me with enough toxins to vomit up when I got out, without my eating some pig fat too.

"Boy, you look pitiful to me. It makes me sorry. Don nobody care about you not eatin! Who you think give a damn? Food gon get wasted one way or the other! What you think some-body comin for you? I had ol Martin Luther King in my jail one time. In the mornin a big pink Cadillac come for him when they bail him out. Where yo big Cadillac, boy? Hm?"

I came to hate the sheriff with his miserable joking. On the second evening — to punish me I suppose — he didn't show up at all, and that night I was starving. By the third day the worst pains were over, my pride was up, and thereafter I refused everything he brought. On the Fourth of July he came in eating delicious barbecue and lemon pie, and stood there offering me bites and licking his fingers and laughing at me denying him in the trap! It's counter to all lore of survival. In his eyes I saw his small sorrow that he couldn't have me ten or fifteen years, which he'd need to make his subtle points. Later, I would bring the food in and touch and smell it, and lie on my back concocting long fabulous recipes which I promised myself for when I got out. Once, I lost control and grabbed a bite of beans, which made it to the back of my throat before I gagged and coughed it out again. For minutes I stood at the bars hawking and spitting. I washed my mouth out at the sink and had a nice long drink of water.

The first week the pains were bad, but after that my stomach shrunk and the region numbed. In the streaked mirror over the sink, I watched my face grow thinner and thinner. The hollows of my cheeks hid behind my beard the way the joinings of the steel around me were being blurred by a gray fuzz. Though I rubbed my eyes, it wouldn't go away. The balls in their sockets felt coated. Like a goldfish in too small a bowl, I was shrinking. I reached for my shirt and missed. My image seemed sunk in the glass further than the distance that I stood from it. I rolled over and over on my bunk, seeking a comfortable distribution of my bones, but it seemed to change shape and angle, affording me sleep and dim visions but no rest. I looked out the windows for days on end. The dusty road and few blades of grass retreated, and the music from the pool became a strange foreign chant that eventually was indistinguishable from silence.

One day the sheriff brought in a drunk and locked him in the cell next to mine. He slept all afternoon and into the next day. When he awoke, he began singing and complaining to himself.

I called over to him, and it surprised him there was anybody else in here too. After that he would walk to the bars, and complain to me.

"I got a bad suspicion that man I work for ain gonna get me out. He know I'd work overtime every day till I pay him back, but how I'm gon pay it off up here? They give you a fine but how you gonna pay when you under a lock? Honest Jesus! I wasn that drunk they gotta lock me. It ain right! I'm like a rabbit — always on the run . . ."

Tonight I didn't spitefully ruin my dinner, but instead handed it around to my time-partner. He couldn't believe it. Hungry as he was coming off a binge, he tried to make me take it back and eat it, especially when I told him I hadn't eaten for two weeks. I promised him if he gave it back I'd only throw it on the floor. The sheriff didn't often bring it over anymore. He gave it to his boy to bring, who came with a mop. In return for the extra meal my new buddy rolled me up some of his Prince Albert tobacco to smoke.

The taste of it was thick and harsh, and I puffed hard on the expertly rolled cigarette hoping to get a little buzz. But if you haven't eaten anything for a while, some fresh P. A. will knock you out! My mind blacked — I came to on the floor, with it still between my fingers. Damn, I felt nice! And my head was spinning. The jail which had been wrong as a tin can in a green field seemed natural and inevitable. I gazed at my surroundings as if seeing them for the first time, and in peace. No star, twig, leaf, and not a breeze unless I waved my arms — yet here was a solitude sweet as a watch on the sea or a walk through the forest. When this world began to ebb, I smoked more. I took deep tokes and held each breath. Off flew the roof — this was my illusion — and I found myself in the bathhouse of a municipal pool in a southern city where I spent summers as a little boy. All the sights and sounds were right. I was relaxing after a nice swim. — When the roof came back on I remembered I was in the zoo that was adjacent to that pool. — And then in came the sheriff, with a friend.

"This *him?*" asked the man.

"Yes tis, this the boy," the sheriff told him. "The ringleader a that trouble they had over in Meansville."

By his clothes he was a farmer. His nose was long as a pin, and his whole face converged at that sharp beak. His lips were drawn upward to it, his eyes sneaked looks around it. I was a white lynx caught by the hunters, given over to keep by jailers and feeders at the zoo of the Man and his friends.

"I guess I ain ever seen one of em before."

"You can tell em by the eyes."

"Dirty ain he!"

"Huh! Some kinda beast!"

"Beard!"

They make me an animal and then demand I stay clean! They don't like it when I litter the floor and piss on the walls, but I've reached an understanding where I am! I never wear a shirt. I lie on my bunk without hardly rising. The farmer came close to the bars which seemed to vanish in the terrific strengths of hate and fear that separated us.

"If'n you had belief in the Lord, you wouldn be in here in this mess!"

"If you were a good Samaritan you'd open the door for me!"

"Don't play with the Lord, boy!"

"Jesus moved mountains with a mustard seed an you got the key in your pocket!"

"Cain't talk no sense to that one," the sheriff intervened and led his friend away. "He lost his mind, probably LSD . . ."

With my tongue, I taste the steel, as the eyes of the cat follow them from the chamber. A vile acid spreads through my mouth into my brain. It strikes my hands that shake the bars that are *fixed*. Devil! What Will did you hire to alchemize this cage for me from Noble Iron? Close to the rock where the rainbow crashes — I'm in a cold sweat, and there's the mystery of the birds soaring up on drafts to lofty multiples of the falls . . .

Horror! The walls are converging! Faces of tombstones and diamonds! Murderous intent masked by the uniform slow gray . . . and my initials . . .

I shook that one off and stumbled to a bunk. I had glimpsed what Knight and I were flouting. I saw what would kill or ignore him if he lost his balance. Waves of suffocating loneliness assaulted me, bringing memories of other jails and college and desperate anger. We cannot march! Don't draw on the Law! Get a bead on it from behind a tree, and over a rocky crest as it rides in fat column. Do not slap power, because power don't play. — I didn't enjoy the stock I was taking. It was true but I was tired. Nonviolence and marching didn't work. When the sheriff's trusty showed up with dinner I grew more irritated than usual. With my time-mate he thought he'd found a bridge. He'd stand up there and jive with him, and keep trying to switch the conversation over to me. He asked me, How could I do myself like this? He was for the movement, he told my friend. He didn't see how my fasting could help the movement. — I told him I didn't either, really.

"Don pester the boy," said the cat, trying to help me out. "Man's got to do what he got to do," he said between mouthfuls.

I was glad when he left. As the night began, my buddy sang a plaintive song that told it all, in blue and silver, and I fell asleep.

I slept twelve-fourteen hours without any problem these thin days. In the morning I had a surprise. I was woken by the movement lawyer, who brought me mail and told me my situation. It was a pleasure to see his courageous, arrogant black features through the bars. Yes, a little arrogance on the side of freedom please! He spoke ironically to the sheriff, not hiding his contempt, just running it a little above his intellectual level. He told me that Knight and the others had already been tried, and that I was going to court soon — he couldn't be sure when — and that if I was convicted I'd be bailed out by the movement. He shook his head at my physical condition. He advised me: Eat soup for a day or two after you get out of here. I didn't feel lost any longer. My mood changed for good.

Now my hours were spent in eager expectation of a sound or sight of freedom. An indistinct sound outside — it's them come for me. Sight of a car on the road — it's them come to get me. All day I drank cups of water, I was so dry. I would've paced the floor if I had any energy. My spirit was taking big leaps over the land. But by nightfall, I knew it was all over until morning, and I got my buddy to roll me a few P. A. reefers, and I lay back and smoked. Lack of food as the month's end nears does far-out things to your head. Outside in the night it seemed to be raining. At the place where the road disappeared in a mist, I saw a great hunk of a rock like granite. I cracked up, and laughed and laughed at myself. Who would believe this? — But there it was, causing me to relax even more. I laughed at myself yearning to be outside when I couldn't be —

"Brighten up!"

About all that could disturb my pleasant dream before sleep was the sheriff.

"Don't kill yourself! What a sulk!"

In his heart the true fear of the keeper that the animal will die; not knowing himself how long the cage is timed for. But I don't die. I don't deny the victory to my persistent and perverse refusal even to talk, beyond a few words of refusal. Evidence of that I saw in the Man's eyes, who (I learned) had to spread lies to the outside about nutriment I received smuggled in capsules, possibly by my lawyer. Now that he had paid me a visit, the sheriff came by every evening to interrupt my thoughts. Maybe he was afraid my dirty starved appearance would give his jail a bad name somehow, I don't know. In the metal picnic grounds with no picnic all you can do is burn your mind. In the hole, you can dig the scenery that's never photographed! He didn't distract me for long. When I didn't talk to him for a quarter of an hour, and all he could get was the usual yassuh, nossuh syllables from my mate, he grew embarrassed and left.

ten

THE DEPUTIES came for me at seven o'clock in the morning.
While I was putting on my torn shirt and scuffed shoes and
messing up my hair and beard some more in the mirror, I told
Sheriff Dick, "Dick, someday I'm gonna put all this shit down in
a book, I'm gonna capture you on my pages!"

"Shit, you do that, boy! An I'm a write one about you too!"
— his last words to me as I got in the squad car.

We headed toward Meansville. I recognized certain signs
along the way. Like the sign that read: WELCOME TO HARK CITY,
on a rise in the road. I'd noticed it as I rode in on the Trailways
Bus to Meansville months ago — and again I looked for Hark
City. But there was nothing to see, not even the burned-out
foundation of an old shack. Man they got some small towns in
Georgia! I thought, maybe it's off the road a ways. I asked my
guards about it, but they didn't want to talk to me. "Maybe
they live in the trees," I mumbled, not sarcastically, almost lov-
ingly, for the mystery.

But it pissed them off. "Open the door and throw him out,"
said the driver as he accelerated . . . seventy . . . ninety

. . . "We jus say he tried to jump out." The cop in the back seat reached across me and opened the door. He pressed his fat bulk against me and squeezed me toward the whizzing pebbles and colors of death. I threw my handcuffed wrists around his neck and hugged the grizzly devil for dear life. Bap! Bap! he threw some blows at my body — but I jumped all over the fat man and when I got my foot up on his gun, he started hollering, and the driver braked. He pulled over on the shoulder, and they all got a turn beating on me. When it was over I was sore but alive. I was lying on the floor of the back seat with two big feet on my back but I wasn't kicking. My cuffs were connected up to an iron bar welded to the frame of the car through the floor. I was beat. I was so tired and sick and weak that I just gave up my life and let it take care of itself. I resigned myself, I relaxed, glad to be breathing even the exhaust that seeped up into my nose through the floorboards. Fear and shadows had been my lot for weeks, and I was humbled. My bitter rage, which smoked at the bottom of my heart, I saved. Later! In time I'll get some back. I wanted no freedom through any kind of death, so I let it all go, and replaced the present bad news with my memory of that first bus ride into Meansville. Maybe it had gotten me into all this trouble, but there was something pleasant in my recollection of that trip into town, through the railroad yards and industrial flats, the hamburger strips and chrome motel stands, the shacks and cottages of the Negroes on the outskirts and the white suburbs within. It was nothing other than my sense of many glimpses of the *river!* rolling peacefully sometimes no further than fifty feet from the road, though once or twice I saw some vicious-looking eddies. The sense of a dream flashed by my mind — and then I remembered it: roses big as boulders in clusters in a field! The red petals big as giant cabbage leaves are crushed beneath bulls settling down, and tiny birds are squeezed from the flowers' fibers no bigger than teardrops. They flutter and begin to hop along the ground. I see the birds and the bulls are the same, downy little creatures with eyes like black beads. Schools of tiny fish in the river swoop through wild erratic figures . . . When the dream passed, the calm, determined feeling any wide and lovely river gives ran with me. When we must have been getting near, the cop unlocked me. We were driving down the wide street that divided the black downtown area from the white. Shortly we veered off into the white and in a minute we pulled up in front of Meansville Courthouse.

The courtroom was too much. I got a belly laugh that drew mean stares from the redneck idlers with stubby unlit cigars in their dentures when I saw the twelve-by-eight-foot version of the forty-eight star American flag that would look down on the proceedings I had no doubt would be strictly kangaroo. I guess they never got the news about Hawaii and Alaska, or else they're too cheap to buy a new one. The cops directed me to a bench and urged me to shut my mouth while I kept on laughing and brushing the tears of despair off my cheeks. But when the movement lawyer walked in! Man, it was a change in the weather. The heat I was feeling lifted like a night breeze. This cat drew all hostility like a magnet and proceeded to move and stalk through the room just like it was his. He greeted me solemnly and slapped a sheaf of papers on the defense table — sound like a bullet. Nobody liked it, but nobody challenged him. He must've met and beat too many in the past. Damn, I had a glow just watching him! I threw my arms back up on the bench back and crossed my knees. Whatever last ounce of strength I still had in my body I threw into enjoying this good

show. Every gesture he made he seemed to wound these courtroom crackers, and he had a way of prolonging his moves, and
leaving his elbow crooked on his hip, and his arm straight out
in the air, and his eyes lingered, but nobody sought his *eyes*.

I heard some commotion and turned my head. The cops
were bringing in another white boy. He was a movement
worker whom I hadn't known too well until he took a seat next
to me and we started rapping, waiting for the show to begin.
He was caught in some shit just like me — arrested in a march
in the south end of town, a couple nights after the march of
CME. And he had the same bad tales to tell. We were friends
at once. He was a big chunky dude from the West Coast, and
was looking bad himself. Had a nice beard. We sat there and
softly badmouthed the crackers together, and watched our man
the lawyer getting ready. Something he said to me struck a
chord. He said he'd had an idea of doing some "good" when he
came down here. And that was his idea in marching. But all
the misery that we brought down, not least of all on ourselves,
he wondered if there was any "good" to it. He said one day
before the little girl had been murdered, some cat's car had
stalled on the road he was walking, and he helped him push it,
and it started. And now that was about the only "good" he
could remember actually accomplishing. I got a chuckle out of
that, and agreed with him. But I told him, though I was vague
about it before, what I'd been through now, I got but one desire
and that's not do good but be bad! That got a smile from him,
but I knew that really he was a more responsible cat than me,
and would go a long ways with the Director.

Only us white boys were being tried today. The blacks had
been tried separately. But some kids and a few chicks had
come to watch. Finally the judge came in and we all had to
stand. My impulse was to put my feet up and stretch out on the

bench. But I didn't want to upstage the lawyer — nor to delay
these proceedings which might lead to freedom. As I stood
there waiting for the judge to adjust his robes before sitting, I
started to feel dizzy and had to fight just to keep my balance.
He was big, fat, and pink, and he took his sweet time getting
settled. "Aw justice is blind, ain it!" somebody muttered behind us. "Deaf, dumb — but hungry!" laughed somebody. He
spent some minutes reading items and ordering his pitcher refilled, clearing his throat, and cleaning his ears. It didn't do any
good; he didn't hear a thing.

The figure he cut was of a pyramid-shape cartoon lead
weight stamped 3000 lbs., set on a wooden platform shining
like the nation's penny: IN GOD WE TRUST. As the prosecution
went on, he pulled a big cigar out of his robes and began to puff
it. He ordered a Coke. He seemed to be enjoying himself —
often he laughed and repeated a phrase of the prosecutor, who
looked just like him in civilian clothes and was smoking the
same type cigar. And then all the cops and flunkies whispered
it brightly and nudged each other as our guilt became obvious.
The defense blew holes in all the charges which were resisting
arrest, attacking an officer, disorderly conduct, damaging
public property, and drunk. But the judge didn't seem to listen.
What a sad conduct for a judge! His eyes sleepily closed and
didn't fully open, until after I'd taken the stand and the prosecution began cross-examination. After asking my name, this
300-pound prosecutor with a one-inch cigar in his mouth sarcastically wanted to know my racial origins. I said, "Well sir,
America is a melting pot — everybody's a mixture, you know?
So it's hard to say but I'll try. One side a my family is from the
South — right here in Georgia as a matter of fact. And in the
South, one thing I've noticed, all the blacks have white blood
and all the whites got black in their veins. So I don't know!

The way you so-called Caucasians act around here one a those ships full of convicts that landed on the Georgia coast must a come from outer space!"

The whites in the room were now purple. The blacks were tittering, kids hooting. It couldn't have helped my case much but I was having fun!

Suddenly I saw Cara Lee — and her sullen eyes were bright with pleasure. She smiled at me.

The judge was rapping his gavel. "Guilty as charged!" he screamed, and sentenced us to ninety days on the garbage gang. The case would be appealed to 5000 lbs., but this one-and-a-half-tonner would have to sign bond papers before we could be released. Reluctantly he did. Sam made bond.

Walking into the streets was a rare experience. Everything was new, fresh, soft, clean, clear, shiny. I wanted to go everywhere and taste everything. We drove to the office, and all the way Sam lectured me. "Well you started somethin! Okay! But you coulda tried plannin it a little! You didn plan no follow-up. When you all went, wasn anybody else to keep the fire goin. You didn use your head. You shoulda told somebody you gonna march! You better be glad we didn't let you cool your ass on the garbage run. We got lots a work to do."

I didn't want to do any work. I didn't even want to talk. I wanted something light to eat, but there wasn't a thing in the kitchen. Sam let me have a dollar, and when we got to the office, he got out, and I drove on to the Stocks' house. I'd save the dollar. It was late afternoon, the old Chevy wasn't there, the deacon was still at work. Somebody was home — only the screen door was latched. The long-tailed dog trotted out from the backyard with its nose up in the air. I went around the way he'd come and found Mrs. Stock nearly hidden, hanging up a

wash. I could see her feet, stockings rolled down, and her practiced fingers pinning the edge of a sheet to the wire. I called
out in order not to give her a start, and she made an opening
between some sheets and peeked through —

"Well," she said softly, surprised. "You out!"

I tried to smile but it didn't make it. "They can't keep you
locked up forever." But immediately I knew it wasn't right.
She didn't require cheerfulness.

"Yes they can too, an you know it!" she said. "Thank the
Lord you out an alive! But you look sick!" She ducked back to
the sheet. "I be finish in a second. Whitefolks got kina dirty
this week."

"Can I help you?"

"Naw! You walk over in the house. You look like your bones
shrank. Go on in the kitchen, get you some water."

A yellow shade drawn against the heat, the kitchen was
suffused with an even copper glow. Spoons stood in a row next
to the sink, pans inserted one into the next like hats, their
handles rays from a silver top. I got some ice water and went
into the front room where it was cool. In their wedding picture
over the mantelpiece, the Stocks looked only younger. Their
eyes had not changed — hers calm, ironic, shy; his bold and
earnest, the brows jutting confidently. With some ice in a cup,
Mrs. Stock came into the room and sat next to me.

"Well I've sure had a bad time this past month, my God," I
said. "It's terrible to be locked up . . ." In my own ears, this
sounded strangely like an admission of something. "And on top
of everything, I haven't eaten anything, like a fool."

"You look like you lost twenty, thirty pounds in there," she
told me. She didn't ask me why I hadn't eaten anything.

"Yeah my stomach must be big as a walnut," I complained
with a grin. She warmed up some bean soup for me that was

very tasty. Slowly I got it down, with long pauses between spoonfuls.

"Lots a folks been prayin for ya," she said. "You got to be thankful for that . . . Probably they give you a hard time in there." She was gazing at me thoughtfully. "I know they very good at callin names . . . I want to tell you a story, I don know why I'm put in mind a this story, but let me tell it." She touched my arm and leaned forward a little. "I was takin care of a child — pretty little blond gal come up no higher'n your calf. Her folks was rich an educated, the kind that *run* this town. Live out in Silver Springs so you know they weren no ordinary poor white folks. Bedtime, I play, I beg, I laugh with her, but I can't get her to sleep. All of a sudden she run on in her mama's room, slam the door. I walk down the hall on tiptoe an listen against the wood. She in there cryin — *cussin* in her pillow — you know what? — *Nigger! nigger! nigger! nigger!* — It was pitiful! You see how it is with these folks? Now if I hear that word I'm thinkin a that little mouse so sorry for herself." She tapped my arm again and smiled. "Well I don spec that story be of much use right now. But one day you gon be proud a your time in jail, an the pain an trial of it be over. You an your frien famous! The whole church been thinkin of ya. Pastor gon be mighty happy to see you. JP gon be overjoyed!"

The specks of my suffering cast thin shadows in her eyes like pebbles flung into the late sun. I felt lighter, slightly refreshed. The soup was warming my insides. But church? No — I didn't want to be a movement hero which I wasn't. The pastor would shake my hand. The deacon would slip another pamphlet into it . . . I gave an excuse, and thanked her with all my heart for the soup, and the story. I wished I could thank her for just being here. I left and drove the car over to CME.

eleven

THOUGH THE SUN had not yet set, a moon was up in the sky, shining with a cold light like a medal. I pulled up in front of Knight's mother's house. The tin roof seemed very frail, like it was made out of thousands of silvery gum wrappers. The gray boards of the house looked brittle and weathered as sea shells. In front of the steps, so that I had to jump over it, was a cast-iron kettle used for collecting rain. It was dry as felt.

In a rocking chair in the front room, his mother was sleeping. Her snores were little chirps. I didn't knock. In one hand she held a paper fan, and in the other, dangling over the arm of the chair, a wire flyswatter. Between her feet rested a huge straw pocketbook with plastic violets braided into its handle. I tiptoed past. She stirred, and closed her legs against the bag, but didn't wake. It was a *shotgun house* — each room opened into the next and you could see straight through, like down a barrel. Passing through the bedroom, I could see Knight in the kitchen standing in front of the old cracked full-length mirror kept tilted up against the wall. A kerosene lantern in one corner of the room threw a cross-light, illuminating one side of things and throwing the other into shadow. There were several jagged seams in the glass. When I stepped inside, he was knotting a tie around his neck.

"*Hey brother!* When you get out?" He stuck out both hands, which I took.

"This afternoon — you didn't have to put on a tie for me."

Grinning, he turned back to the mirror and admired himself. "Wear a tie an drink scotch tonight!" He patted the knot and looked at it from different angles. "You ready for that?"

"Sure, but I don't have a tie —"

"Forget the tie. I'm jus doin that. A friend a mine's back from New York! We gonna meet at the Paradise. Ita be a double party for both a y'all."

Carefully he unwound the scarf that bound up his hair. The dull black of the cloth was replaced by the glistening black of a new process.

"That a hell of a wig you got there, boy," he said to his image in the mirror. "For such a *young* man."

With gentle fingers he smoothed and combed the few rough places on his sculpted head. He picked up a flake of mirror that had broken off, and held it up behind him for a back view.

"That a twelve dollar job, that I got for seven!"

He bound up his trophy once again with the scarf, knotting it behind and inserting a silver nail into the knot. He sat down on the bed and bent over to search for something beneath it.

"You ever polish those shoes?" he asked, staring at my feet. "Here," he said, pulling out a can of brown shoe polish and two rags, "you work on yours, I'll work on mine. You probly got some nice shoes in there someplace." He frowned at the stains on my knees when I sat next to him. "You don have no other trousers? Damn, I better let you wear a pair a mine." He got up and looked in the closet and brought out a pair of shiny black pants which I tried on and found too long. "They fine!" he said. "They too small on me but they jus right on you. They sposeta be wore up high like that. They some stylish Italian pants!"

Sitting on the edge of the bed, we worked on our shoes. Knight was deft at it — he snapped his cloth in intricate rhythms around the silences of polishing.

"So, how was it out there in Weary?"

"Nothin. Nothin happened at all. It was weird. Silence. Nothin to hear but one song from next door. Listen — they played the same song over an over."

"Drove you crazy I bet."

"An nothin to eat."

"Damn!" He looked sideways at me. He felt my arm. "What! You didn eat nothin all this while?"

"It sounds foolish I know, but I haven't. Once I got started, I couldn't quit. It got to be a fight with the sheriff."

"Well I understan that! I fucked with them police downtown! Stuck toilet paper down the sink an cause a flood — it was a waterfall from my cell, a captain a traffic slip on his ass! I did lots a shit, Jim. I take some ol hangers somebody forgot in my cell an unbend em, wind em all roun the door. Then I start in cussin — man, I *talk* about them police! Here they come — 'Nigger shut yo mouth! Gonna beat the shit out a you!' — I talk louder. They unlock the door — an en they see all at wire still lockin it! I lay back an *laugh!* Took em twenty minutes with clippers an I never stop laughin . . . But I *ate.* May as well not let em *kill* me. You like a skeleton, you oughta ate *somethin!*"

"Well I got some soup. Tomorrow I want to hit the menu!"

"You can eat at the Paradise! Paradise got some good food of every kind — pork chops, steak, chicken, shrimp — chittlins, red beans, corn bread . . ."

"They got some soup?"

"Yep! *Good* soup. An good liquor an good company an good sounds. Paradise got it all. Make The Raindrop look sick. Paradise the main place!"

Finished with his shoes, he jumped up and took an iron from the top of his bureau and plugged it into the wall. He stretched a towel across the little table that would serve as ironing board.

"Your shirt gonna look a whole sight better once it pressed."

Even more carefully, he ironed a white shirt for himself. He took off his tie, put on the new shirt, then redid the tie.

"Hey — you know that damn paper? The *Meansville Standard?* Not a word about the march, man — how bout prejudice reportin! We stop it comin in CME. OD get his boys out in the mornin — take *care* a them newsboys! Made a bonfire a the papers! Sheeit! I wish the *editor* come in CME one time!"

Standing in front of the mirror, he arranged his shirt, unwound the head scarf again, and once more went over his hair.

"I don't see how you see yourself in that mirror," I said. "You look like a jigsaw puzzle somebody finished, an bumped."

His eyes squinted, widened, blinked — he tilted his head. "I don even see them cracks — I musta got use to em."

"It shows the future, if they ever catch us again." I stood in front of him, very close to the mirror. Steadily, I inched my body from side to side. My form followed, by chunks: its edges catching in the cracks like a fluid, and running free of them at different moments. My arm and leg and the side of my face away from the light vanished altogether at the extreme point.

Finally only a sliver of elbow was all that was left of me on the edge of the glazed glass.

We sat around for a while and talked more about jail. Knight mentioned that he had some scores to settle, but he said he didn't want to bring down his mood too much right now by talking about it. He had a half a fifth of Thunderbird wine in a bureau drawer, and we got started drinking on that. I was high right away. It seemed like all I had to do was sniff it and I was high, my stomach was so empty. Finally it was time to go.

"Hey, we can ride!" He was ecstatic about that. I'd kept the car as a surprise, I hadn't mentioned that I had it. I was supposed to have returned it to the office already for one thing, and I didn't want to think about it.

We were on a downtown street. I parked the car and we walked. It was quite a change from CME. The lights and people on the sidewalk were momentarily confusing. A strip of tin whirled around a yellow bulb above a doorway, casting quick yellow streaks across a green neon sign: PARADISE.

Knight pushed the door open —

Bobbing in the flow of dancers like a painted duck, a jukebox splashed up webs of pastel pink and blue and green light. Smoke rose in folds through the air-conditioned air to the ceiling hung with *parachutes* — an effect of billowy rainbow sky. At the bar a cat had a crowd around him. He broke away and pulled us in —

"Hey baby! What you say, Knight? Hey man, how you doin . . ." He poured whiskey over ice — handed us full glasses. "I was tellin about this broad I met at a dance in D.C. Naturally she dig my conversation, I'm jus down from The City, an well that like Atlanta to Meansville, you know. But what get *to* her though — my *steps*, man! Say, 'You gotta come home with me, baby, teach me to dance!' . . . Gray broad, you dig," he said flicking his eyes at me —

"Nothin wrong with white girls, I like em myself," I said.

"Yay! Say, 'I wanna learn from you baby!' I stay a month. Didn do *no* work — sheeit! Lay up an stay high — showed her how to *dance*, yay!"

He passed the bottle around to all the appreciative chucklers.

"Hey what you been into, Knight?"

"Well I tell you, I ain doin nothin but take it easy an play. My needs satisfied you understan, so I'm jus playin . . . Tore up a police car last week, Broomer. Like the ol times today! OB ol lady screamin *Stop thief!* Man jump out, say, 'Stop thief!' too, whippin his gun! — Got the battery! Got the tires! Got the spotlight! Beat the shit out a his new paint job with chains!"

"Say, this here — this is a real *bad* man!" said a man of thirty-five or forty with strange bright eyes, under a little jaunty hat, at the edge of our party.

"Who you?" said Knight, glaring at him.

"Whata you call your gang?"

"Ain no gang —"

"Ain no gang! I thought all a you bad boys had gangs."

"Well you the same man I left!" said Broomer, chucking Knight on the back. "But homeboy, I want you to visit me in the City!"

"Tell you somethin else!" said Knight, who was getting a little hot. "Did you read in the paper how the water in whitey's pool turn green las weekend, can't nobody swim for a week while they clean her out? I did that!"

"You did!" I asked him what he used.

"Threw three U.S. Army dye bombs! Shit, that water look like piss!"

"Say, you keep some *bad* company!" laughed the man with the hat.

"Who *you!*" cried Knight.

"That's a bad motherfucker you travel with!"

"I'm askin you mother!"

"Call me Jones, Jones," said the man, losing his smile. (Or had he said — "Call me Jones Jones?") — "I steal! I don't play! See me with whitey, I be cool, I'm out to do him in, an build me up! I don't play with no law! I *break* the law!"

"Shit, I hate a sneak thief! If I want me somethin, I walk up an take it!"

"You nothin but a *boy*, boy! You live in the movies an think life a show! I seen a million of you. Ten years, you be drinkin that wine. You ever see a thousand dollar bill? I might have one in my pocket right now but you never know! I'm cool."

"Yay! If you can stay hip to some *steps*, you jus naturally make it!" Broomer was trying to pick up his audience that had tuned into the argument and forgot about him.

"You jus an average nigger, tryin to sneak somethin you oughta fight for," said Knight, with hurt in his voice.

"I keep my feelins right here!" He slapped his pockets. "So I got both hands free to deal with a sucker!"

"Yeah, I see — you drinkin on Broomer jus like me!"

"No I'm not," said Jones, and got one of the bottles that were on the bar, and walked away toward the corner of the place. He was a curious sort and a good talker but I was glad to see him go; he was cutting my friend. My heart was with Knight.

"Yeah! Here we go!" cried Broomer, as a waitress brought in plates of chicken and barbecue. "Help yaself one an all!"

A pungent steam was coming up from the feast spread out on the bar. It was raining and storming in my mouth. For my stomach's sake, I knew I shouldn't eat a lot of solid food, but this was like one of my dreams in jail come true, and I couldn't stop myself. Words stopped among those of us gathered around the bar, and the sounds of champing and chewing prevailed. Everything was mellow. Everyone was happy and easy.

And then all of a sudden, there was a strange interruption —

Crack! — crack!

It took us a few moments to accept it, to register the sound of bullets. Then drumsticks dropped, glasses were set down. As Knight and I arrived in the red doorway, so did Jones. Almost at once, two little boys fell from the roof above our heads, right in front of the Paradise. The sound of their bodies hitting the ground was a dead *plop! plop!* but at once they jumped to their feet.

"Run! Run!" cried Knight.

One did — at high speed. The other made it only as far as the curb before his knees gave out.

Crack! — crack! — crack!

Poor aim — the runner whizzed over a fence like a quick mouse.

Crack! — crack!

Around the other boy, down on his knees and knuckles, the bullets were kicking up a ring of dust. His lip drooped and his teeth chattered. The lids of his eyes squeezed so tight together they were wrinkled — two little prunes above his nose.

"*Run* little boy — goddam!" screamed Knight.

Above our heads a white hand and a silver muzzle, smoking. A cage of bullets for the criminal until two squad cars and a motorcycle roared up and circled him, small and crouched as a bowling ball! His nose was running. His eyes blinked, darted, shut again. There was a triangular rent in the shoulder of his T-shirt. On one foot was a tennis shoe laced with twine, the other foot was bare. He tried to stand up while being handcuffed to two fat officers, but they knocked him down and dragged him to the car like a dead fish.

"You boy!" called the cop from the roof, pointing his gun down at Knight. "Watch yo step!" He began to make his way down the fire escape.

"You too, officer, sir, don trip now!" cried Knight in a voice almost giddy with hate.

"Nigger!" Waving his pistol. "Only reason I don't take you in for aidin an escape — I *like* niggers!" He jumped in one of the squad cars. With sirens shrieking, the raiding party tore off down the road.

"God*dam* them cops!" Knight walked out the Paradise to the curb and looked from the pockmarked earth to the squadron vanishing from view.

"Yeah, now they gone, damn em!" leered Jones. Knight had at least spoke back. The sight of the cops reminding me of jail had shut me up, and I felt poor about it.

"Damn all you motherfuckers stan aroun don do shit!"

"Yeah, damn all you ol boys love life!" Jones told the bar. The smell of jail had made me sick, I needed air —

"You ain shit, thief!"

"I'm free!" laughed Jones.

Knight called me. Already he was getting into the car.

Broomer stuck his head out the door and yelled to Knight, it was early, where was he going?

"I got some business, Broom! Come by an see me tomorrow!"

He drove. We headed away from the downtown area, but not toward CME. Knight was mulling something over in his head, like looking for a way to phrase something. He was burning up about the cops shooting at those little kids, who probably tried to steal some trinket from a pawnshop.

"Listen man, they was a girl in the girls' cell, I don know where she came from. I never seen her. Runaway from out in the country I think, I don know how she foun our march, but there she is, an she sick. She got the *fits*, you know? I couldn see her, but I sure could hear her floppin. It was awful, Jim! After we complain about two days, here come the doc, who take a look at her, say, 'Lil nigger, don play!' an slap her, you know, wake her up. They got her out in the walkway — she don wanna wake! — 'She posin! Wake up!' Slap slap! Slap slap! Slap! She never did wake up man, but he beat the shit outa her! He just went crazy! — Listen man, I got my revenge in the jail, I had some fun with those laws, you know, for what happen to us. But that doc, think he can stan in front a *me* an beat *mine!* I shout at him *stop!* I promise myself, when I'm out, I'm gon hurt *him.*"

We took our time getting there. We made a stop by Knight's house for a can of paint and some brushes. He knew the route through the black neighborhoods by which we would avoid exposure. We parked inside the black, about a half mile from our target, and began to walk. We took the alleys. The air was soft, and seemed shot through with a fine, invisible powder, so conscious was I of it falling against my hands and face. My sympathetic anger didn't conflict with fear of the cops, they strangely canceled each other out, and I felt insubstantial, as though there were not enough of me here, walking in the moon shadows, to be happy or afraid. The air felt like snow — snow falling over me and through my heart, but not reaching the secret place from which would come the action. We came out of the alley onto a paved street and we were in a white area. We crossed the street and continued in the alleys that were now a bit wider and more even. Only at the last did we walk half a block on a sidewalk, along a well kept street. It was a small modern house on the corner, which was drawing us to itself with the pulsing force of the prey. As Knight pointed to it, I was victim of a withdrawal of emotion that left not even a numbness I could know myself by. I felt like I would drift into action, and later have feelings about it.

We didn't run but walked casually and quietly to the house. A bronze oval on the front door announced the doctor's office. It was polished to a high finish that made our defiance shine. Knight went immediately to the side of the house which looked away from the corner and was protected from view of its neighbor by a tall hedge. He broke out a pane and unlocked the window. I climbed through first, and he handed up the can of paint and the brushes before he followed me inside. I was in a room full of unfamiliar shapes, some soft, some covered, some standing up out of the shadows, metal and sharp: the doctor's instruments and ornaments, poised about the floor. Knight moved among them as if after long practice. If by chance he touched a chair or a small laden table, he shoved it aside ruthlessly as though it were out of place and offensive to him. He went into the hallway and paced out its length, his footsteps veered and were muffled . . . I stood in the middle of the strange room with the paint can dangling from my hand. I

could sense no personality in the shapes around me. Inscrutable, silent, blurred, they seemed to be experiencing *me*. It
was of no matter to me whether or not I kicked aside the unknown object I found in my path to the hallway; I found it
easy to kick it. By the sting of my toe, I recognized a force that
had passed out of me. I felt very light, as if bobbing on the
surfaces of the room like water. In the hallway Knight held
two metal beakers belonging to the doctor, and I poured paint
into them. He gave me a stub of candle and took one of the
brushes. A tiny light perhaps from the moon appeared around
our hands at this moment but it seemed to reach no further
than our forearms and cast his face into heightened darkness. I
returned to the curious room and lit the candle. I dripped a
little puddle of hot wax onto the glass surface of the doctor's
desk and stood the candle in it. A ring of yellow light com-
menced a few inches from the base of the candle and seeped
slowly in all directions to the walls and corners. The smiling
faces of the doctor's family stared up at me from under the
glass. Hinges, silver frame of a short bed, metal pans, the glass
protecting a framed diploma, all glinted in the candlelight. I
lettered with large strokes, taking up a big space of one
wall . . .

NEXT   TIME   SLAP   ONE   OF   YOUR   OWN

The letters glowed faintly — hinting of huge colorful flash-
ings. A heat began to stir in my breast. Outside, the night was
silent right to the stars, but in the small space where I stood
was all possibility. In another room, Knight's hand swept a
shelf clean of all phials and fragile jars: a sweet chiming of
splintering glass streamed to my ear. Then I heard his knife

tearing and slashing the upholstery of chairs and sofas, the can-
vases of waiting-room paintings. The muffled crashings of
heavy objects came one after another in a continuous shattered
flow. A little girl's face outspoken of lost child's fear floated
near my thoughts. Then I saw the face of the doctor — the
tormentor! It was the sheriff's face in a glass! The intricate
shining of a set of scales behind the glass caught my eye. By
degrees I had arrived at this moment, in this office. Under pressure of experience and inspired by Knight's example, I had
come to this place that we would try to destroy. In a world that
seemed misordered, we would find an inimitable joy in destruction. I had followed Knight to the doctor's house, and I was
surprised when the joy hit me. I had been distant at first, but
now I was angry. I opened the little doors of the case and tore
the scales from their balance and pitched them overhand
against a wall. I shut the glass doors, and threw paperweights
through them. I tore up stacks of freshly typed papers. At this
moment I thought of Deacon Stock. By some logic of my own
heart, I thought: I'm doing this for him. I knocked every object
from every shelf, and pulled out drawers and dumped their
contents of small cylinders and tubing onto the floor, and
stomped on piles of light metal accessories and the glass cylinders that crackled like thin ice . . . I thought, The night will
have its day. An eclipse I envisioned, prolonged night, to can-
cel the old terrorized night of the Klan. A life for fire was
needed — far from the homeland with water and the forest and
the blue air, and fire perched comfortably like a pet on its little
ration on the stone, the *elemental* fire to be loosed like a rainbow, that men have always fought, and always splashed with
decorous fury on the objects of their love and hate. In the room
was a memory of this spectacle —

"It a beautiful mess, man!" cried Knight, kicking over the can of paint I had set on the floor with a vicious jab of his foot. On the wall under my sign he painted the letter: K. I thought this dangerous, but he laughed. A single strand of his process was pointing straight up above the center of his forehead like a fierce black Indian feather. "If they ever get us this time, they get us *for* somethin! We given this man a beautiful reward!"

With regret, I snuffed the little candle, the fire-seed. In the darkness we jumped back out the window and started to run. My stomach flipped. I should never've eaten so much on the first night off the fast. I tripped, and fell, and on my hands and knees disgorged the ribmeat and barbecue chicken I'd packed in at the Paradise. I got it all out, while Knight laughed and hooted with abandon. Now we ran for dear life. I felt very clean. And the air was cool and lovely, and the dust of the clay hid the sounds of our flight.

twelve

BY THE TIME I'd got out of jail, things had returned to normal on the outside. The little girl wasn't forgotten, but the anger couldn't be sustained. The vote drive was full speed again, but I didn't return to work on it. With Knight, I had entered a new phase, accepted a new idea, but of course it might still be said that we were with the movement. The movement was where the next meal always came from. It was with the movement's aims in mind that we considered any violence. Hadn't the movement wanted to vindicate the girl's death somehow? The days slipped by quickly. I hung around the movement office and talked with anybody who came by. I sat on the porch and enjoyed the sunshine and regained my health that had been wasted in fasting out in the Weary jail. The office was the place to be in the mornings, when some chicks might be around, making breakfast. Some SNCC paychecks arrived on Fridays, and on Saturday mornings we'd have great breakfasts of meat and eggs and grits and bread and quarts of orange juice. We'd waste some money! And top it off with a pot of real coffee and

a pack of fresh cigarettes. I never missed a Saturday morning.
And the rest of the day was easily passed in talk.

Anybody might come by. There was one cat named George
who used to pull up in his red, white, and blue Mercury. He
worked out on a big farm in the country that he described like
it was a plantation. He bred some champion dogs for the man,
and he was indispensable to the man's glory, so he could come
driving into town about whenever he wanted. But he never
talked about the dogs. He loved to talk about the movement.
He was sweet, firm, and earnest — and a hard worker for the
vote drive out in hard country. I believed he could mold some
beautiful dogs. He wasn't shy, he was adamant about his freedom ideas and he loved to talk and to laugh; he was very kind
and always talked to everybody, even the timidest most vulnerable white kid whom *I* might even have trouble talking to.
George loved to dream aloud about the plantation workers
striking one day, and I loved to listen to his plans. It was always a pleasure when George came by.

Another regular was the Avon lady, who was a great organ-
izer for the movement; she must talk to hundreds of people in a
day's work. She would come in and remark on the wonderful
job us kids were doing, that always made me feel good, if a
little guilty. We were way overstocked with colognes, deodor-
ants, perfumes, and other far-out products, thanks to the Avon
lady.

After he got out of jail, sometimes Cousin Yellow came by
and brought us some nice river fish for our dinner.

Most days Knight might be around by noon. Maybe he'd
have a bottle of wine that he'd saved from the night before.
We'd sit around and I'd listen to him tell me stories about the
bad old days in CME. One day some kids were hanging out in

the front room. OD was there, trying to make some time with one of the white girls. I thought I'd help him out. I put my arm around his shoulder. "OD, what's happening! I didn't think they'd ever let you out. — OD personally took care of a whole gas station full of crackers that night we marched in CME!" I told the girl.

"Sheeit!" OD grinned at me. "I had to! They woulda try to bust us up if I hadn't hit em first."

She was regarding him with new admiration. She was a pretty girl, and a lot of these voter workers were good-looking. I was mildly surprised that I wasn't really interested in them and it caused me to think. It was the girls of the town, like Cara Lee, who caught my attention, because they were all new. I was progressing, I thought, in my appreciation of women. I saw that Cara Lee held the way to new worlds of experience. It would be the strangeness and newness of it. Maybe OD and I were into the same thing. I decided I'd kid the white girl a little.

"Hey — listen to this one!" There was an article posted on the bulletin board from the Honey Hill, Ohio *Gazette*. "Unlike most coeds at Barclay College," I started reading, "Sara decided to forgo the pleasures of surf and sun in order to devote her summer to fighting racial injustice in the turbulent South —"

"Shut up!" shouted the girl.

"Sara can have my vote," grinned Knight, dropping his hand to the ballot region. "Hey," he said, "why they write about Negro girls get raped all a time?"

His eye had caught on a clipping from *Mohammed Speaks* that had also been tacked to the board. *Mohammed* was the only newspaper in the country that reported on it.

"They plenty white women get raped! — Hey OD, remember when the Stars cut off the power? Shit, half the town went dark! They weren't a goddam thing in no paper an I rape one myself that night!"

This evening Knight and I were walking over to Cara Lee's house. But just before we got there, he turned away. "She don wanna see none a me," he said, "but she been waitin to see you." He winked and was gone.

Cousin Yellow was shelling butter beans, motionless from the wrists back at the far end of the porch, smiling. As always, I was heartened by the bright calm of his expression. I saw him at the last moment before I went in the door.

"Yellow, how do you stay so quiet!"

"Well, suh, it enough noise, it don need no new contribution."

"Hey, don't call me *suh*, okay?"

"Well, suh, I'm kina fixed."

"Well, suh, you call me *suh*, I'm gonna call you suh too, suh!"

He said no more. His smile got wider.

Some kind of construction was progressing across the street. It had been a vacant lot a month ago. Black men were digging ditches and hauling wheelbarrows. A white man with the mien of a chain gang boss was overseeing their activity. "Ha ha! He givin you the evil eye," laughed Cara Lee through the doorway. I looked around at him and there he was giving me the eye all right, got his hand on his hip and his eyes squinted up. I was kind of crazy in those days. I liked to show off. I walked across the street and asked his men, "Hey what the fuck you cats workin for this fuckin slave driver!" I walked back to the porch and went inside and sat down between the women, who were on the couch. He was in the middle of the street, shaking his finger.

"Mm-mm-mm!" said Mae.

I told her I didn't mean to start anything — maybe I should split.

"Naw!" said Cara Lee. "I pay rent on this house."

"Didn mean to start nothin!" said Mae.

When the man stepped on the curb to approach the house, Cara Lee jumped up and hollered, "Harrell, they a man out here — get y'gun!"

"No! I ain't botherin ya!" The man stepped backward. "Who you got in there with ya?"

"My light-skin cousin from Chicago! Get outa my house!" She stepped down off the porch and made large shooing motions with her hands. She had some big proud eyes that could blaze! The man looked like nothing had been explained, but he turned around and went back to the work. He took it out on his laborers. He yelled for a while and shoved a few and made them run the barrows.

"Who's Harrell?" I asked her.

She chuckled and looked at Mae, who was shaking her head, when she came back in. "This cracker been diggin me for days, you know? Come up the other night wanna get somethin — I called to Harrell, 'Wake up, husband! They a white man pickin on me!' "

That almost made me nervous myself. "But uh —"

"Sheeit!" She smiled and reassured me that she had no husband.

"You fixin to go right on *back* to jail ain't you," said Mae.

Oh no! I didn't think so! But her words troubled me. It was amazing how I'd put any thought of such consequences clear out of my mind. Already pleasures of life had melted away that pain. I couldn't hang on to even the memory when I looked at Cara Lee.

Yellow was cleaning some blue and green big sunfish — like what we call bluegills up North. The perfume of the river came in the window. His slow easy strokes floated and evened the air. He was the same as always. He didn't say much and was very well contented. I stood in the doorway and asked him about his fishing. He said he fished some holes in the river and used crickets.

"Hey — you wanna take me to the show?" Cara Lee asked, touching me with her fingertips.

"Sure."

"We can eat and catch the eight-fifteen show. Okay?"

"Yeah, sure."

"You got a dollar?"

"*Sure!* I wouldn't say *yes* if I didn't have the money." A few checks had piled up while I was in jail and I actually felt rich.

"Mae, will you watch the babies till I get home?"

"Feel kinda like seein a show my own self," said Mae, scowling at the activity across the street.

"Aw *Mae!*"

"Okay, okay —"

"Lemme put on some clothes!" cried Cara Lee, bounding up. She stopped in the doorway, looking down at me sprawled out. "You mean it for real?"

"My word of honor! I'm not kidding! I promise to take you to the show. Yes! If I don't take you to the show I hope the Lord will smite me down with a lightning bolt in this spot."

She looked at me for a while. She knelt down beside me and gave me a kiss.

When she called me into the kitchen, she had put on a pretty green dress and some beige lipstick. She sure looked good! I commented. She pointed to the table and told me to hurry and eat so we wouldn't be late. On a plate was a sandwich. On a closer look, it was a peanut butter sandwich. A peanut butter sandwich! That wasn't my idea of some soul food to drowse me down so I could best enjoy the show. She apologized, but there wasn't time to cook anything. I ate it in about five bites and got her to make me another. I didn't bother sitting down. At the corner store I bought a quart of beer and kept it in the wrapper and drank it on the way. She was carrying a big purse, where I could stash it when we entered the show, so I carefully saved the bottle cap. When we passed through a white neighborhood, she insisted we walk separately. I went ahead first, and she waited a few minutes and followed on the other side. I waited for her on the corner of Main Street and South Street, where I bought a hamburger at a stand, and sipped down past the halfway mark on the label where I wanted to stop for the movies. I was on the edge of the black looking back into the white, and she was a long time in coming. I saw she'd been in a hurry to get going so she could make this detour. For safety? Now I was a little nervous, walking down this street of bars and cafes with dozens of cats hanging out in doorways and nobody missing this! The Grand Theater loomed up in this block, the tallest building in sight. It stood the equivalent of three stories, and the facade rose up another fifteen feet with neon stripings and white bulb dots. *French Love* said the bill. I loosened up as I put my money down on the window counter and got the tickets, and we moved toward the Grand door like the mouth of a fabulous sea fish that lures its eats with intricate and delicious baits grown on its lips. NEXT WEEK! NEXT WEEK!

We sat in the last row, under the balcony. The upper level was filled with young boys and girls, chewing popcorn and kissing. On the lower level, in the middle of the theater, a few

sedate couples were watching the picture. Every dozen seats in
any direction, a hustler with his hat down over his face muffling
his snores. I had wanted to sit upstairs. "Too many kids lovin
up there, can't see the show in peace," smiled Cara Lee. Above
us, the ceiling creaked. Every ten or fifteen minutes loud
laughter and fierce hooting spilled down in the flickering dark.
This rhythm, no matter what the gold-haired girl on the screen
was doing. Nothing much happened but the glittering hair and
gleaming blue eyes, the girl laughing and weeping, showing her
pink hands, the soft roots of her breasts, her light pointed elbows. Around her many men stretching out their arms. In the
hard wooden seat, I found a comfortable position and traded
Cara Lee the popcorn for the beer. Watching the gold girl
dance, sing, play games, richly cry, Cara Lee's eyes got softer
and softer . . .

It was disappointing. There were some phoney Paris sets,
but all the actors were Americans: the husband, the good rival,
the bad rival: jealousy, boredom, anger, envy, deceit, sacrifice
and "true love": a chase. The good guy, who would rather see
the gold girl with her husband than dead, just a few yards behind the bad guy who would kill her to get her, up spiraling
flights to a high place. At the climax of the fight, a boy in one
of the boxes hurled a bottle which struck the good guy square
in the temple. But he didn't flag. Finally, he pitched the bad
guy from the roof. The gold girl could now realize the unfath-
omable depths of the good suitor's affection. She left her husband, who had a heart like the pit of a fruit. The new love was
not wealthy, but he looked okay. Cara Lee sighed . . .

The houselights went up. Four chandeliers from another
era, casting a thin brown light. None of the sleeping men woke.
The rhythm of the balcony was not altered. I stretched, rose,

shifted my weight from foot to foot. Cara Lee did not immediately take her eyes from the screen. We went out through the mouth. A few people had stopped to look at next week's posters. Seeing us walk away down the street, they smiled, grinned, showed blank faces, frowned, paid us no attention.

"You ever been to California?"

Her eyes showed no trace of their usual queenly sullenness. They were wide, very soft.

"Nope."

"You wanna go?"

"When?"

"No special time. Anytime."

"Sure. Why not? I want to go everyplace."

"That one place I sure like to visit one day."

"Seeing that movie is close enough for me."

"Shows ain't *real*."

"Neither is California."

"You kiddin me?"

"I mean the Hollywood you imagine out of the pictures isn't real."

"How you know?"

"I know."

"You crazy."

"Hollywood is probably just like Meansville."

A clipped silence. "You *crazy!*"

"What I mean is that the people of Hollywood aren't deeply a whole lot different from the people of Meansville." I said that, I remember.

"Shit man, I see you ain been west a Pittsburgh!"

We passed through silent streets, rows of darkened houses. The night was black and moist. Half-moon, stars, occasionally lighted windows muted silver like nearly closed eyes. A dog howled. The echo didn't fade . . .

"Maybe Meansville like Hollywood to you, but it ain to me. To me it a sad place, where people only dreamin."

"Some people say dreamin is havin."

"Naw it's not." With that disagreement, we lapsed into the unity of a silence that lasted till we got home.

Mae Liza slept in a room at the side of the house. Yellow was curled up on a pallet in the front, his shoes set down beside him. Quietly we made our way to Cara Lee's bedroom at the back. Her babies were snoring like mice in little padded boxes at her bedside. She set them over by the open door. Who knows what she was thinking as she gracefully took off her clothes? Her motions were nervous and modest. It wasn't Hollywood. We were rising out of Meansville. Clothes hanging from a makeshift pole-tree stirred with a breeze through the door, and the movement softened the still air . . .

Not until the morning did I think of the Director with his inscrutable judging eyes. I wondered would he get a report on this somehow. Ha! Toward dawn, low clouds took over the sky.

thirteen

AT FIRST IMPACT of the rain the clay gave up a thin dust like red steam. Soon the houses drygray as slate were soaked and blackened. The blue drops swarmed down through the yellow air and changed hue. Gusts of wind drove brown mists, coating grass-blades, leaves, the window glass — washed, and coated again. I was staying at Cara Lee's house as much as at the movement office these days. Everybody was gone out of the house by the time I awoke. It must've been noon or later. Yellow was probably downtown at the barbershop or gone fishing. God knew where Mae was — most likely at church. Cara Lee was at her job over at the Sunny-Side Drive-In. — Man I was hungry! After the fast in jail I'd got my stomach stretched back to shape again and it was making up for lost time. If I neglected it, the grumbles and shrill hollers that came up from it were mistrustful and threatened vengeance. For a while I sat on the bed and looked out the window, wishing I'd got started before the rain. Then a bad internal bellow made me jump up, and I took a run to the office. It was late, and everybody was finished breakfast and out working. The beautiful little house with bullet holes in its doors was always left open so the kids or anybody could come in and use the typewriters, chairs, bathroom. I found a copy of the morning's *Meansville Standard* and sort of dried myself off with it. I was pretty wet. This was a good place to be, it was so quiet and mellow, it was a pleasure just to sit in the kitchen or out on the porch, and talk to some little kids who hung out there too or anybody who came by to shoot the shit.

I pulled out a case of canned goods with the labels come off that had been sent to us from up North: a charity case. It must have been unsalable because nobody could tell what was in the cans. Mostly they were low-grade pasty ravioli. But about every fifth can turned out to be spaghetti which was much better. I had an idea I could guess by the weight, and I tested a dozen and shook them next to my ear. I lost the gamble, but with grace. This morning even the ravioli tasted good. In the corner of the kitchen, there was a dining booth made of a card table and two old bus seats still smelling unmistakably of passengers and motion, and this was where I ate my breakfast. I was the picture of comfort sitting on the back seat with my feet up on the front seat when in flew Knight, dripping and blowing the rain. He didn't say anything at first. He blew up his chest and glared indignantly down his nose at me —

"What you doin sit down comfortable when you talk to me, boy?"

We had these jokes between us. I almost knocked over the table jumping to my feet. Scratching my head, I showed my teeth in a sheepish grin and scraped my feet. "Sorry, bossman, I been sick. I been so sick an weak with the eight-day pneumonia . . ."

"Sometimes I think you messin with them movement niggers, boy! Sometimes I think you *is* a movement nigger."

"Oh *no,* bossman! Don even think such a thought. Why jus yesterday one a them white boys you always warn me against, one a them Commanists, he grab my arm, hol me tight, force me to stop while he talk bout how everybody got to vote an how it my *duty* to vote, an how *I* can decide who be *mayor* — an you know what I says to him, bossman? I say, 'Me an my bossman we gets along fine, he good to me, my bossman, what I wanna vote for?'"

Knight rubbed his chin, looking a little pacified. "Well you done right there, boy . . . Maybe you all right after all . . . They one way to find out! I got a plan! They one a them white boys I mislikes particular, an you know the one, boy. Bout your height? Got a funny look in his eye, act smart? Yeah, I want you to brand that miscolored nigger, on the forehead, you got a knife I know. Brand: YANKEES GO HOME. How you like to be makin five dollar a week stead a two, how you like that, hey boy?"

"Oh thata be mighty fine, boss. Heh-heh . . . I know which one you speakin of an I sure like to get that raise . . . I'm gon brand him, yessir! An give him some a this here ravioli, poison him. — Hey, you like some ravioli, bossman?"

"I don know how you eat that shit."

Smacking my lips, I dropped the dishes in the sink, adding to the mountain that grew up past the faucet. Knight was drenched. He grabbed a few copies of the latest *National Guardian,* a stack of which we were sent each week in the hope we would distribute them to the local proletariat.

"This all we got to get dry with?"

"That is the best in the house —"

"Damn we poor!"

They were not very absorbent. He pressed them tight against his arms as though trying to stop wounds. He waved them like a fan. Maybe they helped a little.

"Hey — there any coffee?"

"Take a look. I don't want to wake up, I like dreamin — you got any wine?"

He sort of nodded and then he sort of shook his head, like later. He set about making some coffee. He turned to me. "Tonight, how bout it?" he said, referring to our plans. "Tonight, I'll meet you here at midnight. Where the shit?"

"Under the back steps."

He returned to the kitchen with a can of white spray enamel and two stencils that I'd had made by one of the movement girls, who was a good artist. One read COPS. The other read WHITEY.

"Hey come back here!" he said. He went back in the bedroom, which was more secret. Five cots took up the floor space of the room. On top of them and underneath them and all around the room lay piles of books and clothing, representing the sundry life-styles of the movement. Works on nonviolence and the life of Gandhi, and Chief Albert Luthuli's autobiography lay on the Director's cot in the corner. A work of DuBois' and a copy of *Look* along with an alarm clock bedecked the cot next to it. A green easy chair was jammed in the corner of the room. Missing a leg, it was propped up with bricks. On top of the bureau by the back door were stacked old bills, old letters, notebooks, an unopened cardboard box, a windup clock with brass bells, a bottle of Royal Cologne. Boxes of posters and leaflets stood up against one wall. A clothespole rigged up in one corner sagged under a wide selection of the hippest and most durable clothing to find its way down here as charity in the last year or two. Knight was rippling his fingers through them, looking for his style. When he came to the tuxedo, he stopped in amazement. I couldn't believe my eyes either when I first saw it. He breathed a sigh and then coughed. From out the motley array he got a cardboard stiffener that had come back in the laundry inside somebody's shirt. He stood it at an angle on a table against the wall and grabbed the can of paint. The steel ball inside the can clicked sharply as he shook it. He aimed, but hesitated, thought better of it, and started for the back door.

"C'mon out, I'll make a mess in here. You gon just sit there lemme mess up the wall? I'm gon speak with the Director about you!"

It was a day of restlessly alternating sunbursts and showers. The clean quick drops seemed to come from the light; they flew sideways and upwards. The light was wet as paint. The sky was gray and white, bolt blue stars suddenly flashed, and furled slowly. What did I care about the Director on a day like today? Knight set the cardboard against the wire incinerator basket. He sprayed a gentle circling stream.

"Ah nice . . . nice an heavy, so long it don drip." He was telling me this but I knew something about painting myself. But I just nodded my head, I didn't mention it. He held the can upside down and shot a clear stream to clean the nozzle. He dropped the cardboard into the basket and admonished me not to forget to burn it later. I slapped his back. Yeah I was so ready for tonight! I was ready for any adventure . . .

In the back room, he flopped down heavily on a bed. I pulled out a folding chair from the corner and set it up and sat down on it. "Yeah, we right!" he laughed, stroking the plastic button that triggered the paint with his thumb. "Tonight!" he cried, and tossed me the can. "Dig it!"

I turned it around in my hands and flipped it into the air. Tonight was going to be some fun . . .

"Feel nice as a gun, don it?" he remarked. He settled himself more comfortably on the cot. "Oughta *be* a gun, sheeit!" He sat up. "I been takin it easy too long! The bad days too long gone! Cuz we useta had some bad Negroes in CME. Even before me . . ." He lay back down again, real comfortable. "They was a man — that was way before the Stars — they call him Big Black, like that, Big Black. He a cousin to my brother-in-law, so I useta hang out with him, big an black, bout six foot six an *wide!* Ha ha! Damn! Even when he smile he have a sneer on his face, an when he laugh, he look *terrible!* One time a little police stop him for drunk on the corner. Right by The Raindrop. Took him by the arm, you know, an when he felt how big that arm was, which he couldn even get a grip, he pull out a pistol an hol it under Black nose. — That was a mistake! — Wave a gun roun front a Black like that when he ain done no real wrong he can think of that evenin. He was insulted, what it was — he grab that pistol quick as fire! That police ain ready for nothin like that! Who go grabbin guns like that so quick? But he don have no time for no surprise. Black take that gun away like it a baby toy an throw it clean over the cafe. You seen how it longer than it look in front, with the kitchen an the shed out back. — That gun go sailin, lan clear back in the alley someplace. Some boys foun it after. I reckon it in CME right now, in somebody drawer —"

He paused. His eyes focused on some point neither near nor far — wondering, perhaps, which drawer. Could I believe Knight's stories that attested to a tradition of violence against the setup in the South? The idea where I'd come from was that the Negroes down here had been in a more pitiful shape. But to me college itself was an illusion, and I'd left it behind. I loved a good story, and I loved to listen to Knight's good stories, and I believed them with my soul, and I believed in our acts —

"What happened after Black threw the gun?"

"Happen? Sheeit, what you think happen? He knock that police flat on the groun an stomp him. Big police too. Bounce on him an kick him aroun awhile, then he just walk on his way, calm an cool, like he stop for a little conversation that got lame . . . How they stop *that* Negro, they got to stop that *heart*. Nother time, Black don get the gun firs try an get six bullets instead. Man, the peoples was sorry! He was so popular in CME, the pride a all us young boys useta look up to him, a favorite with everybody. Had a big fancy funeral. Couldn see the folks for all the flowers. Musta been a thousan people come to mourn that man . . ."

A moment of silence for the name Big Black. A name maybe only Knight carried forward, impressing it where he could. I listened reverently to the echoes on the air heavy with the sad memory — but joy in the images cast on the future. Into this moment came a light *tap-tap-tap.* I opened the door and stepped into the front room to see who it was. On the front porch was a young girl, not quite assured in her straight stance, very solemn, not quite inside the door.

"Hello!" I greeted her, as we always welcomed any new-comer to the office.

For a while she stared at me. Then she looked at all the walls of the front room, tilting her head as she moved her eyes, as if the place were slowly spinning or flowing upwards.

"This the movement?" she asked at last.

She began extending her foot and drawing it back, in the practiced but tentative flexure of a little child exploring. Very gradually she came into the room. Carefully I started back into the backroom, and she followed. "Can I sit down?" she asked.

"This is the movement," I said. "You got the right place. Have a seat."

She looked down and up rapidly as she walked to the far corner, where she sat on a big cardboard box full of leaflets.

"Hey baby!" said Knight.

She opened her mouth but didn't say anything. She looked only at my eyes or his eyes, at nothing else, as though expecting a revelation. Her eyes were large, black, and demanding as gems. "What you doin?" she asked finally, the words seeming a slight shock to her tongue.

"Well nothin much, talkin about some things . . ." I was amused. She was beautiful.

"What *you* doin?" asked Knight.

"I was jus passin by," she said. "I been hearin bout the movemen . . ." Her stark gaze made the words somehow precise. She nodded, adding to the effect.

"Where you home?" asked Knight. "Weary? Dalton? Spot?"

Her small body slouched. She looked down. She looked straight ahead as she walked to the door as if she was leaving. She stood right in the door.

"You got somethin to read?" she asked in a tiny voice, turning around at the last.

I gave her a leaflet on voting out of the box.

"What's your name?"

"Bell."

She sat down in the green chair — settling lightly, she didn't disturb the bricks. She scratched her knee, then her elbow. She adjusted the leaflet in her lap. Knight gave up trying to talk to her. He took up his story: "Black was the man! Nobody like Black today cep me . . ." He got up and began to pace. "You see how hard it is for me to go along with this nonviolent! I ain doin nothin but restin. People wonder an remember, they comparin the past . . ."

Bell rose and stepped softly into the kitchen, peering in first to see if anyone else was in there. The leaflet was still in her hand — but in a minute sounds of water and dishes rattling could be heard.

"Since the Stars broke up it's been so quiet it's a shame!" Knight declared in a loud voice. "You know when we kidnap that police, that the las thing the Stars did together. One noon Buddy wen out in the woods to feed that police an ain never come back. Them polices huntin they frien naturally. Some way they got wise an caught ol Buddy when he givin him to eat. Bud like to feed him dog food an shit, he like to mess with him. He gone in the chair! An his brother Jake sen up for natural life. He on the chain gang an gon be there, I reckon. But he ain never said a word about none a the rest of us. *That* the kind a spirit some of us had! But the Stars broke up. Mos everybody lef town, wen up north, didn know is they gonna talk or not. — Not me! I knew . . ."

"Scuse me," said Bell, entering the room. With the straw broom she began sweeping up the dirt around our feet. Small staccato strokes of the broom like pecks —

"Oh thanks a lot," I said, thinking what a blessing such a girl was to the movement.

"An the dishes," she mentioned.

"You already did all those dishes?"

"Those little dishes? My mama have me workin all *day* not jus a few little dishes you can do an then have fun . . ."

"Where home?" Knight asked.

"I ain got nary'n."

"Didn she say *her mama?*"

"That by Forks — my mama."

"When you leave?"

"Yesterday."

She flicked the broom under the beds and in the corners, she even moved things to get at the dust. She swept it out the back door. "An I ain never goin back," she said, and went outside and swept the steps. "An nobody care an I don care."

"I see you do care," said Knight, as she walked back in.

She pouted her lips and shook her head and walked straight on through to the kitchen. Knight returned to his story, that he'd referred to many times since I'd met him.

"So the Stars died! Man, I didn know what was happenin, I couldn believe that shit! I wen aroun talk to every member still in town, but they didn wanna see me. They show me how they don have no spirit no more. An pretty soon I see little boys wearin the Star shirt all fade, an I hear em jivin use Star secret code they never shoulda heard. The gang ain nothin but a memory! But one day they gon be another gang I swear! CME gon be bad again if I am the president an the only member a the gang that do it, sheeit!"

"Could I have a cigarette please?"

Bell was sitting in the easy chair. Out of her blouse she took a long-handled pink plastic comb and pulled it through her hair until I got up and shook out a cigarette for her and lit it. She drew deeply. Letting out the smoke, she sighed. Having done a job for the movement, she was altogether more sure of herself.

She inhaled the smoke in through her nose and savored it.

"Somebody water been boilin," she said, gazing indifferently toward the doorway of the kitchen.

Knight leaped up. In a moment he was standing in the doorway with a steaming cup of coffee in his hand. With the other, he made a gesture of laying it on the line — "Well now you come to town, sugar, what you gon do for yourself?"

Violently she crossed her legs. There was a break in the smooth funnel of smoke that went up from her lips.

"Listen, don worry bout me cuz I ain studyin you!"

She trembled. She slipped the comb back into her blouse and set the leaflet on her knees and bent her head over it. She put her hands over her ears and swayed from side to side as she read the same line again and again. When she breathed in she came up a little, and when she exhaled she sank way down. Deep within her, she struggled to get the last wisp of old air out and to absolutely fill her lungs with the new. The leaflet fluttered to the floor as she jumped up and fled through the front door.

"My Jesus!" said Knight.

We walked clear into the middle of the street for a view but we couldn't see her.

fourteen

The shock sent Knight under the porch in search of a bottle of wine he had stashed there. "Damn!" he said. "I was so tore up las night when I pass here, say, 'Save this for in the mornin!'" We took it back in the bedroom. The Director didn't like us drinking in the office, so I took the precaution of shutting the front door as well as the bedroom doors. I turned on the light. I was content to drink in silence but momentarily Knight had picked up on his story. "Talk about gangs! They can talk about bad cats over across the river but they ain nobody with heart like the Stars. A lot of us could be inside right now — I could be in there right —"

Suddenly somebody was trying to push the door open. There was no handle on the other side, and they began pounding. Knight put the cap on the bottle and slid it under the bed. Outside Sam started yelling, "Hey y'all freedom riders, lemme in! They a pack a Klan out here, they got a rope, they comin for me!"

When he recognized his voice, Knight got out the bottle. I

let Sam yell a minute, then I twisted the old spoon bent in the lock for a handle, and he burst in.

"Damn, time you open up I'm *gone!* — Act like you doin somethin wrong — yeah, gimme that wine!"

Peering through some wide-angle shades, Sam moved to take the bottle which Knight held behind him.

"Where you been so thirsty, Sam?"

"Plantin a tree," said Sam, dropping his hand and grinning. "Lemme have some wine fore I throw it down the drain. You know you ain sposeta have no wine in this office!"

"You better hope that tree don grow!"

"Listen at you with your six kids."

"Sambo, it wasn one a them real little gals was it?"

"Knight, don call me that name —"

"Sheeit, out fuckin a little twelve-year-ol girl, oughta be ashame!"

"Man I don care how ol she is. Anyway, she fourteen, you musta got her confuse with one a your whores. Don make me beg for a drink, Knight!"

Knight took another himself. He held the bottle to the light to see how much was left. "Sam, I believe you fuck anythin that move . . ."

Sam stuck his finger up at Knight and looked along it like a gun barrel. He lunged forward and got the bottle, which Knight let him have. "Damn right! Who? I been knowed to get on top a daffodil swingin in the breeze hahahahaha!" He tipped the bottle up and drank . . . Pulling up his sleeve, peering at his wrist with no watch on it, he said, "Telephone time, brothers!" He set the phone on his knee and dialed the police station. It was part of a policy of harassing the police as much as possible while they had any of our people in jail. Sam

stuck out his elbow and squinted at the ceiling while at headquarters the desk sergeant's phone began to ring —

"Hello! Is this the officer in charge? — What — What? —
No, it all right, you'll do. This is the Reverend A. J. Simms
of Philadelphia talkin to you. Philadelphia, *Pennsylvania*. —
What? The name is Simms, S-I-M-M-S, the Reverend A. J.
Simms, yes. See here, my good sir, we been gettin reports up in
my congregation that a certain Charles Cosby an one Robert
Thomas both originally of Philadelphia, Pennsylvania, not gettin
they proper nutriment in your jail. The congregation all three
thousan members is *concerned* an they gettin set to write the
federal — what? Mmm, yes, by all means, do check your rec-
ords for them poor dear boys . . ."

He turned the receiver a little away from his ear and looked
smugly at us trying to keep in our laughter, at his congregation,
the whole outraged city maybe —

"What? You have them? Well that at least is a small relief
they in existence an not dead. But, officer, what about those
reports? What you been feedin —"

Listening, he tapped his foot and held the receiver with a
firm, businesslike grip. When the cop got loud, he ripped it
away from his head and gave it a look —

"Yes yes yes, officer, that certainly grand, officer, all your diet
chart —" He gave the receiver another look — "But have you
got a *heart* specialist? — Wait, officer! Please, officer, will you
do somethin for me? No, not for me — for the people a Philadelphia, Pennsylvania, so worried they can't sleep! For the
Lord up above! Take em a sandwich. Yes, go in your pocket,
officer, an buy em oh say ham an cheese that be all right an take
it to em in your own hands so I can be sure they ain starve. Oh
I can't tell you how it will soothe my poor congregation, how
upset they are, if you only — what? *Busy?* I didn't hear you

right! Too busy for the Lord's work! Officer, think a the here-
after, rest your thoughts on eternity! Consider the Father! —
What? You say you — oh bless your heart, officer! Oh how
the Lord will bless — no wait! Officer, will you please! One
last! Officer, one last small favor not for me but for the Father,
officer, will you get down on your knees with the Reverend A. J.
Simms an pray for the poor starved locked up beaten up fracti-
fied deprived but glad souls them poor boys you have . . ."

Gently Sam replaced the receiver on the hook. "He hung
up."

I came in from the yard where I'd had to run for laughing.
Knight was lying on the floor, tears down his cheeks. Sam had
kept the man on a long time with his hypnotic line.

" 'Take em a sandwich?! Is this a joke?' — A *joke*, officer! I
guess not! Simms don play with the Lord. On High, they askin
for a ham salad for them boys, believe it . . . !"

A fat bee bumped into the room through the open door and
plopped and glanced against the walls like a slow orange fish.
Like a thick gold fluid, the air in the room resisted the breeze
from outside and did not move. We sat very still. The mood
was changing, it was the sadness that was realer than the joke.
Friends were in jail. Sam began to sing —

> Oh-oh freedom!
> Oh-oh freedom!

He stood up on his heels and stuck out his chest, and hooked
his thumb in the strap of his overalls and kept time with his
forefinger —

> Oh-oh freedom,
> Over me,
> Over me . . .

I joined in, I loved to sing. On his flickering voice Knight floated in and out and around the song. His eyes were shut, he was searching for the glassy minimum of sound.

> An before I'll be a slave,
> I'll be buried in my grave,
> An be home with my Lord,
> An be free —

Before we'd finished the verse, Sam's voice fell off pitch — and never recovered. Knight sang louder and Sam began to shout. Knight grabbed a leaflet and wadded it into a ball which he bounced off Sam's head —

"Sambo, if I sang half as bad —"

"I tol you, Collins! I been done tol you don call me that name!"

"You the only Negro I ever knowed can't keep nary tune. What you spose yo mammy done wrong?"

"Don talk about my mother! Don make me fight you, Knight! I don wanna hafta hurt ya."

"Yeah, I better not talk about yo mammy. I need half an hour to speak proper on that subject —"

"An leave the bottle in the middle of the floor for the Director to step on!" Sam grabbed the empty bottle, waved it in the air and under Knight's nose, took a windup, and pitched it out the back door.

"Where is the Director step on a bottle? Where? I ain leave shit!"

"Knight, you ain got no sense. Set in the *office* drink wine!"

"If you wasn drunk, we wouldn be arguin! Who's actin drunk?" Knight appealed to me for a decision. I would've said, both you cats, and me too, listening to you. But I didn't get the chance.

Sam said, "You still askin a white man to settle your arguments?"

Hearing it, Knight stiffened. Then he leaped up from the bed and grabbed Sam by his shirt collar and hoisted him into the air.

"Sambo, I'm gonna take you outside an throw you in the mud, I swear I am, less you take that back!"

"What mud?" grinned Sam. "Ain no little rain like that make no mud."

"Go turn on the hydrant, man, make some mud."

I walked outside, and, insulted in my own right, gladly turned the handle. The water gushed out onto the clay. Out came Knight carrying Sam in his arms. We stood and watched a wide red lake quickly form. Knight held Sam over it.

"Take it back, Sam," beginning to release him.

"Hell no I ain't!"

"Take it back!"

Feeling the hands beneath him seriously loosen, Sam shouted, "Okay, okay!"

Knight dropped him beyond all hope — and caught him a foot above the pool of mud and stood him roughly on his feet. Sam adjusted his overalls and pushed his shades up on his nose. He brushed imaginary dirt from his elbows. "Boy you don play do you!" He looked really aggrieved. "I was only jokin! This black nigger here!"

In the sun the sodden clay was sending up a red vapor. The heat made us lazy and we just stood in the yard without moving.

"Georgia, Georgia . . ." sang Sam, but he was still off-key.

"Damn, boy, you don give up do you?" said Knight.

"That what they tol Ray Charles when he was a boy. You

cain't sing! You won never be no singer!' — He born right here in the country. Look where he is now!"

"Ain down here that for sure! He *from* Georgia, he can sing about her."

"Georgia, Georgia," crooned Sam, squinting up at the sun that had broken through the clouds, "you always on my mind . . ."

Then clear through the office we heard some girls' shouts. Knight jumped up in a fright and charged into the back room. Then he changed his mind and charged out again. He ran across the yard toward the fence but Cara Lee and another girl burst around the side of the house and cornered him. Cara Lee's eyes were big and bright and full of scorn.

"This where you been hidin out, Knight Collins!" shouted the other chick.

"Hidin? Who!"

"I want my baby, Knight!"

"I tol ya, Brenda, I ain got no money. How many times I gotta say it? *I ain got no money!*"

"I don want no money. All you gotta do sign your name on a paper."

"What on the paper, Brenda?"

"How I know? They say, 'The father he gotta sign on this paper fore we let your baby go.'"

"That paper got a *figure* on it, girl! I wasn born this mornin! Look here, Brenda, you go say the baby ain got no father you can name, they ain gon keep your baby."

"I can't, Knight. I already tol em bout you."

"No you didn't! What I tell you to tell em? What I say —?"

"I scared they won believe me —"

"*You* scared! Jail for me, baby!"

"They won put you in jail if you pay."

"Good Lord! Oh good Jesus! All the babies they got to take care of, you think they wanna keep yours?"

"I want my baby! I *want* my *baby!* Knight, I'm goin to your mother."

"Dumb as they is . . . you ain got the little teaspoonful a sense . . . Brenda, it so easy an simple —"

She turned and ran back the way she had come. Knight moved to chase her, but Cara Lee elbowed him back and ran too. He dashed through the office and met them in front. I followed and stood on the porch.

"Brenda, you goin to the hospital?"

"I'm goin to your mother, you lazy ass!"

"Ahhhh . . ."

He leaned against a tree as if he meant to knock it down. "Wait, goddamit, I'm comin."

Sam was asleep in the back with a newspaper over his face. I could hear him beginning to snore. From the porch, I was watching Cara Lee. I think I loved her since the day I'd first seen her, when Knight and I hid out from the cops in her house. I loved her eyes, so large and proud. Her hair was short — a shining bowl around her head. When she hung back from the unhappy couple, I went and stood beside her. Knight called that he'd see me later. About ten feet apart he and Brenda were walking down the road. He called be sure and get a car for tonight, and I called back I'd take care of it. The two of them went off in one direction, and I started walking Cara Lee to her place.

"Your frien sure think he big, don he?" she remarked. "So damn big ain got time for his own chillern. He make babies, he well satisfied, don give a damn to growin em up."

"Well —"

"Well nothin! Knight crazy an selfish both. You seen a rooster, jump this way an that, want all them gals an can't never make up his mind. That Knight. He chicken! You oughta tell him he got a duty to his chillern."

"Well —"

"You think I'm bitchin but he lucky he ain shot dead by a woman long time ago. You oughta try lookin at things from another side than Knight an give him some good advice."

"Well I guess you're right. You quit work or what?"

She turned and looked me in the eye, acknowledging my having changed the subject, allowing it, showing me in the same quick glance that she resented the fact that she worked and I didn't. "Yeah them cracker high school kids hang out over there drove me crazy . . . I *wish* I quit, sheeit! I need that job . . ." She fixed me with a canny gaze. "Listen, don you an Knight never come out that way, you promise. That one place I don wanna see nary one a y'all."

"I don't even know where it is —"

"Yeah good . . ."

Why was she so suspicious? Actually I'd never thought about it till now. Maybe she really wanted us to come out there and cause some integration-type trouble so she'd be fired?

"An don let Knight give you no ideas neither. In case he ever say he comin out there you persuade him he don wanna, please! Cuz Knight *hunt* trouble an I wanna keep that job! If he would spen half the time hunt some food for his chillern . . . You been in jail cuz a Knight but you still don know nothin . . . Say, you min if we walk a little faster?"

I guess she really did want to keep that job. I looked sideways at her, and saw how tight were her lips, how tall she was walking, and how terribly wide were her eyes, but I didn't think there could be anything wrong until she said, "Don look now, they some folks watchin us . . ."

Out of the corner of my eye I saw — behind us — white men staring. Wearing white aprons, khaki shirts and trousers, the flash of their eyes made an ice-blue haze. The shape they made all together was a bomb with a fuse of the last of them still easing out beneath the canvas awning of a grocery store.

"Damn, you'd think we were a parade," I said.

"We sorta are," she said, not looking back, walking very fast, tugging at my arm.

"Look I'll walk to the corner with you," I told her, "then you go ahead alone, it'll be safer."

She was agreeable to that! Even better had I told her to go ahead right then. And I should've run for it. But I couldn't just skip off and leave her in danger, that was my idea. So I kept her in danger a little longer. I was slightly afraid, yet I have to admit I was looking forward to the confrontation that might take place if I took this route back to the office. Once this had been a wealthy section of the town. The houses were huge and seemed empty and forsaken despite the little white kids playing in their yards that supported only a few tufts of wiry gray grass. A tiny girl ran ahead of us, dragging a stick along a picket fence da-da-da-da-da-da like a Morse code of excitement or danger. She turned in a walk — a small white dog ran out as she ran in — it yapped at our heels.

"He won bite ya!" called the girl, not much bigger than her pet. "He don bite nobody but . . ."

Cara Lee's eyes were fixed straight ahead and slightly bulging as though she might pull the scenery past us more quickly with their help.

"Come an see me tonight," she smiled at the corner. "Cut aroun the block or somethin, don be no fool!"

And she was gone. She was small and thin way down the road and I was watching her and I didn't know what I was going to do next. I walked back down the street. Inside my head, I was tightening up. If I could've rapped on my soul right then it would've sounded like a cold drum. When I passed the grocery a squat man in a white apron ran out toward me, rolling up his sleeves and shaking his fist —

"Hey boy!"

Boy! Me? — That's what I was all right but I resented it on his lips.

"You!"

His face was fat with rage — he grabbed my arm. "Whachu think you doin walk down this street with a nigger gal in broad daylight?"

His concern that it was daytime intrigued me, but I took it from a different angle. "What nigger? The only nigger I see is you!" I gave him a big smile, trying to give him that compliment. I had a strange approach to things in those days.

He drew his fists up next to his chin that was red. "Whachu wanna come down fuck with our good goddam Georgia niggers?"

"Now wait a minute! I won't talk about you! That could be my wife you're talkin about."

"Your —! You —! You smart sonofabitch! Where you come from?"

"The United States of America! We won the war, remember? I'm a citizen —"

"The United —! Boy this ain no united nothin — this here Meansville, Georgia!"

He was squinting at me like a bull. More men were appearing out of the grocery store. They settled around us in a slow wreath that shrank continually.

"Now I ast ya? Whachu doin walk down the sidewalk with a nigger gal?"

"*What sidewalk?* All I see is the damn dirt road!"

"Boy, you don know what you playin —"

"No I'm not. I'm registering voters. My wife is a prospective voter." I thought I would get that in. If all this led to real trouble, he would be attacking a voter worker, and that would be violating the Constitution.

"Boy I'm gon stick you like a pig!"

The blood began leaving my legs — it seemed to be running up the outside of the skin of them. I should've wanted to run, but I was strangely distracted. This could've been something I'd once read about in the newspapers. I waited for a move — but he let the stark pronouncement just hang in the air. The eyes of the men around us glinted. Their silence screamed: *Go on!* Or maybe they were all waiting for me to run, as if I had some good sense —

The whine of a motorcycle cut through this scene . . . Through the ring of watchers I saw a cop pull up and dismount. He removed his helmet and wiped his forehead with the back of his hand. With the tips of his fingers he parted a way for himself through the audience and stood next to the grocer.

"What's goin on here, Bill?"

The friendly way he spoke the man's name sounded bad, but when he chuckled right afterward my little hope vanished like dew under a blowtorch. Nevertheless, I started to say something: "This guy —"

"Shuddup!" said the cop.

"Oh nothin much goin on here, Bob," said the grocer. "Fixin to cut this here nigger-lover." He never took his eyes off me.

"Oh that what he is!" said the cop, opening his eyes real wide. "Well lemme get on out your way . . ." He walked on back to his bike, settled himself on it with some care, adjusted his helmet, jumped on the starter, and whined away.

"Mm-hmmm!" said the grocer. He hooked his thumbs in his belt under the apron and pulled himself up so that he was looking directly into my eyes.

"Mm-*hmmm!*" said somebody in the crowd.

"I oughta cut you right now! I oughta cut you damn throat!"

I ought to hit you in the mouth first! I ought to run like hell! But I didn't do anything. Weirdly, the scene was both unreal and fascinating. Maybe it was *too* real. It was just too classic a confrontation between a civil rights worker and a southerner. This wasn't the first time I'd been in trouble — yet it didn't seem like he was talking to *me* — maybe I wasn't really there? — and maybe I wasn't talking to *him*. As if this was a play and we'd both forgotten our next lines, we stood there staring at each other. Or maybe my line came next, and I knew it, but I just let it go, hoping to provoke something totally unexpected.

Finally he said, "United States! I fought in the War, boy, you don tell me bout no United States!" and again fell silent. But his face was getting redder.

I just stood there breathing. All of a sudden I was stifling my laughter —

"I'm gonna give you a gift!" he shouted. "I'm gonna give you until in the mornin to clear out. Hear me boy? *Till in the mornin to get outa this county!*"

Well it was time for me to go. "Pardon me, scuse me there, mister sir . . ." I made my way out of the crowd, but I couldn't keep from smiling.

"*You hear me?*"

"Yeah, I hear you," I said. I was out of them now, I started to run, "But I ain't leavin now or anytime!" I was speeding along. "I *like* your county!" I cried, and let my wild laughter overtake me. Nobody pursued. I ran clear to the office, on shaky legs, in echoes . . .

On the steps of the office sat the Director, humming to himself. Sam was next to him, shelling beans into a pot.

"What's new?" asked Sam.

"Well a cracker just told me to get out of town by sunrise or he's gonna kill me, that's new."

His shades glittered as he tipped his head. He put his hands on his knees. "You goin?"

"No I'm not goin! Goddam, Sam!" He was sitting there with the Director, that's why he was acting so different.

"Maybe you better," he said. "Them rednecks sure can be mean. What you do to him?"

That made me angry — "Damn, Sam, nothing! Cara Lee an I were walkin by —"

"Oh yeah, nothin!" interrupted Sam. "We had another white boy jus like you las year. He think he in love with some girl an think cuz she black that very special, so they downtown one day an he kiss her on Main Street. They arrested, cost us plenty to bail em out. He talk jus like you — 'I didn do nothin!' — Only when they come to get you, they maybe get me too. If you can't remember *you*, think a *me* — how I love life!"

The Director said nothing. In the dark I wouldn't have recognized the Director by his voice. He seemed to think a thought should be rolled around on the tongue a thousand times before let out in words, and he rarely let any out. Sam spoke for him, he spoke of his likes, dislikes, rules, sacrifices, hopes, beliefs. The Director was absent from it. He talked only when necessary and I'd heard him keep quiet even then. I could only imagine how difficult it was for him to be with a newcomer, a stranger from the North, a Harvard dropout who was so clean, and green, not wounded by the terrible discoveries that were freeing his mind into darknesses. Years ago, he had selected seven towns. They formed a crescent with Meansville the largest of them, the central target. A command of voices describing the evil would abolish it all along the crescent. The bright light of many people speaking truly would illumine and then burn it up. He sang of his vision of nonviolence, the people believed, they marched, they challenged the chiefs of the evil, who did not vanish — they grew more wily. The Director was losing his gentle potent righteousness and growing sad or angry. The complex music of the town was drowning out his voice. It was my innocence of this that chilled him toward me. He was afraid I would stop at too shallow a level and return to familiar planes without understanding. My arrival in town had nearly coincided with the end of the period of strong belief in nonviolence. The recent marching might be the last the town would see for a long time. I wished I could explain myself to him. I respected his imbalance and admired his uncertainty, though it was Knight's anger that moved me. He didn't look at me as I passed. His eyes were nearly shut. Lightly, far back in his throat, he was humming.

fifteen

SOONER THAN I'D EXPECTED, Knight returned. The energy was gone from his step, his gaze was scattered. He flopped down in the green easy chair — and jumped up when it collapsed. Wearily he stacked up the bricks that made up for where it was missing a leg and sat again more carefully.

"How you make out, Knight?"

"Oh man, I put my name on that paper. Eighty-six fifty by the end a the month. How I'm gonna get that? I don know what kinda champagne they been feedin that baby."

"Look," I whispered, "you put it right, you might get some of it from the movement . . ."

Momentarily a faint light appeared in his eyes. Then they shut and he rubbed them with the heels of his hands. "A woman bring you down every time. They jus ain got good sense. By this time I oughta learned. All the experience I had! I deserve to get shot down . . . You know, when I was seventeen year ol, I was a married man. I drove shine all over this state for a big bootlegger out by Weary. I made me a heap of money, think I'm a *man*, gotta get *married*. My ol man — he a sergeant in the army up in New Jersey — he pay for a nice weddin an pay a month rent on a house, even put a TV in it for me. He pay everythin — an I got a pile myself, make big money haul that splo cuza the danger. Times was lovely, man! I make six, seven big trips a month, rest a the time I lay up in the bed an fuck till I can't fuck no more an en watch TV. Heaven, man! An I like drivin that shit. It peace an quiet like you wouldn believe it up behin that wheel. It a secret where I am an a secret where I'm goin, an the onlies light throw by my truck. But one day the man get busted. Politics. He say, 'Wait on me, boy! We be right again in a year.' They fine him an he get some little time too. He still ain right! But they don catch me. Not *me!* An I got some connection, so I figure I go to work for another man. But my wife, she start in complainin — 'They gon get you nex time! What I'm gon do you go to jail?' You know. She get on my nerves, start me to worryin — she jinx me, what it was, an I decide to take a vacation. I got plenty a money so I don need to work. Lay up all day, take it easy, for a while I convince myself I'm enjoyin life. But pretty soon, I can't deny it. I'm bored. Same happnins, gettin me down. I start hangin roun bars at night an I'm in a fightin mood an don do myself no good. Outa bed me an the ol lady fight plenty. I need to do somethin for myself stead a stay drunk an *wish!* One day, we fight, I tell her, 'It all yours.' I tell her, everythin in the house, an the *house too,* she can have it, cuz I'm splittin. I give her some money an slam the door on her cryin an throwin stuff. I remember it was rainin a drizzle in the sunshine, an I felt sharp an clean like that water. You know — that when I met Bud an join the Stars. I ain jivin. That same day hones to God. We gon have our own lan in the woods, an control it! We gon have a house an cars, an we will be unstoppable because we be together! Step outa my house — felt so free! Felt like I could do anything . . ." His head, high as he talked, drooped down. He sank back into the chair disgustedly. "Yeah, you see what I do. Let em fuck over me like a boy . . . put myself in a bind . . ."

After the right kind of silence I said, "Yeah, well you're not the only one had trouble today." I waited for his attention, for his eyes. "Cracker told me be outa town by sunrise or he's gonna look for me . . ."

"Who?"

"Right down the road, that white grocery. Cara Lee an I walked by, that's what did it. When I came back that way, he grabbed me — 'Boy, I'm gon cut you like a pig!'"

"*What?* Who he think he is! Can't let that go, man think he can threaten folks an get away with it. Be a shame hafta go clear roun that store every time you head for CME . . ."

He stood up — I said, "Look, they were kinda pissed off about it," motioning toward the front porch, "Sam anyway. You know — I should've been more careful."

"Sheeit! Nonviolen don mean run like a dog, do it? We ain gonna do nothin but a little nonviolent!"

Though Knight respected the Director, he never spoke to him. He expressed his respect by not speaking. "Jump up, Sam!" he said, as we passed them sitting on the steps. In the street, he looked back over his shoulder. "Sam, lemme talk to ya."

Finally he came on, regarding Knight curiously.

"You hear what happen?" Knight thumbed at me.

"So?"

"So you gonna jus let it pass?"

"It his fault — it wouldna happen —"

"But it happen!"

"You gonna go ask for trouble?"

"I just want that cracker know we don play that shit, Sam."

"Yeah, what good you think that gon do?"

"Good! Oh man, don come talkin bout no *good* —"

"What *you* gon get out of it?"

"I'ma tell a white man he ain the bigges thing in the worl, it ain nothin more to it but that."

"So what that gon do for you?"

"What it do! God*dam*, Sam, it make me *happy!* What you think it do?"

That got him. He laughed. I had a feeling he might — he was coming along with us. We walked three abreast with Sam in the middle. "All right, what we do when we get there?" asked Sam.

"What kinda candy you like? Baby Ruth? Gimme a nickel, Sam. We all buy some little thing so we get in there — I'll decide after that."

Knight was springing off his toes. He seemed aware of every muscle in its place, rippling over the bone. Every now and then: *Ha!* he snorted. And in his eyes, warm light.

"Tol ya to get outa town did he?" said Sam, as though I had just related the incident.

"Yeah motherfucker — an all I did was kiss Cara Lee!"

The late sun was a purple ball lighting up the earth with pinks. Burning in the window of the store, a yellow bulb held pale influence over the edge of the street. As we entered I glanced at the shelves. Hominy, cornmeal, sacks of flour and potatoes . . . An old man in clothing the color of cardboard cartons moved himself and became visible. He began whistling "The Halls of Montezuma." The curve of the grocer's back,

stooped down beneath the counter, was in motion of him looking for something. We took places around the counter, which
was shaped like an *L*. I was around the far side of it. Knight
tapped a nickel on the smooth board. The man's head tipped
up, then the whole man —

"Help ya?"

He sounded friendly, which surprised me. It was too good.
Though he had seen Sam out of the corner of his eye, he hadn't
spotted me yet.

"Butterfinger," said Knight, gazing down into the man's eyes.

"Sho."

He bent down again and came up with a thin orange-
wrapped bar. Handing it to Knight, he turned slightly toward
Sam, raising his eyes for the request.

"Butterfinger," said Sam. The word, repeated, and coming
slowly from Sam's lips, sounded so clearly foreboding to me that
I was amazed the man didn't stop right then and demand an
explanation. But the good salesman obligingly stooped. Coming up for the third time, his knees, straightening after the
squat, and his hand, holding the candy, clenched tight as his
teeth as, for a long moment, staying in this crouch, something
became clear.

"Boy, you thrive on trouble!"

"Butterfinger," I said, and that made him almost writhe.

The next move was his. He was holding the candy. He
flipped it angrily — it bounced against the bib of Sam's overalls. Insulted, Sam watched it spinning down the counter. He
threw his nickel at the man's apron. Their hands moved simultaneously, covering the candy and the coin. As usual I didn't
really understand what was going on, but I could see the effect
and I almost laughed. I wanted to slap him on the back and

have a good laugh about it, all of us, it struck me that funny. I leaned my hands on the counter and stared into his eyes as I might've had I just asked him for the contents of the cash drawer, though I had almost no such mean intention; if I was excited I was also pained by the rage in the air, that I reflected —

"You do a lot of trade with colored folks, don you, mister?" asked Knight in a pleasant voice.

The man ignored him. He reached under the counter and found my candy and chucked it down in front of me. A vein had swollen up to the size of a candy bar in his neck and his face was blue. He opened his trembling fingers for my nickel.

"Uh mister, maybe you didn hear me speak to you. What I said, you do a lot a trade with Negroes, isn't that true?"

"You wanna buy somethin just tell me what, I ain a-gonna talk no politics with you."

"This ain no politics! It a simple business question. You get a lot a *black* trade in this here store or don you?"

"I got a good relation with the colored come in here. I don swindle nobody. I don need yo advice how to run my business."

"You on such good terms how come you ain got none workin for ya in the store?" cried Sam, taking advantage of the situation. "I oughta see a black face behin that counter stead a your ugly one!"

"What you got against two young people walkin in the street?" Knight insisted. "Hmm? Mindin they business, a boy an a girl — might be in love an happy, how you know? Got to run out your store an butt in! See somethin nice but you can't have it, got to shit in the street! What wrong with you, mister?"

"I done tol ya! No politics!" The man's hands began climbing frantically over each other. "If you ain gonna buy nothin else I'm gon ast ya to please leave outa my store." He pressed his hands onto the counter, he made fists of them, he jerked up a finger and drove it into his ear.

"I'm gon leave, don worry!" cried Knight. "Jus as soon as I tell ya one las thing. Don mess with folks! Hear, mister? *Don mess with folks!* I hate to see you lose all your nice window glass out front! I hate to see you lose all your good colored trade! I hate to see you lose all your whole store!"

He held the stunned man in his gaze another moment — then he walked out the door. The old fellow in the cardboard suit looked like he never saw anything like it in all his days. He followed Knight so close with his eyes he was actually drawn into the doorway. He jumped back for Sam. I followed, staring back at the grocer who seemed to be sinking behind the counter, diminishing in size for a final late explosion . . .

Laughing and touching hands, we fell into the center of the road and paraded down it.

"You an actor, boy!" grinned Sam. "Yes Lord, you out a sight, Knight! I see a great future for you —"

"Well he know you ain leavin by no sunup," said Knight.

"— if you live another few years . . ."

At something past eleven when I got up to go and meet Knight, Cara Lee told me I was crazy one more time. "How many crazy things you want to do in one day?" she asked. I'd been doing some bragging about the episode at the grocery store. I told her, *one* more. And she did laugh. I made it over to the office. I had arranged to borrow the movement Studebaker, the least car belonging to the movement, and I was glad to see it was parked out in front. It was a moist, cloudy night,

156

without actually raining. Just perfect. I got the spray can and stencils from under the back steps. I sat on the front porch and breathed the deep air, and listened to the good night sounds. When Knight showed up, he was bare chested and wearing black pants, for camouflage.

"You picked a perfect night," I told him. "Ten feet away and I can't even make you out it's so dark."

"Who so dark! Button down your shirt sleeves! I can see *you* for blocks."

We got in the Studebaker. Reluctant as an old cow, the sporty green and yellow car heaved away from the curb. He floored the gas pedal, but we went no faster.

"How y'all come by this tank?" he asked.

"Somebody up North sent it down, I guess."

"Yeah, man say, 'Save me twenty-five bucks tow it away, better give it to them needy Negroes down South.'"

There were no stars. The silver of an occasional streetlamp washed away in the night like a too delicate dye. We drove a few blocks. Quickly, under a cluster of poplars we parked in shade like tar and gently rested the doors on their locks. Over the silent clay we ran past a warehouse to the corner. No one on any stoop. In the distance, no headlights. Somebody's bumper had recently clouted the stem of the stop sign, it was a difficult angle. I slapped the stencil up against the red octagon, and Knight sprayed —

It stood at a grave tilt as if directing the sky. The paint lightly glowed when I struck a match. Knight's eyes rushed

with joy like stones in fast water. We got the other of this pair
of signs and ran back to the car. Knight paused to leave a message on the side of the warehouse: FUCK MEANSVILLE. We hit
all the stop signs in the vicinity of the office — we wanted our
work to be seen by friends even more than enemies. Knight
had an accurate idea of the routes and schedules of the police
patrols. We saw squad cars as close as a street away, but we
were never in motion. In CME, we painted the main corners.
At the crossroads by The Raindrop Cafe, there were four stop
signs and we used both stencils. Our hands were white from
holding the stencils. I glanced at the cafe, thinking this is
where Big Black took away that gun and threw it clean into the
alley. A drunk stumbled out of the place. He stopped a half
inch away from me.

"Whachu?" he asked, "Indian, me."

So he was, a red man.

"Sailallverthworl — cnspikfrenchtalinmexcnzulunportagis.
Wenschoolfourteenyear — whagood? whagood?"

People were idling out of the cafe to watch us.

Idly I asked the red man, "What tribe are you?"

"You talk to anybody, don you," said Knight. "Look here!"

In the tarred intersection, he had written STRIKE BACK. The
drunk Indian had a bottle of wine and I got a few swallows, and
so did Knight. We circled around the letters in the middle of
the street, admiring them. The Indian started dancing and we
joined him in some steps. But foolishly he began to holler —
we were running immediately, away from the scene. We
jumped in the car. On the downhill we shot past our work,
through the stop sign. The Indian was waving both his arms
like he wanted to come too, but this was too serious for a drunk.
All night we painted until the stencils were pulp past using.

We painted all of CME and entered a white suburb and painted to the edge of Means Park with its confederate cannon, its monument to old Means who barreled salt pork for the Dixie army, its zoo, and the notorious segregated Means swimming pool.

"I got the power but I hate to waste it on jus a swimmin pool," said Knight, referring to some dynamite he had. This reminded him of something. We drove on through the suburb to a great white mansion nearly hidden behind a grove of pine trees.

"This where Maddon live, who own the pool," he explained, "in this fuckin barn."

We walked along the edge of a long drive that was like a cinder road through a forest. Finally we came to the front steps which rose majestically to a big glass door black as ice, in front of which stood an iron coachman. Silently we ran up the steps. The coachman was a large fellow, reaching up to our chests, with shiny black cheeks and grinning red lips and teeth like diamonds, and his buttons and every detail dabbed in with a fine brush. On his head was a little cap, and in his gloved hand he held a brass ring. We admired him a moment as execution-ers. We wasted the rest of the spray can on him. We left him white all over, lips and elbows dripping.

It was an hour before dawn. The sky was clumped and folded like dark gray cotton. In a vacant lot we dumped the empty paint can, and in an alley, the remains of the stencils and the newspapers that had protected the interior of the car. We made a stop at Knight's mother's house for cleaning fluid, and headed for the office. In the trunk of the car were rags with which we wiped away every telltale streak and smudge we could locate and did the best we could for our hands. Suddenly I noticed spots of paint everywhere; I picked at my fingernails, I took off my shoes for a closer look. In the incinerator basket behind the office we burned the rags — lovely pale morning fire. We entered by the back door, decorated like the front door with bullet holes — old wounds or medals that made sleep proud. A couple cats I didn't recognize were asleep in two of the cots. You never knew who would flop down here for a little rest. All the girls of the movement stayed in a house that was rented for them down the street. Neither Sam nor the Director was here tonight. In the quiet light — Knight was already snoring. I heard a gasp, like a cry. In the easy chair in the corner, there was the little girl, Bell. She seemed to be fighting for air, her hands clutched her throat, she would choke, recoil. Out of surprise, I nearly shook her; I made a slight move, incomplete. It was one of those moments when my identity kind of traded around, and I was her fitful slumber. Then she relaxed, the bad dream tension collapsing, her limbs finding temporary comfort. She seemed to be gaining strength for new terror: run far way from home, the little body of hope and fear come to this corner.

sixteen

I AWOKE a few hours later, mid-morning. I was tense — I couldn't sleep anymore so I went outside to relax, breathe, and see what was happening. Bell was sitting on the edge of the porch, swinging her legs. I welcomed her home. She didn't seem to want to talk so I shut up and sat in a chair and savored the thought that every stop sign within blocks bore my signature. The sky was still overcast today. Through the bushes like giant weeds, the view of a few houses and a strip of clay road seemed very beautiful. I didn't think to try to figure it out, I just enjoyed it. I had never much liked this section around the office where the people were poor but trying to be respectable and middle class, but last night we staked out some territory. A lot of black people saw us. I wondered if the cops would haul us away for vandalizing public property. Can beauty be the flower of fear? I looked forward to people showing up with the news. I asked Bell, "Say, you want to see something?"

She said, yeah she did, and I led her toward the corner. But before we got fifty feet, she stopped abruptly and grabbed my arm. Her face was tight and frightened and I thought oh my

God she's not going into a thing! She said, "Listen! Hear that crackin?"

I listened. No . . . Yes, maybe I heard a little crackling or pecking noise. I don't know. She was pointing at a big tree that dominated the air between here and the corner. "Haints in the tree," she said. "You wanna bring trouble on yourself go on stan under it!" She was pulling me back the way we had come.

"What!"

"Listen boy, they a lot a things you don know! Haints skittish — *nasty!* If you gon try to scare a haint you got to know how. I bet you been to college but you nothin when it come to haints. They musta roost up there las night . . ."

I really didn't know what to think about that. It amused me. But was she putting me on? — No, I didn't think so. There was something very for real and urgent in the little kid's voice. Feeling strange and kind of foolish, I agreed to turn away, and we walked in the other direction. It didn't matter. Almost any corner around here would do.

"I heard em — scittin an scattin," she went on. "I hate to see em mess with folks! — Yeah, you spec a haint, get away fast! They fly like *that!*" She clapped her hands and grabbed her throat — "An cling on ya!"

I shook my head. "Whew!"

In fact this was an even better corner for purposes of showing off our work because it had four signs. I walked her around and showed her each example of our art. She seemed impressed. She touched the letters and said they looked very nice. "How you get em so straight an nice?" she asked. I explained the idea of a stencil.

"Hey, I brung you somethin in the movemen. You see it?"

No, I said, I hadn't, what was that? She wouldn't say. We

started back to see. — But here came Knight out of the office. He didn't see us as he made the turn toward CME and headed toward the evil tree. I hollered to him and he waited as we came up.

"Well look who here!" he said to Bell.

"So what about it?" she snapped.

I told him to watch his step around that big tree up ahead, and told him why.

"Haints?" He burst into laughter. "What you know about haints?"

"Some folks oughta know better," Bell said.

"You sure some up there," he said quickly, feigning seriousness. She was such a sweet kid, whom he really liked a lot. I could see him make a decision to humor her.

"Hear em snappin twigs — if you listen!"

We went and sat on the porch. There was more than a little strange about this girl. But she didn't say more about the haints. Apparently we were at a safe distance here.

"You wanna know what I'm gonna do?"

"Look here, little mama, it ain none a my business."

"That ain what you say yesterday. Say — 'You gotta know what to do in town!' "

"You the one need to know, not me, baby."

"I'm with the movemen, that what!"

"Oh yeah? Good! That a wise step — you on a good path in life."

"I been march! I'm ready!" She touched my hand and pointed through the doorway. "See what I brought?"

I couldn't see. I got up to look. On the table in the front room, in the plastic container we used to mix Kool-Aid, green shoots and yellow flowers in a lovely spray! Beautiful! Knight got up to admire them too.

"Aw they ain nothin really. I picked em down by the river-bank." Then she remembered. "Oh yes," she told Knight, "them signs you paint very nice. They look like they was made that way, you know . . ."

"Ha ha! I bet they look good in the daylight!"

Nobody showed up for half an hour, so we took a walk. Avoiding the tree, we followed a route toward The Raindrop Cafe that took us through the areas we'd concentrated on last night. STOP COPS! . . . STOP WHITEY! . . . Does it seem odd that a white boy painted such signs? "Whitey" is a retort to "nigger." They are imprecations linked in converse by blood the earth has been drinking for centuries. For instance, the cops called me "nigger," I was at a new place in the equation. It made me happy to see our work in numerous display. At each traffic corner we appreciated it anew! As we walked and walked and cracked up every time we passed a busy, regulated corner, I felt an undercurrent in my emotion, I couldn't deny it, like a light undertow, eddy of fear. I was laughing a lot. At any moment, while we were laughing and leaning on the stems of our paintings, patrol cars might swoop in and uniforms engulf us. We returned to the scene of the crime again and again! Was it not from this almost pleasurable current of fright that the beauty of these streets flowed? Everything, as if I was surrounded by colored liquids held in forms . . .

On a rise at the end of one block — an abandoned warehouse with windows painted over or broken out, and the loading dock overgrown with high hot weeds. Drifted onto its tall door were figures of old paint and rust, lines, oblongs, unnamable spatterings — strange emblem of our passing.

And here, in front of this home, the orange dust had been raked in countless neat thin rows. The unpainted boards of the house were powder-gray and finely grained — wood like shell.

On the top step, a white porcelain rooster with bright red comb arched its neck and silently crowed.

Beauty so bare and common appreciation of it must require if not a hand in its creation or years' unconscious scrutiny — faith.

Even the meat-packing plant, the great shed in the distance, on other days like a cliff of tin where life and land abruptly end, seemed today more like a silver tent. The rich noon blue-silver air blended into the meat shed, and the edges of the building swam away in the air, and the huge ambiguous letter-symbols floated unsupported, bobbing on the air. And I didn't think of what went on inside it, behind the huge red letters s w i f t that were too far apart from one another to be seen as a single word. When I considered the slaughter, I understood even its far-out and timely beauty.

We passed Knight's mother's house. The rain bucket had been removed — with something in it after the recent showers. I asked him, "Hey you got running water in your house, how come your mama keeps a rain bucket?" He answered, "She from the country, man, she specially like the taste of rain-water." — On the corner of this block, was the house of a mechanic. Knight led the way back behind it to a "shade-tree garage." Over the biggest limbs of an oak tree in his yard, ropes and pulleys were slung — like over beams in a roof of leaves. The cat was doing a valve job on a Ford. He welcomed us — he seemed to enjoy making his work into a demonstration. Knight had told me he hung around a lot and helped the man for the experience. He had the engine open, and he showed Bell the pistons and down in the cylinders. I had to smile at a little girl for whom ghosts in the air were so natural and the innards of an automobile were such a wonder! She looked and looked. Knight invited the cat to come and have a beer with us at the cafe. He declined because of pressure of work. Knight said, really he wanted to show him something — and grinned sly. But we couldn't get him to come along, though I added my voice; I had a dollar or two to spend on some beer. Knight had to tell him — had he seen any signs on the corner today by any chance? — Yeah, he saw that shit! Who did that? — Knight pointed from himself to me. The man cracked up, and when Knight held out his hand, he slapped it, and held it up for me too, and he grazed my hand in gratitude and appreciation. It was extra cool here under the leaves so thick lying flat on each other down the branches like green hair, and the clay soil was so cool to stand or sit on, bared by the work and soaked with grease and black oil, so it took the heat straight down. It was a fine place to be on a hot day, I hated to go. But The Raindrop had beer.

In a rut red as a river of wine we walked downhill. The sunlight through the dust was making crystal figures in the air. On front stoops small kids braving the heat in earth-smeared shorts solemnly watched us pass. An old Cadillac rolled by — cane fishing poles jiggling cork bobbers poked through a window. Through the cloud that it raised I could see the faces staring back. I knew why they were staring, these folks from the country, but it hardly mattered. I looked up in the sky and saw the dust flow into a thousand shining veins . . . At the bottom of the hill stood the cafe with its bright roof bluer than the air. Like a cave or a cellar. Inside behind the shutters it was shadowy and very pleasant. Knight ordered beers for us and a Coca-Cola for Bell. The woman was very brusque with him, like she didn't mind his business but she didn't like him. For a while we relaxed and breathed in silence. Bell looked very happy and pleased, but like a little gal on a tour she didn't say much. Knight started talking to her:

"Hey baby, you know where we at, don't you? CME, baby!
You probably heard about this part a Meansville — we got a
rep that flies for miles, but a lot of people don even wanna talk
about it . . ."

Bell didn't say anything. If she hadn't heard of CME she
wasn't going to say so. She could tell he was winding up into it.
He gulped some beer — "In CME the women bad as the men!
Shit! —"

"Mae and Cara Lee —" I started to say.

"Naw man! *Bad!* I tell you bout a woman that was *bad!* Ol
Lou Lester, aunt a mine, hustle stump whiskey, keep a skin-
game goin in her house. Had three husbands an damn if she
didn shoot all every one of em! One time she catch Tony Bass
out at the Playhouse after she tol him not to go out drinkin at
none a them places. He was her man after she done kilt her
second husband. You hear I didn say she was his woman.
Didn have nary word for him when she find him — whip out
her blade an be all aroun him whoo-wup-wup! Ha ha! Hack
that sharkskin suit she bought him clean off, he stan there look
foolish in his undershorts. She go in the bar an send for this cat
Lucius Tip, an when ol Tip brung his cab aroun an they got
Tony laid out on the back seat, she say, 'Take him on home,
Lucius, an stay there an don neither one a you go near that
door till I get there if it ain't till *next week* —' "

Bell was giggling loudly. Two drunk cats at another table
were snorting, and even the woman behind the bar was grinning. Knight went on, "I'm her nephew an it run in the family.
I been bad all my life an I don know how to play nothin else. I
fuck with whitefolks when I was a *child* cause I wanna make
my rep. One thing I know — if you a crazy nigger — if you the
crazies nigger they know — they don wanna mess with you.

Cuz they know! Yes, they know, whatever you doin now —
the nex thing could be worse! Ha ha!" He finished the beer
and called for another. I got another, and Bell got a fresh Coke.
"One time, I remember, I wasn but a boy. I wasn doin nothin
one day, an I took it in my head — Ha! I got an idea — I'm gon
climb on this big white man house. I'm gon climb right to the
top an see what is they to see way up high . . ." He laughed
and laughed, remembering. In three long swallows he finished
his second beer.

Triumphant, on the difficult peak, his arms shot straight out,
framing his mirth. He laughed before climbing. He laughed at
the thought of it, not bothering to climb at all. All the way up
he laughed as he breathed, thinking how he would tell it
later —

"An en at white lady come out the door, say, 'Boy! Whachu
doin on my roof?!' "

"I say, 'Watchin the sunset, ma'am.' "

" 'On my *roof?*' "

" 'Yes ma'am, they quite a view. You don mean to tell me you
ain never took it in?' "

" 'You *crazy* nigger!' — She leave me see my fill a sunset."

I dug his tales. I gave him fame in my heart.

When Sam burst in the cafe with something obviously on his
mind, Knight didn't stop. But when he sat next to us with an
angry, glum expression and didn't try to interrupt him or anything — just sat there looking bitter and sad — Knight finally
gave in: "What wrong with you, man? Look like somebody
mess with you!"

Still Sam didn't say anything. He was gazing at Bell, so I
introduced them. Sam nodded and then suddenly shouted,
"What you drinkin?" He grabbed Bell's glass and looked in it,

got a little taste, and jumped up and strode to the door and tossed the contents out in the dust. He returned to the bar and asked the lady, "What else you got beside Coca-Cola?"

"What buggin him?!" said Knight — and really it was amazing.

The lady held up a light green bottle. "This here Mountain Dew drink, nothin else."

Sam took that and poured it in a new glass and gave her a dime. He brought the fresh drink back to Bell and sat down again. "Listen man," Sam said to us, "there was a meetin last night, about jobs, we got to talkin about boycotts —"

"Shit man, I don want no job!" interrupted Knight. "Hey — you seen some stop signs this morning, man?"

"Yeah, I seen em an I been hearin about you too," said Sam, cool and friendly. "Dig, I think you cats did a beautiful thing — but listen, Knight, lemme tell my story —"

Knight nodded, "Okay, okay —"

"It's black money make em rich, right? You got to admit it, Knight, everybody ain't like you. Some folks would like a job for some bread. — So dig, this mornin I went out to Coca-Cola with some kids, try to talk with the man, why ain't any Negroes in the operation when we drink as much Coke as anybody. — See what we got?" He rolled up his sleeves and showed abrasions on his elbows. He stood up and pointed to his ripped pants. I winced seeing it. "That all we got, man," said Sam. "They won talk — like it's national Coke but it's a Georgia bottling company — they pitch us out on our ass an we got a boycott on Coca-Cola startin today!"

"Damn, Sam, I useta work out at Coca-Cola myself," said Knight.

"What you do out there?"

"Oh carry some shit, you know," Knight smiled.

"You ever seen a nigger in the *operation?*"

"Shit, Sam, I know that man run that place — you sure it wasn't jus some crackers hang aroun the neighborhood? I like a Coke, if I can't drink beer. We like Coke, don we, baby!"

Sipping her Mountain Dew, Bell made no reply. "Bell's with the movement," I kidded him.

"Okay man, if you know the man, go on out there tell him the boycott is on! I never even got to see him. We want a promise a ten percent Negroes trained to *work*. That ain nothin for Meansville!"

Knight looked pained. He looked brought down. It wasn't his type of thing at all.

"You don know that man!" Sam taunted him.

But it struck me that it might be some fun. I was so high on last night's accomplishments, I was ready for more. If there was any fear in me now, I felt it as excitement. "C'mon man," I encouraged him, though I didn't know what I was getting into.

"Why not?" He stood up. As if wishing there was somebody here to tell him why not he repeated himself. "Shit, why the fuck not?" he said, starting for the door. "I know that man — hey I probly work out a contrac for you, Sam!" he said with sarcasm.

Quickly I explained to Sam what a help Bell had already been around the office. I asked him to give her a ride back to the office with him, and I told her — later, Bell. Knight and I walked away down the hot road toward the industrial outskirts of Meansville. I'd never seen the Coke bottling plant. Knight said it was out about another half mile past the meat-packing plant. He really did work out there a few years back, he said. He started laughing: "Ha! I'm gonna talk some shit to ol man

Rogers! We useta get along pretty good. We useta joke an have a drink a rum together. Rum an Coke on a hot day with some ice! Nice!"

We hadn't walked five hundred yards when Bell came runnin up behind us. "He askin me all kinda shit," she complained in a sorrowful voice of Sam. "Where I come from? Who is my mama? I don think he want me aroun."

"He jus want some pussy, that all. Try to see is it safe," Knight laughed. "C'mon with us, baby! We have us some *negotiations.*"

"What that?"

"Yeah what is that?" I joked. "I sure hope he still has some ice to put in it!"

But when we got there, a guard barred our way at the gate. Behind the tall Cyclone Fence that surrounded the place, the big red script COCA-COLA flowed pretty as ever. But the guard showed an ugly scowl as he told us, No! Knight protested. He emplored the cracker to go tell Mr. Rogers it was Collins' nephew out front to see him. Somehow he persuaded him. Securing the gate behind him, he walked away to a door of the plant and disappeared inside. When he reappeared he wasn't alone. And I could see at a glance it wasn't Bo Rogers who was walking with him. Guards were pouring out of several doors. Seven or eight crackers bearing down on us — "Bell! — Go on, start walkin!" I told her. — But she froze too. At this point we should've run — "What he say?" asked Knight, as the first guard opened the gate. Nobody answered. Two of them pinned my arms and began shoving me toward the street. One was aiming kicks at the little girl. And the rest had Knight — they had him off the ground and were running him forward like he was a battering ram. They gave him the heave-ho —

through the air he sailed. Bell was weeping and screaming little curses as the man pushed her way from the fence. When they gave me a last shove and a few cuffs, I whipped around and started swinging.

"No! Stop man!" yelled Knight in the dirt. I retreated, taking kicks and punches in my back and neck. Drooping at the waist, Knight moved off. "Don hit us no more, boss! We sorry! We don mean nothin! We ain bother you no more!" He was sort of crying and grinning at the same time. He was giving off a sorry cowed vibration! And it worked. The crackers turned around and went through the gate and locked it behind them and went on in the plant, except for the one who guarded the gate. I couldn't believe it! I felt sick! I couldn't look at Knight and I couldn't seem to move. I covered my bleeding eyes and started to sit on the ground. But he yanked my arm — "C'mon man!" he hissed. "Save it!"

Tonight we carried gasoline, not paint — three five-gallon cans in the trunk of the car. We borrowed the cans from the mechanic. He bought the gas for us, to raise no suspicion. After midnight we took a trial run out to the plant, without anything.

Knight remembered no watchmen, nor any alarm system either — but he'd been surprised by the guards this afternoon. He was sure we could get in any one of several windows without raising anybody — but we wanted to be double sure. So we took a cruise around the plant in the Ford that the mechanic had been fixing up. We stopped and got out and talked to each other in medium voices. The sky was clear, and there was a seven-eighths moon. It's a big bright red moon down in Georgia in the summertime. Knight hit the fence and climbed over it. He found his window. Nobody! If they caught us now, at least there'd be no arson in it. But the coast was clear. It was nice. What trouble could they expect? What can you steal from a bottling company?

We sailed back and switched cars and got the gasoline. We didn't waste time. Knight got up on the fence and I hoisted up one can straight-arm above my head. With a mighty effort he swung it on top of the fence, and climbed on over and climbed on down the other side with it. He scurried back and got the other ones the same way, and I followed him over. We ran the cans to the side of the plant. He jumped in his window that he'd already jimmied open, and I handed the can in to him. While he worked inside, I made a fat trail from the window to the fence. I sloshed it all over the wall under the window and made a puddle on the ground. When I'd done my job, I still had a gallon or two left in the can. I called to him to get it, but he told me to save it, I didn't know why.

Momentarily he jumped out with his can. In five seconds we were back over the fence. The trail I'd made extended just a little beyond the yard of the plant through the fence. With the heel of his shoe, Knight formed a big letter *K* in the dirt, while I shook my head and smiled. We stashed the cans in the trunk. With joy in his eyes, my friend handed me a book of matches. His words: "Would you like to do it up?" — With pleasure, man! I struck a match. It was a *fine* moment in my life. I tossed it into the gasoline and immediately the trail flared! In no time it hit the plant and — who-o-o-ff! a flame twenty feet tall reached up toward the heavens! Knight had soaked the place well. It was afire! And we were speeding away . . .

Behind us the Georgia sky was lit by a moon and a fire! A fire for real! A big fire! I was shouting and Knight was laughing.

But he made a detour off the fastest route and soon he was cruising slowly through CME. *Hey man, where you goin?* But he made a sign with his hand to wait. — *Hey man, this car is hot, man! Let's get outa this car, go dump it back a the office. Let's dump these cans, man!* — But no, wait! And I see he's got something else on his mind. He's cruising and looking — but now he brakes — what? I don't see a thing. Houses, parked cars. A finger to his lips, he shows me with his hand to stay right where I am. Stealthily he gets out and opens the trunk, and through the window I see him douse the inside of a car. He opens the hood and dumps the rest of the gas on the engine. A match! Bam — we're off again — and behind us the car is blazing. "Hey man! — That Jack's car. Remember that motherfucker I tol you with the sheriff? Jack! Oh no! Ha ha! That his bran new Chrysler! Ha ha ha ha!"

We left the cans off behind the shade-tree garage. Wiped clean of any fingerprints, they were just so natural in a mechanic's garage! The man was awake to greet us. What a great cat — but he looked a little nervous. And now we drove to the office and parked the car behind it in a covey in the alley. I was so satisfied with myself. I whispered, "John Brown! You meant nothing to me back in school when I had to read about your body, man! But tonight I meet you in the air!" On foot we jogged away. We took the low ways and the alleys back to CME. It was time to separate. We touched hands. Knight was on his way to Brenda's to spend his night, and I was going to Cara Lee. In a split second he was gone, and I was running. How can I express how I felt? Like a painter who has seen his painting in a vision. (And when it's done he may never see it again this same way.) I was very proud and excited. But I knew what to expect from Cara Lee. That is, if I told her.

Maybe I should say: "Hi sweetheart, I'm sorry to be coming over so late, I had to do some work at the movement. I had to type up some reports."

Or I would riff, I would really riff . . .

"How you feel?" she asked, when I was done with my vivid story. She was asleep when I came in. I could have pretended but I was hot! So I told her my story, and only near the end of my words did I know I was weary. "Tired," I said, turning my face into her neck.

"Sick an tired," she muttered. She sniffed. "No I don smell no jail. — Yet."

I began to lose myself in her, starting in her neck. She welcomed me with her body but began to assault my mind and heart with belittling words that undercut my bad and heroic high. She was trying to make me feel sneaky and mean, like an arsonist that might've burned somebody up. I soon overcame this. My head up in the free air secured by our triumphant sabotage and escape to good beds, I surveyed the beautiful scene, the woman spread out before me, through the window the quiet moonlit yard and alley humming peace, contrasting the violence we had dared against those who are always violent with impunity. It was a warm denouement.

Before we slept, she told me, "Baby, I don know bout them crackers, but Jack! Jack gon be lookin for somebody an he got a nose like a bloodhound. Don go out tomorrow. Be right here when I get home from work. Don get with Knight tomorrow . . ."

seventeen

IN THE MORNING I had a strange dream. On its cinderblock stilts the house was beginning to move. The noise of its uprooting was terrific, red-orange dust spilled up into the sun behind its swift glide over the road. I gazed out a window, not daring to jump out. Overhead, birds flew past in the opposite direction. As we passed other houses people withdrew behind doors; the cracks sealed up behind them. Cara Lee was in another room someplace, I could hear her rattling around cooking or something. Passing The Raindrop Cafe, I waved at a crowd of boys and bums standing there with beer cans in their hands, and they stared back with soft shocked eyes, one or two smiled hesitantly. Then they were gone behind the curtain of dust, eyes like last flickering embers. The house was leaving town, with us inside it! We entered silent country — and the house made no noise on the road, and no dust anymore either, a shining black road. Glistening yellow landscape that was very pleasant flowed past, and with the yellow sky, it made a tube with a bulge in it, that's me in the house. I knew myself by this kind of *buckle* in the scenery, that straightened out behind.

And now everything was slowing down. And the sky turned red, and then darker. The house veered off the road, but very slowly, and stopped in a field of yellow sunflowers. For a moment, there was complete peace of the strange motion ceased. Then in the distance, out of a protective forest, people were approaching. They looked friendly, the aspect of it all was warm and watery, though not understandable. As they came nearer, I felt a keen warmth to speak to them, my anticipation grew with every step they took. But suddenly there was a wind, becoming violent. Trees in the distance, then the meadow flowers chunk away. As they near the house, the people with grins on their faces fly off. Then the house — we're in the air. For a while the people turn slowly behind the house, like pale fish on lines, being drowned . . .

During the days of hiding and waiting, I realized that things were going to change. I felt afraid and desperate as if I were already in jail, and of course I wondered if I was soon to be locked up. The clearest feeling that I had was that if I made it out of this predicament, I wouldn't get myself in another one. I admired Knight's way of life, I thought I felt about things as he did, but I couldn't go on. I could only envision myself drinking and idling, as I was doing now, only with freedom of movement again when things cooled down. But undeniably something was dying or changing — this made me sad. The sadness made me want to write. I wanted to celebrate the way of life it seemed I was already growing away from, and I wanted to celebrate my friend Knight, with whom I'd lived that life. As the long empty hours passed, I penned some sketches, remembered conversations, our small adventures with the law, times in jail. Every day I wrote, and I hid the pages under the house. Though later I was to lose these notes, they form the basis of this story. It's not clear to me if I've succeeded, but my intention has always been to glorify the memory of my friend.

It was only a week before the heat started lifting. And it was only real bad at night, when Cara Lee and Mae argued about this scene I seemed to have started. Mae was showing a mean side of herself, and referring to me as "this white boy." It was weirding her out to have me around as a member of the house. Gradually I realized this was not so much because I was white, but because my identity as "movement" had disappeared. It was one thing when the movement boy had come around for a social visit. It was not clear to her whether Jack's car had been burned by Knight or by me. Half-heartedly I tried to tell her that really it hadn't been my idea. But, obscurely, she put the blame on me. I was more worried about the damage we'd done to the bottling company. We all felt the heat — except maybe Yellow — but in our dreams we must put a different face on it. Cops. Jack. Crackers. Jack's friends. The law . . . Sitting on the floor, peeking out the window, I started feeling unreal. An end was put to this when Knight shot Jack. Knight was waiting for him, when he came to get him, in the country. Jack and a friend tried to sneak in on him, and he put them in the hospital. Cara Lee came home at noon to tell me. She said they wounded him, but not badly. But Jack got a bullet in the stomach and the lung and might die. Somebody said Knight was in Boston. Somebody said a white girl from the movement went with him to the West Coast. The rumors were crisscrossed covering him, and all she knew was he was gone. So the heat was off. I couldn't really feel this. In fact it seemed a few degrees hotter. But Mae said the same thing. She put it differently: "You can come out now, boy," still bitter, but no doubt about her relief. "You ain in it," she assured me with some scorn. With all my heart I wanted to believe that, but I just couldn't figure it. Cara Lee made some ice lemonade and bought some gin. Over the bedroom window, she'd put up a sheet, but the cool inside was only relative. Outside the sun was white and scorching; it hadn't rained for days. It was like a holiday, with both of them not working. Some ladies came by and had a drink with Mae in the front room. At dusk some cats stopped over. One was the boyfriend I'd met seemed so very long ago, the evening of the march. We'd had a nice conversation that time, and I happily greeted him. They were drinking wine, and I accepted a little glass of that, though I'd been drinking a lot of gin. But tonight everything was on the surface. Like the cat was being polite or something. We didn't talk about much, and I felt some distance, and then some cold. In my head I had one explanation for this: Knight had taken care of business — but I'd done nothing. Nothing? That's how it felt. The vibration I was feeling for myself was . . . outsider. I didn't know what was going down anymore. Did these cats even know I'd helped burn up Coca-Cola? What did they think about that? I sure didn't ask. I couldn't even joke or brag about it. In the air was a pall, and I realized it had one source if I didn't know why: me.

"Listen, I'm gonna take a walk, I'll see you later," I told Cara Lee. — "Okay, don't worry," she said. She made me come in the kitchen a second. She said, *take it easy,* with some gestures and more words. *Be cool . . .*

With a bad head, I left the house. Crossing the bridge, I paused awhile to look down at the river. It was dark green and lovely and slow — you could see for quite a distance upstream. Under the bridge, it got shallow, and white water broke over logs pinned in the rocks. Tin cans and debris and a thick muck covered the shores as if in the life of the water, the bridge was not right. I let my eyes flow downstream where nature returned — but a bend in the river soon cut off view, and all I could see were the leafy trees. I love water, and I wanted to take a walk down this old river one time. But not now, when I felt so shaky. The river would be a fine trip, I thought, reasoning with a part of me that wanted to start right now. I'd make it later if I ever felt bad enough — or when I was gladder and freer. Just now I needed to be with some people.

eighteen

HALF AN HOUR LATER I stood inside the door of the Paradise
getting a look. I thought I might see Broomer and beg a dollar,
and have some beers and still have enough for some wine for
Cara Lee. In the long mirror behind the bar rose a blue light
mist, and a metal twist whirling between blue and green bulbs
in a far corner sprayed aqua flecks across the floor. Silhouettes
of dancers, drinkers, rims of tables and glasses — sound of ice,
music, paper money smacking plastic. Mirrors on all the walls
made the place deep and brightly swarming — inside a doorway like a slot. I saw nobody I knew. I ordered a beer from the
bartender in a gold shirt who was working almost in front of
me. In a few words I gave him heartfelt compliments on the
Paradise. I was aware of the combinations of feelings now un-
winding invisibly through his and the hearts around me. I was
used to it. Things got better or worse for me quickly. I always
wanted to make something easy. — "No place to even come
close to it in CME," I told him.

"CME!" A place that didn't pop in his mind when he looked
at me!

"It's a long walk, but worth it." I looked around again appreciatively. "Say, the atmosphere — it really hits you and relaxes you —"

"Might be forty miles to me," said the bartender with a friendly chuckle. "Swamps an alligators out that far!"

I drank in the beer with all five senses, allowing a slow stream with my tongue. Nothing got past unsavored, amber vapor wet my eyeballs . . .

"Hey Georgie — gimme two more a brand this man here drinkin!"

Hearing the familiar voice, I glanced up into the mirror in which, out of the blue mist, eyes of Jones Jones gave off their sure light. Now this was a pleasant surprise. Confident tilt of his smile, sly angle of his hat, wide green eyes aglow and too round, energetically protruding from the lids like the thief's secret's protected by something faster —

"Cause he's noddin down in his glass!" he laughed shortly, as he slid onto the stool next to me.

"Say thanks, Jones!" I thanked him gratefully.

"That's *all* right, it's a pleasure," he said, "*stormy weather*, I see you motionless," spreading down a bill on the bar.

" —— " said the bartender with a slack mouth, picking up the bill and wondering what to take out of it.

"Jones — " I said.

"I take out what he owe — " he said, avoiding slight to Jones.

"I'm busted, Jones, but I'll straighten you — " I lied. But it was practically the truth.

"Please forget it," said the generous thief. "I understand about luck. Like the weather, ain't never been there, but we feel the power!" He raised his hat. "In the brain is luck!" he said. "Like the man invented the wheel, up on his chariot, got the power he could figure where the pebbles gonna fly. He want to make somethin! But folks can't believe it. He looks fine — they say, 'Ain't he lucky!' — *Speedy!* Got your game together, luck is momentum!"

I didn't really see it that way: luck was what I seemed to get by on, *without a game.*

"Where's your boy tonight?"

"Knight," I said, after a pause that said my objections to that. "He's around, but I haven't seen him for a while."

"Yeah, say God looks after fools, an they need it, cause a fool ain't never been lucky. Yeah," his voice took a dip away, "I seen plenty cats . . ." Scowling slightly, his eyes cast aslant at the memory, he said in a sad tone, "Yeah, five years, *Knight* be *straight* all right, pumpin gas — or wasted."

He missed the point about my friend, which was his past and his spirit, not his power or future. He must not know him at all, but he's got a prejudice.

"Not even a gang," I said. "Too far out in his own world war, I couldn't keep up — "

"He's so far out, done fell off the edge an *lost!* Playin! call himself bad. That ain't bad what he do! That ain't even foolish, it's pitiful — "

I started to say something because I hated to hear it —

"You!" he cut me off, "hang around with him and let what you got in your brain go to waste! Don't blame it on luck, you got bad habits!" He reached up and pushed his hat down in his eyes, glaring at me. He delivered a little lecture on the subject. He spoke softly with force. He sounded like a teacher with his talk about brain waste, his words came faster to dramatic stops. I didn't know what I wanted to do, nor what I should do, and it was almost laughable. I'd deserted my loyalties, and I'd broke with my recent past, though I wasn't waiting for anything. I was just enjoying my freedom. I was listening to him easy. I wanted the *easy* way (it didn't matter if it required work) — never calculable beforehand, but on an impulse irresistible. My luck couldn't be *too* bad, drinking the beer . . .

I started hanging out in the Paradise night after night. I didn't have the clothes for it, and I didn't have the money either. But I kept running into this cat Jones who would stand me to some beers. I would drink them and listen to him talk, and he always said the same thing: what I'd been into with Knight was child's play, boys' games. But dangerous. Dangerous for nothing! I was listening. When I went home at night, I always had some money, and I bought a big jug of wine on the way and brought it to Cara Lee, who smiled with surprise. After that I didn't bother taking any money when I headed for the Paradise. And Jones would usually let me have a dollar, and I returned home with real presents of blackberry, Thunderbird, or Red Hurricane wine.

One night Jones was haranguing me, and anybody else who'd listen, on the subject of how bad a thief and how cold and fine a businessman he was, and taking some shots at the movement, and us movement boys who didn't know where it was at. I was listening. There came a time when nobody else was — I was his steady companion.

"I'm the invisible man with the invisible hand," he said to me. "Got a name that disappears an reappears an can't be pin down! *Jones* — a real thief wins — you can't name him!"

"Me," he said softer, in a tone almost of changing the subject, "I made five hundred today wasn't spose to be made." He caught the bartender's eye. The man in gold reached under the bar and handed him a long roll of papers he must've had stashed. Jones pulled off the band, already his face smoothing, his eyes showing the pleasure it gave him to spread out the glassy blue plans, which he continued caressing moments after they were perfectly flat like they must feel wonderful. For the first time I noticed his hands, which were fluid-fingered as I'd unconsciously expected, but also thick calloused. I reached out and smoothed down a corner myself. — He gave a little side-eye glance of recognition — "Yeah, beautiful, *blueprints*," he said. "Plans for a buildin I'm puttin up — factory shell, prefabricated job, ever see one? I don need no prints! I got my *own* plans — you hip to that?" He cast me an appraising look, and finding nothing in the rapt gaze I returned him to indicate I wasn't or couldn't be, went on — "Like the laws you got to know where they're at so you get around em, just the same with the laws a construction — they're to protect the money from the new men coming on, and I am *new*, and I *love* money!" His voice was low but ringing. On his face, a few inches away, an intense excited expression became pensive, like his secret had many aspects and in the pause its complexity gave him, he was wondering if this was the right time to develop it. When he turned back to the prints, his hand widespread on the topmost, his mind had turned, too — "This is the stage I'm in now — the grading. In a couple days we pour concrete — " he flipped a sheet — "up she goes. USA Builders. Whole thing comes on a truck — " As he spoke this, the plans, which were wider than the bar, buckled and slid. He caught them, held them out in front of him as he walked away from the bar, and, shoving aside glasses and bottles, spread them down again on the nearest table, where two fine-looking chicks sat back surprised.

He thumbed through the prints to a sheet near the bottom, which he pulled out and set on top. "When you done, looks like this . . ." He pointed to a glossy color picture of a tall shiny tin-covered structure with a lot of landscaping around it, pasted onto the print. Smiling, he turned it around so the girls could see.

"What that?" asked one, who had a streak of silver in her hair. "You got a barn?" The other giggled.

"No baby," said Jones, with a drag in his voice, "that is a factory gonna make refrigerated bodies." That brought a silence, and he smiled, "You know, for ice cream trucks an like that." Rolling up the prints, he said, "Pleased to meet you, ladies. I'm Jones, I'm a contractor from New York — this here is my partner—" Feeling raggledy and just a few moments ago not even sure of a beer! But I tried not to show it. "Uh, I don't believe I had the pleasure before," Jones continued, "but by your look an style you must be down from the City too —"

"He know we ain't from no New York!" laughed Silver.

The other smiled and sipped her beer which Jones had replaced before her. She was the more beautiful, with a long smooth neck.

"Yeah, what we need some fresh hops!" said Jones, waving to the bartender.

"An I bet *he* ain't from no further than Damascus!" Silver was cracking up, but moving over, like her friend, for me and Jones to sit down.

"Baby, if you don't *believe*, how you gonna come on to the good things of life?" asked Jones.

"If you take things on trust, life comes easy," I managed to add.

Both the girls were drinking the beer Jones bought. They talked and laughed, mostly listening to the piccolo. Jones was spread out on the seat opposite me, his arm around Silver's shoulders — eyes changing their focus, as if following something through the air. "I call my shots," he said, attention stopping just above and to the bar-side of my head. "I called this money — you remember. I'm not lucky but I'm sly." The wonder of it was, of course, why was he hovering around and bragging of his game to me? I had to have a little money for the things of life. I saw he was the kind of cat who now and then dropped a dollar off his roll, and that was why I hung around *him*. I was happy to listen to him, and reflect his ideas. My hope resounded in the music from the big jukebox, all those fine old tunes. But I couldn't believe he had it on his tongue to tell me his game. And I thought he'd cool it with the chicks, but maybe he was very secure because he was winding up into this. He focused dead in my eyes. He glanced at Silver — "Here, play the piccolo." He put some change on the table and got up, and I got up. They got out and went over to the corner and picked some songs. A line of chicks was bobbing and dancing next to the box, lit up with delight, and they joined them. In the booth again, Jones looked intently into my eyes as though trying to recognize something. I did my best reflecting the possibility it might be there . . .

"I pour concrete *thin* except in areas of stress of I-beams, by grading slight *hills* underneath," he said quickly, and laughed, and looked desperate or mean, "so there's a saving, which I will share with the man delivers me the concrete cheapest. You see — this the type operation. There's a concrete war. I choose *Black Star* Concrete Co., which ain't exactly at the top of competition, also I know this is one white man ain't long on scruples." He took a little breath, and as whatever of caution that was operating in him vanished, his eyes came out sharply. "How do they test the floor? They don't test it! They get a

declaration on the truckloads he delivers — where is it gonna
go? They all white. Except one black sheep slip his pencil for
five hundred, an I get the other five, when he pours me a thousand of concrete and writes down *two*—"

"My brother work for that *boy*," said Silver, suddenly sitting
next to Jones in the booth. "He could cop some favors for
you —"

Jones, still smiling, but the light went out of his eyes. What's
wrong? She had showed up again way too sudden. His face
lost its warmth, he was smiling grimly up in her eyes suddenly
confusedly moving around the things on the table.

"Rogers? He ain't shit." She seemed to have to continue.
"That boy? My brother got a thing with him, the sucker —"

"Rogers! Are you speaking of Mr. R. Rogers at Black Star?"
cried Jones, getting up now with his face barely brittley concealing alarm he revealed by some angry arm motions adjusting
his plans in his pocket, and his collar. The other girl nervously
hedged into the booth next to me. Jones pushed Silver out the
way and seemed headed for the bar. But he stuck out his arm
and leaned on one of the silver poles dividing the booths. "Who
are you ladies? I don't believe we've ever met," he said, with a
distant, perfect enunciation. Standing up very straight, eyes
lifted off them, he didn't glance my way but waited a second
before heading toward the door. I watched him, not playing —
there he went, out of the Paradise. My God, there went my
chance. I couldn't understand the cat — one minute brash,
next minute uptight. What the hell came over him?

"And could run through the office fire!" said somebody.
Though I glanced around, I knew I couldn't locate the voice.
Confused, I stood up and looked at the girls, who we had
something going with plain to see, and I almost sat down again.

I said, "Is it after eleven? No! Yeah? We're late — but we'll be back, *wait right here!*" Curiosity and — suddenly — ambition sent me on my way, no coins in my pocket to slow me down.

About halfway to the corner, I caught up with him, I saw: determination, in light fear. His furious steps were firming — regaining his cool, expression brightening up and hardening up, but something else lingered. I couldn't follow it, though I thought I could follow him to whatever came next. I had to ignore it, for I wasn't sure I'd been supposed to see it. But as bad a change as that, it lasted in my memory. Because never again, right through the rich fast days, did I see that.

"Simple-minded bitch!"

At this cross of streets, on the corner, in the pale neon glow of many bars and one streetlamp, I watched maybe fifty people, mostly men in white or brown stingy brim hats set horizontal, making their way gracefully between bars, cafes, poolrooms, girls, stump liquor kitchens, the movies, and motels. An image of the woman's smooth neck came into mind, I didn't know her name but I knew her face, and I wanted to walk straight back as soon as Jones got right.

"Yeah, that's all, a little lame," I assured him. "Not a danger — !"

"I don't need no favors, blame, brothers, and no kind words! Thank you! Her countryass brother an Black Star *my man?*"

We were standing there on the corner, in front of the poolroom. I kept my silence, which was not understanding, but cool.

"You're a young boy. They ain't the last bitches!"

A movement like light across the street caught my eye: in a pawnshop window hung a palely shining picture-portrait of a black man in a simple cloak with long straight hair and a raised prophet's face; it was done in luminescent paint which, in the reflective light quality of the night street, gave ethereal force to the shapes of the colors. The expression of the man was bright and direct, and openly pleased, and I couldn't take my eyes off this picture.

"Yes, you got to take care of business —" I said vaguely.

"Maybe I won't be in this *state* tomorrow!"

"Because —" I put that one word out into the air, still looking at the prophet.

"— the general danger," he interrupted.

". . . *Ninety-five!* You say what, boy?" came a loud voice from down the street. A short round man with a beret over his eyes and maybe a dozen whiskers on his chin was cracking with some Courteous Cab drivers, sitting on the hood of one of their cars, and he had just increased his volume. " '. . . Yassuh, whitefolks,' I say, 'I see a sign — *ninety-five!* How I'm speedin?' — Law tell me, 'Nigger, I hate to see you on highway two *hundred* and five!' — Ha-ha! — 'Officer, please suh, don't give me no ticket, cuz ain't but two things I have *belief:* the Lord above, an my good whitefolks — ! ' "

When he finished his joke, he started walking toward Jones and me on the corner, saying, "Here come my man, Dr. *Power* — Jones Jones — been to more states than I been in liquor stores!" When he came very close in a brotherly low voice, "Lemme hold a dollar, Jones . . ."

"Leo, I wouldn't give you no dollar if I had seven million in my *hand!*"

Leo began moving his body in jelly jerks, bending his knees. He was squinting off across the street. When his laughter came it was real — "Jones a cold motherfucker!"

Jones started across the street, saying, "Cold? I posed as a preacher an beat broke down asses an ol bent-bone elderlies outa their last savings! I been a doctor an beat mothers outa their paychecks! Cold? I don't miss nobody. Life is cold, dig it? She scatter you. But you in a good crossin, you better get somethin. You steal, you win, that's law in this life, you dig it? That's the highest law that nobody break, an people talk against it, but they all follow it. See, you read a book, you steal. A smart man might read five thousan books, he might read a wrong book, an know, see?"

Jones had a far-off look in his eyes. He almost seemed to be talking to himself.

"A man is a lie, or else he die, yeah. Some lies last longer than others. Don leave no openin you can't get out of before they get in! Put it out there first — *talk* don't wait — don ever stop. You watch people and see if they ain all like me down deep. You listen careful! — Hey walk faster!" he said. I was straggling behind, but he was moving unnecessarily fast, I thought, since he'd taken care of business. "Walk fast," he said, "even if you ain't goin no place. Walk fast enough long enough an places'll show up by themselves."

A voice sounded out of the poolroom — "Hey, Jones, did you call me?"

"C'mon man! We late, man!" called Jones at once, turning around and walking back. The doors of the poolroom were ajar, and a slant of light from the tables reached our feet. The painted poolroom window tingled red as the Red Rose Snuff it featured with roses strung along the top.

"Well I got to go," said the voice loudly from inside, and out the door came a thin man in an open trench coat, long fingers playing up around his bony jaw.

"Hey nigger, I thought you was a sport!" shouted another voice inside.

"You play for sport!" said the thin man, crumpling with winner's mirth.

"You low!" from in the poolroom.

The man's hand drooped down, and he bent his knees and fell down laughing and brushed the tassles on his shoes. With a luxuriant cough, he stood up, looked up in Jones' eye, held his palm up, and Jones grazed it saying, "What you gonna do, Suitcase?"

"Oughta go home to my wife, put me in bed, feed me hot rum with a spoon!"

"Naw don't do that, Case . . ."

"Cuz I feel sick," beginning to laugh again — the man *in his world,* blood vessels standing out in his neck and eyes red as the window; ones, fives, tens . . . and twenties! spread in his left hand gazed at by himself, Jones, me, and Leo, the fat man in the beret. Suddenly four little girls darted past us fast as fish, two on each side. One held a piece of green cellophane over her eyes and shrieked at the funny green world, and the others stabbed fingers at it for a look. Force of the little running school had me stepping away from the curb — again the flicker hit the corner of my eye, but when I looked at the pawnshop window, the picture had changed to a blue river winding between trees, with some lambs feeding on the grass beside it. The image hung me up for a while — it was one of those pictures that change depending on your angle. At the curb, I walked back, and, hitting my old angle of focus, the prophet reappeared. His arms hung loose at his sides, his head was up floating.

"Yeah, well let's drink it up then," said Case, and my drunk attention was brought back to the corner scene. I saw the man called Suitcase stick two twenties in his shoe.

"Case, you know that bitch Peggy got a stripe in her wig?" asked Jones, referring to our recent companion.

"Yeah, yeah, yeah, yeah, yeah!" said Case, in recognition. "Big titties an talk a lot?"

"Yeah, a damn lot — !"

"Stupid bitch!" he shook his head again in recognition. "An her mother useta live next door to my mother in the project. I was over there one day, she come up, 'Case, I'm so down-hearted an depressed, an I'm poor even to look at, Case. I wanna commit suicide but I don't even know how to do that!' 'Poor!' I think, 'Stone ugly!' Say, 'Here honey, I got this gun here an you can have it. Stick it under your lef breast an fire.' An she did. She took it home — shot herself in the *kneecap!*"

Leo was laughing, studiously applauding Suitcase high on victory, and in a strange way the effect of his mime had been accumulating, now dazzling me with his presence. From him came a falsetto cry. At this moment, Suitcase seemed also to be reached. "Leo, cop us a fifth a Beefeater's!" he beamed, handing him a ten.

"I want to take her home an get me some head," complained Jones, "but I'm afraid she bite it off!"

"Ha-ha! Jones, look out for this boy's mind!"

"Sheeit! This boy got a bitch out working for him . . ."

The compliment brought me out of the slight unease slipped over me by Leo splitting on his errand. The way Jones said it made me proud. (It amused me, too, actually thinking of me and Cara Lee, who was out working for no one but herself.) A rush of eagerness followed, not for anything I could name, because the story was only beginning.

But Case wanted to drink the Beefeater's in the Paradise. Jones shrugged, and let him walk on, with Leo at his heels. In Jones' eye was a curious distraction, like he needed nothing, he was content to stand here and see what would happen. At this moment I felt a soul similarity with the man. And sure enough, something *did* happen . . .

Down the street, in front of the Grand Movie Theater flashing strings of light bulbs on a phosphorescent orange paint job like a hundred New York City fresh orange juice stands, out of the intricacies of lights and posters that must have been hiding him, a red-faced white man in a limp white shirt was waving his good arm and a stump at us. He was yelling, "C'mere!" again and again. I disregarded him. He didn't let up.

"Say Jones, who is that?"

"Who? — Nub, uh, harmless, he's manager of the show."

"You gonna go see what he wants or what?"

"Me?"

I saw it was *me* he was after, and I was living like that, so I started walking. But he didn't stop waving till I actually stepped up to him; he said, "Say, look here! I'm the manager, I'm happy to see ya. Say, you with the movement, ain't you?"

Well I didn't discourage this because I saw he was wrought up with an idea. Watery eyes jumping, he remembered, "You use to come in for a show, but I ain't seen you for a while. Me an the theater — I want you to know this here — we are behind you. That's straight from Atlanta, not only my personal attitude! — I showed you the cushion seats?"

I was unprepared for the torrent released by my simple answer ("No") — he apologized, "Oh I'm very sorry, oh no! I'm sorry!" and made profuse gestures of welcome, as he stepped backward into his theater. Okay, I'd like to sit in a soft seat.

Looking over my shoulder, I saw Jones start drifting over. In the dim sparse lobby the cracker asked me, "He with the movement?"

"Absolutely. That's the treasurer, really," I said.

Nub led us into the movies.

There were some cats from the country in the new seats, which were on the aisle in the last row. They were viewing in fine style, cushion comfort, they were enjoying, and you could hear it right through the backs of their heads, incipient low chuckle. Got their elbows nudged in each other. It hurt me to see Nub get them up for us. But not so much, I guess, because I remember the time when I would've just flat refused something like that. There was a time when I had so much respect for any existing beauty. Jones heard the impulse, said, "Shit! Fuck the countryass motherfuckers! And don't act phoney!" — When they did get up, their eyes looked down, a little drawn back in the skull. Nub indicated the seats like rare flowers with his fingertips. I said they were fine, and we sat down and pushed back. Up the aisle, the country boys were looking for three seats together, and one looked back when they turned in a row, and right then, under his shy disappointed glance, I felt how something warm and alight was maybe burning out of me. I put those words together in my mind and for a second that's how bad it felt. And yet my head was easy — in that pure state when anything *must* happen to you and you are guiltless — and soon the incident and my sad feeling had vanished. Jones was on the aisle, I felt his gentle pleasure at conning such seats in the movies.

"How you like em?" Nub had knelt down right behind us and whispered, "By New Year half the house be like em! Yessir, the *Grand* Theater! We *been* integrated!"

Jones got his hand up on the side of his face, curled around his eye, then with his fingertips he pulled his ear forward — not to hear better, but to cut off Nub's quivering self-promotion. In the movie — it was Jerry Lewis going into an Oriental bit — and immediately I felt embarrassed, but Jones broke up, and laughed for a long while, thereby dismissing Nub. By me, the joke didn't get there. Jones was an old cat and might have been in the World War, but for me it was the lowest level bigoted farce.

"Well you boys enjoy it," said Nub, after Jones let up. "Anytime you want to see another one, just ask me."

I nodded and thanked him, as I didn't have any way to get in again but free. When Jones cracked up the second time his laughter was caustic and denigrating and getting louder as rat-face Jerry turned the corner into self-humiliation. The outburst sent waves over the half-empty theater, rolling dozens of others into harsh cackling at the almost evilly ridiculous behavior. The meanness in Jones' throat exactly compensated the level of unintended self-caricature Jerry was attaining.

"Well I'm *with* you, don't forget it," said Nub, patting me on the shoulder.

"Okay," I said, and he waited awhile longer, finally got up, patted me once more, and left.

We watched the movie for a while. Jones sunk deep in his chair, and his eyes drooped, like he was going to sleep. Then they did close. He straightened up his suit, and adjusted his shoes. "Jerry Lewis?" he asked — he looked surprised and amazed in fact, to be here, and said, "Let's move it" — and we drifted away through the sour popcorn gases into the sharp evening air, Jones leading, and he seemed to be aimed. He was in a brand-new mood.

nineteen

WE REENTERED the Paradise. Suitcase was nowhere to be seen, neither was the girl called Peggy. Beauty with the long neck was sitting in the booth alone. She had waited! A look of relief that broke over her worried frown was lost in a full petulant scowl by the time we made it over to her.

"Hey baby!" hailed Jones, glistening friendly, and sat down across from her and took her hand.

"Do I know you boys?"

". . . *Hey* baby!"

"Maybe I met you in the past someplace?" coolly, and taking her hand away from him.

"We weren't so long!" I said.

"Peggy gone *home!*"

"Well I'm very glad," Jones spoke courteously, "that you're still here — because we had to go —" He appealed to me and I expressed yes, regretful, absolutely. "Business is business an don't wait but we shoulda taken you along."

"Hey, what's your name?" I asked.

"Peggy say don *nobody* make her wait, ain no freedom rider gon make her wait!" She didn't smile but her bad look cracked.

Jones, standing up, made a sign to the bar. She had a little beer left at the bottom of her glass, but she covered the top of it with her fingers and delicately shut her eyes. When the beer came, Jones gently parted her fingers, and as he poured, her eyes opened. Into the glass went a nice shot of the dark unlabeled liquor from the gold bartender, who left the bottle on the table.

"My name is Angel," she said to me, "an sometimes I feel like one." Now she smiled, but with a little edge, and up came her head, showing her neck long and lovely as an angel's. Eyeing her glass suspiciously, she nonetheless picked it up and took a tiny sip.

"Jones, how bout that Pontiac he's got in his drive?" I laughed. — Out of a nameless enthusiasm, reference to some sensed myth —

". . . Yeah! An that is this year's. Have you seen the new models? I got my order in on a dark green Grand Prix —"

"Bonneville convertible is very pretty —"

"Yes it is, some boss shorts! an I'll have me mine as soon as they can send it down to this damn backass Georgia! Hey baby, ride all you want this winter — ride with me on Christmas Day! I may go up to Detroit an get it myself, see everything is right an avoid these damn crackers in this damn fumblebum state!"

Her denying look had come back a little. "*If* you get it," she said in her glass.

"*If!* Ha-ha! Hidden, fast, an ride-blinding, color forest green that'll be me. Ride to the coast! Angel, ride in the best ain no *if!*"

That got away with her, and she gave a light chuckle like a light two or three tone chime, "Sheeit!"

Which freed us all to drink our beer plus shots. Jones' eyes fell out of focus as he concentrated on drinking, and neither Angel nor I cared to break the silence. I felt how Jones' mood had become almost leisurely again and I had no idea what he was thinking, but I wasn't surprised when he laughed once to himself. But he didn't say anything, and when he rose, we both finished up and got up too. On our way out the door, I set the brown purple bottle on the bar near the bartender ringing up the cash register.

The sky was thick with stars. A hush had fallen over the street, and there were fewer people, moving more slowly — and a very few moving fast. Rounding the poolroom, collisions of balls could be heard, low curses, low cries. We passed the cabstand with one last hack asleep in the chair. I was looking around at things with a sharp drunken curiosity. There was the American Insurance Agency with a lot of posters in the window. Cracks' Ribs, as narrow a store as I've ever seen, behind a steamy window a man cooking up ribs dinners and barbecue. My eyes came down on a set of big tiger paw prints painted gold, black, white, and pink going into a bar with no name on it. Past another couple of bars or stores, then a gas station on the corner, through a lot filled with cars and trucks, Jones headed into the alley. Cutting between parked cars, Angel banged her knee and swore angrily, but happily. Jones comforted her and started feeling her leg, "Goddam you feel good, girl! Hey man feel how good she feel!"

Beautiful and soft! And thus we made our way three blocks uphill along the crusted clay of the alley arced by shadowy tree branches. We arrived at a project of big new apartments, and here the alley became an asphalt lane, one of several running between the individual buildings. Maybe this was an endeavor of New South moneymen — modern housing for Negroes, with replaceable thin green sod, smooth white walks, reinforced glass doors, Thunderbird straight lines, new brick glowing like red glass — each of the dozen or so buildings L-shaped with a square courtyard. Way down the block, I could make out one word of a neon sign ASTRAL . . .

The lobby was burning up with big mirrors, cooled here and there by rubber plants in modern vases; in the spaces between the large oily green leaves our images were flickering: I'd sort of halfway noticed it before but, reflected a dozen times on three sides of us and dimly in the glass doors behind, it vividly hit me Angel was dressed all in red, Jones in his green suit, and me in a black T-shirt and Knight's high-cut black slacks I'd borrowed the night I first met Jones. My shoes had little polish left on them, and the T-shirt with a hole back of the shoulder made me wince, and I promised myself I'd find a way to get clean if I was going to hang around the Paradise and these parts. To compensate for nothing but lint in my pockets, I felt extra cool in my face, I lit my last cigarette (I'd been saving it for such a moment). We were waiting for the elevator. Over the door there was a board with the names of the tenants in raised plastic letters. I looked for a Jones — no, he's in love with deceit. As we got in the elevator, Angel was looking nervous and pleased like it's been a long time since the last time. In the shiny imitation wood walls, there I was again in sharp reflection, smoke at a good angle. I guess I was as excited as Angel, but Jones was very cool. We were standing in the hallway and he was opening the door to his place.

"Excuse the crib," he said, "things come and sometimes take a while to go."

Some stolen items, I imagined, but I wasn't ready for wooden crates — scattered ranks of television sets, boxed phonograph components, transistor radios, table lamps, and clocks — a lot of clocks showing every different time like a clock-shopwindow's essay: free time. And a long rack of suits, trenches, slacks, dresses, furs. (Angel saw the fur coats right away and slipped something like a full-length silver beaver off its hanger onto her shoulders and began to laugh) — like he'd copped half a department store. Struggling up under all this hot load, still visible in places like trellises in a vineyard, low-slung dark green and walnut futuristic *astral* furniture. In the big front room, only two chairs and a small table were really free, no other surface was unoccupied except for a circular piece of the floor tremulously containing the chairs and table like survivors of a forest growth pushing inward a round clearing. A narrow path led out of it, to the kitchen, and then a big bedroom. Holding herself in her fur and laughing, Angel was making it to a big double bed. And I was following her.

"Oh you got some sheets, thank heaven!" she said.

"What you mean thank *heaven!*" said Jones in the kitchen rinsing out glasses. "Thank Jones, baby," he laughed. He brought out some whiskey, and we had a drink. Angel set her glass on the thin headboard of the bed and took off her clothes. She stepped up onto the bed and had her drink looking down at us. Soon as Jones let us in I knew he was into a wilder thing than I'd ever expected, but in this back room besides stacks of closed cartons and more clothing, there was something else — an *arsenal* of rifles, shotguns, pistols in holsters, boxes of ammunition. And opposite the big bed stood a barber's chair! porcelain, steel, leather — polished, and well sat in. I climbed up and sat in it, and started laughing drunkenly. "Hey, how bout a *barber* chair!" cried Jones, and cracked a long comfortable laugh filled with some meaning of that. The cat was into more than ordinary thievery! I had some more whiskey. Opulent private successes and ironies — these I now realized in the thief. I thought I smelled flavors of extravagance. But in the person of Jones I saw professionalism and bitter ambition, and, I wondered, How do you sell a barber's chair?

Angel jumped down and got her fur coat. Giggling insanely and cozily, naked, in her fur, she rolled luxuriantly from one side of the bed to the other. Jones stopped her with his hand. He drew back the fur and got his hands on her thighs. I climbed down off the chair and from the other side got a hold too. "Lookin nice, baby," Jones spoke softly. The lights of her — lavender, and dark ash brown. She watched with half-closed amused charged eyes, and now raised up a little on the backs of her arms, slightly bowed her legs, eased back her head pointing her chin — generously shifting the inner axis of her body. I let the moment swell, and still. Then I unfastened my pants.

"Hey! Take off y'damn shoes!" Angel told me. And so I did, and what the hell, pants too. I didn't have any socks or underwear.

"An turn out the light," she said. Jones let go her breasts he'd been squeezing, moved back behind me, clicked out the lamp.

"Hey man," I mumbled, coming down in her, in way of excusing myself for jumping first like that.

"Oooh . . ." said Angel. I was grooving in her, sound of the letter *h* continuing to rise barely up out of her parted lips.

"Ha-ha-ha!" laughed Jones somewhere in the room, "showin off like it's the first," he said, as if to someone with him in the dark. It was only a moment before I realized it was Angel he'd been talking to. Directly he said it, she said, "He-e-eh!" and came up, faster than me, and I drove down, twisting at last —

the undertow. Behind our occasional voices, fine light rustling of our bodies — sound like lock oil between your fingers. Richening it — touch of the fur. A hand pushed my shoulder — "Hey hold it a minute, Jones!" my first alarm reaction, was he going to push me off before I'd finished?

"Get away outa her face, man."

I took a new angle. Jones knelt —

"C'mon baby, till it get hard."

"It *is* ha——" but on that vowel he got it in — "A-ahh! Mm . . ."

A half hour later when we'd all had enough, on his way back to the lights and some more whiskey, he remarked, "Ain't that a lovely seat?"

I was standing there looking at the barber's chair. I sat in it again, felt the cool of the white arms, with my arms on top of them — and the soft leather seat and back: headrest let you loll back, iron rest for your feet. In my imagination, an air of the pleasant service — head scratched, neck rubbed, steam towels. Jones got ice cubes in the kitchen, and poured whiskey in our glasses. I tilted back in the chair and relaxed and drank.

Jones set his drink in the only unoccupied flat space, middle of the floor, and disappeared into a closet. The rich scattering of stolen goods was amazing — I admired the place and the loot — *loot* had never been more to me than a flashy word. And it's a memory now. But I took this out of the thief's vault: the image of it. A lot of folks' toys in here! Everywhere Jones looked, a prize, a trophy. Eyes glittering like steel, he came back into the room with a thin leather box.

"Want to see something pretty?" he asked us. I walked over to see. He took a gulp of whiskey and balanced the glass on the bed. He flicked a little catch that unlocked the box, his eyes relaxed in love on it opening. Later, in their energies, I'll see glints of denial and traps' green metal, such sharp lights diffused now in the glow of opportunity. I sensed he was letting me in, near as a symbol anyway, and maybe I barely realized at this moment that the sight would have its price. I came close to see better. He showed us mirror-steel compasses, in velvet. I could read the German embossed trademarks —

"Look at them points," remarked Angel.

"Yeah, precision shit, stole from old Kirksey himself. Compasses — and I ran circles around that man. Kirksey, even the bank got to his ass . . ." After a pause, he gave me a look, he asked, "What did you do in your day today? Anything?"

Nothing. I didn't say anything . . .

"Work for me," said Jones. "I got a use for you, and you make good bread. You done any construction?"

"No —"

"Don't matter."

He turned and began to walk around the room, compasses in hand, looking for something else.

Yes, I thought, I'd help him steal, I could enjoy it. I couldn't see how I'd do him any good, without skills or experience, with my white skin. And I'd do it, I thought, as long as it came *easy*.

He found what he was looking for — a steelworker's yellow hard hat. He brought it over and handed it to me, and I tried it on — a good fit, and I liked how it felt. Inside it, beyond the leather headstraps, on the concave inner surface, a few words lettered: STOLEN FROM J. W. KIRKSEY & CO., JUNE, 1962. Jones was pulling on his shoes. "You ready?" adjusting his green hat. "It must be late an we got business to take care of before dawn." What? Well, I was going to work for him as of tonight.

"Hey baby," he addressed Angel, "see you later." But she didn't answer, dead asleep in the bed.

Out through the mirrored corridor — I got a glimpse of green Jones, me in the yellow helmet. I had decided to wear it on my drunk head the rest of the night. Down the backstairs, to the alleyway, we got in a truck with a flatbed trailer, and clattered swiftly away from the center of town, and into CME, toward the industrial area over the familiar dirt roads black and silver in the starlight. We drove past The Raindrop Cafe, deserted at this hour — I wished Cara Lee would come out on her porch and see me roll by. I was tired of Mae telling me I was lazy, but I was even more tired of Cara Lee defending me. I glanced at the playground of the school from which we'd marched that time to jail, bright and empty as the moon, and for a moment I was put in mind of the forlorn triumph of that night. I never walked out in this direction from Cara Lee's, I just walked into town. Now we crossed the first tracks and headed past the Swift's factory I used to see so often. Tonight it glowed friendly. We hung on the industrial road that led us to nowhere else but the Meansville Welding Company. The coincidence rang in my head so loud I hardly gave it a second thought. This was where Deacon Stock arrived for work every morning! We parked the truck and got out. Over the loading block, a form that must be the watchman was moving toward us out of the shadows.

"Who there?" he challenged.

"Me," said Jones, jumping up on the dock and walking straight at him.

"Ha!" He spat, stopped walking, and waited for us to reach him. "Lay somethin on me, Jones."

"Shit!" said Jones, brushing past the man — "All I done for you!"

"Jones, don't jeopardize me without paying! Because I ain't free, an I don't play!"

Jones handed me a bill and I took it back to him.

"I'll flash a light," said the watchman.

"No, I need that light." Jones called to me that I should take it from him. I brought it on, and pointed it down off the end of the dock, turned it on to light our way.

"I'll shout!" the watchman called.

The back lot of the works was thick with waste rods, tubing, bomb-shaped empty oxygen and acetylene tanks, jagged steel shapes. Tall grass grown up in every empty space half concealed obstacles — with the light we picked our way to the rear of the yard, where, next to an alley, groping up into the sky like a monstrous insect stood a crane. Jones was grinning and exclaiming at it like an old friend. He told me that not long ago it too had belonged to unfortunate Kirksey, when he'd worked for him as crane operator. When the man bankrupted, the Citizens' Trust Bank repossessed it, and parked it here, where it'd stood unattended ever since, lacking a buyer. It was an old model crane: warm, rounded lines of the rusty cab painted red faded almost pink, but there must be plenty life left in it I could hear by Jones' excited voice. Under the beam of light I held for him, he began an examination that took about half an hour: gears slightly rusted — but all that was needed was some oil and grease. Brakes, gas lines, electricity — it needed a battery and plugs, and new points. I took a walk back to the truck for a good battery that was in it, and Jones installed it and we got the engine going. We drove it backward and forward. We checked the transmissions — cables and hooks. Finally his investigation took him up the long arm of the crane. He slid up the crosspieces like he was well used to climbing and almost at the top he straddled the arm and I shone the light on the pulleys. He checked them and shouted, "Okay!" I felt it was my triumph too. A wind was blowing and the bottoms of his trousers flapped. The points of his handkerchief had come way up, they waved gently at shoulder height. But not a ripple in the smooth metal sheen of his jacket. He lifted his head in the breeze. On his face was a look of satisfaction, like it all looked good to him, and the view was fine too. Out of his pocket he drew white work gloves, and when he'd pulled them on he held his palms up ready. Falling to one side, he grabbed the steel cables and slid down.

twenty

I DIDN'T MAKE IT BACK to Cara Lee's that night. Jones and I
slept on either side of Angel on the big bed up in his apartment
or warehouse. I saw Cara Lee a couple times more, and then I
stopped going by to see her altogether. I was into something
else, that's all. It was a long way to CME from the central part
of town. But sometimes I'd see her on the street, when she'd
come downtown to shop. We were always friendly. Once she
had news of Knight. He'd returned to town for a few days, and
while he was here, he'd been swimming in Means Park pool.
That's right, he'd followed his dream, and climbed the fence,
and dove in the pool, got a swim, and walked out the front gate.
The whites, the lifeguards, and pool attendants were too
shocked to do anything but watch. Cara Lee said he'd come by
her house soaking wet and out of breath to tell her about it.
She didn't believe him at first, but when she heard about it
from certain sources, she knew it was true. He asked her to tell
me what he had accomplished. Maybe he came back to town
just for this, I don't know. She said he'd gone to New York, and
months later I knew he'd made that too.

I was standing on the corner, wasting time. A young kid I knew from CME came up and handed me a newspaper folded open to an inner page. There was Knight's picture on it, among other photos of a riot, and its aftermath: looted, burned-up streets, cops, and occupying troops. It was somewhere in New York State. Knight was the one wearing the straw hat, with a medallion around his neck, standing up on the hood of a car and laughing. The picture was one tight move in a subordinary dissection, a beam of light off the cameraman's eye. The account of the riot I do not remember. There was nothing of my friend's exuberance in the words, assessing causes and damages. I could have written a better report that began:

> Well satisfied with the destruction around him, the fire, the burned-out car beneath his feet, smiling victoriously atop the car, among his friends who are in control of this area temporarily . . .

The moment won't fade, it'll be apparent in the stream later on. But right now it's been discarded in the dot paper cycle, lost in the stacks of tomorrow's editions. I'll always admire Knight Collins' successes, small as this one, cat in a crowd who jumps into view at the right moment. Man who comes to town to jump in a forbidden swimming pool! On his face, the smile almost of a patriot or outlaw, the jubilant smile of my old friend. It made me laugh, to see it. He'd been doing damage no doubt. Now he gets some glory.

With a cat like him, you would always expect the end is just around the corner. "It don matter how you die, if you in ya thing . . ." He wouldn't last, I thought. This was Jones' lesson for me, and I was ready for it. But Knight'll reappear in this role. This is the meaning of winning. When the end appears, you lose. Instead of the possibility of the triumph, it's the possibility of the fall that affects you. If I can get high, I can do without the glory. If I can get mellow. This was my only aim, and I tried not to think. Jones seemed to know a way.

Next morning up in Jones' truck parked in the lot of Citizens' Trust Bank, feeling mellow from the night before, I dozed and smoked, my gaze sidewind through the windshield, and I saw: savers clutching little books coming in and out the decorated fortlike bank, moving eagerly through the brilliant multicolored auto maze; I heard locked sleek money sounds in parentheses of tires and brake arcs, and my eyes turned inward to bugs and rain marks on the glass, then the floating cellular creatures on the retina (or in the sunshine) like magnetized tiny rice grains. Man I'd drunk a lot last night! I was on a new trip, though I could hardly remember it. It'd been thirty minutes, by the Citizens' tower clock, since Jones went in the gold door with his plan to cheat them out of four, five hundred dollars' use of the crane. Plugs and grease we took care of last night — but he's in there pretending it's much more. It's an engine job at least on that crane, he was telling them. Kirksey for bankrupted or stranger sentimental reasons verified his special crane operator's knowledge; plus Hobshead, Jones' connection for these jobs, put in the right word. It'll cost the bank several hundred anyway — but Jones would put the crane in salable shape *free* in exchange for two days' use. It's in the open that everybody's getting something. Cranes rent forty dollars an hour. Jones was gambling they weren't sure what they got there over in back of Meansville Welding . . .

Only a second or two after the clock chimed the hour — out

the big marbled glass door came Jones. It gave him hell of a
happiness to mess around at the bank I could see, and I could
tell he'd met with success. As he kicked up his feet, steel toes of
his boots flashed in the light, top of him was slung down in his
hips; his lucid stride, his thumbs up in the front pockets of his
jeans, his leather jacket open over a green T-shirt, and his helmet pushed back off his head, showing off a grin — all testified
to a smashing success. Suddenly I saw a fat white man at his
side — as if he'd just materialized like that and at once begun
speaking with the professional attitude of a football coach talking to his quarterback, I suddenly saw him. And Jones was listening with fitting professional deference, nodding his head,
blinking his eyes that were glowing. This ruddy confidence in
expensive business clothes couldn't be fallen Kirksey. It was
Hobshead, the contractor, and this morning Jones had said,
"You'll meet him sometime and he'll be happy to see you, believe me — I know what he'll think . . . here is one a them
civil rights workers doin some shit, an I'm gonna get the effect
of a white man in the crew for a Negro wage. What he don't
know, ignorant red pig, *you* gonna get more outa this shit than
him! So be cool and act like a graduate." That I was trying to
do, stepping firmly off the running board, and getting some little lines into my head. I gazed into the pale interested eyes of
the contractor, who was saying, "Robert tells me you been at
Tech —"

"Yes," I said. I thought, *Robert?* Who is this guy I work for?
"I had a year up there, yessir. I'm looking to get some practice,
you know, and make a little money over the summer." I spoke a
mix of accents — South and North. I hoped my words reassured him I wouldn't try to get into his concerns, and he
seemed to pick up on that. "The South," I added for good

measure, "my people are from down here, although I wasn't
raised down here."

"Well that's fine," he said, "that you know the South, because
we walkin on eggs out there with the people, you can understan, and you *can* be a help. I don't know how he foun you —"
sly glance at Jones Jones Robert, who smiled — "but that ain't
my concern . . ." He will play on you, I thought; yes he will!
Hobshead went on, "Robert says you can handle it. You got
one responsibility, foreman, and that is *talk!*"

Foreman! I resisted the temptation to glance at Jones, and
Hobshead went on, "You understand, the local folks are curious, a buildin goin up in their midst that could mean so much,
an the uh crux, the *Negro crew.* They're just ordinary ignorant
country people out there. Your job, keep em happy, answer
questions, explain the progress — to them *you* will have the
power —" He glanced at his watch; seemed in no hurry to
know more about me. "Well you boys get to work! I'll be out
to see you later in the week," he said to Jones. He hesitated just
in case I wanted to say anything. I had a lot of bullshit ready,
but it wasn't necessary, having been not only accepted, but promoted. I told him I was happy to be hired, and he said it was
very much the same with him, he had every hope. Nice southern manners. Jones walked him over to his car, which was a
responsible trust-provoking late Ford. I climbed back into the
cab and lit a cigarette. Jones had some more words with him
before parting, and then he jumped up with his grin and threw
a key up on the dash —

"Can I talk!" he announced, laughing and revving the engine.
"Jones, where you learn to talk like you do?" taking off with a
jolt, and an accidental honk of the horn, we were heading out
toward our crane at the welding works.

"Say Jones — *foreman?*" I could hardly stifle a suspicious laugh — I let it out, slyly.

"Yeah, how about that? And with it comes a raise."

"I know a lot about airplanes and spaceships also," I mumbled, with sarcasm — but I felt joy.

"You don't have to *know* nothin! Talk, that's all. I'm hip you can talk. I'll give you a book. A catalog for the salesman. You study that, you know what to *say!*"

He had his reasons, and that was one thing I didn't have. You can do anything, I told myself, as long as it's *easy.* The idea of stealing appealed to my heart which contained no desire to put anything into this endless world. I saw he had a use for me, and I'd steal a *way* from him. This was my idea. *Don't ask too many questions!* I kept quiet, and worried I'd see Deacon Stock at the welding company, it being mid-morning of a working day, and I wondered what I'd say to him if I did. How could I even greet that solid churchly individual who might see more about what I was doing than I knew!

But I saw nothing of him. Jones jumped on the crane and it started right up, and he took off down the alley, and I was so relieved not to have seen the old man, I hurried the truck on after Jones. Not allowed on the city streets, having not bought "an oversize permit," Jones ran straight for the town boundary, and we would have to make a partial circle on back country roads to the site. Jones' speed — perhaps top speed — was exactly starting speed, and after that first lurch, he settled into an even fifteen miles per hour, by the truck speedometer. For more than an hour we rolled through brown-black swamplands, under heavy intricate vegetable odors, long stretches of pine forest in spicy dry breezes that opened onto hilly pastures on which cows were grazing. Sometime before noon we approached the site; we had made a circle, so that it was as if we were coming into Meansville from the south. Topping a hill, I caught sight of the cleared rectangle of red clay. I saw in the distance a silver globe and two gold steeples — the water tower, the biggest church, and the Citizens' Bank, sinking beyond yellow-green trees on the horizon as we descended the hill to the dark-red newly graded factory site in the center of the flat valley, on which my mind began flashing images of the completed structure, shining like the high points of the town. New hope for D. W.'s Good Eats — that was the only house or building in sight: a faded one-story wooden structure about a hundred yards down the highway, with its name on a sign on the roof.

It appeared the grading was all finished. In one corner chicken wire already had been laid down over plastic for the concrete, and a wooden mold for the concrete had been erected around three sides. Two medium-sized bulldozers were parked on the grass, and in the shade they cast, their operators lay napping. Jones pulled up near them, but they didn't move. He walked onto the clay, located hammers and a sack of big bolts, and walked to the area where work on the molding apparently had stopped. I came over from where I'd parked the truck near the road and got a hammer. After studying the plans briefly he was pressing out on the ground, without taking his eyes off them, he started yelling at the drivers to wake up and get to work on the siding for the fourth side. They didn't seem to expect more work might be required of them. Slowly they lifted their brimless straw hats to see. The three of us set to work fixing the planks with pairs of stakes, and Jones, with the plans, sunk the long bolts that would pass up through and be fixed by concrete and hold the I-beams. The graders worked quietly — hammers and breathing. They had the sullen sealed faces of farmhands and seemed scared of Jones, who started in rapping, "Hey you ever been to Germany? They got some beautiful chicks — them German fräuleins." He tapped the nearest workman on the leg. "When I was in the war one time, I had four of em in a little German short pick-me-up outside Munich. A little Volkswagen. I could count the heads slowin down — *four!* We had some pleasure that night! Four a them plump, white — virgins they was — yeah!" He started laughing. He smacked the man again a couple times. "But in the morning, man, I wake up with a piss hard, I balled em all till noon, buddy, and then I had em bring up a lunch! Man I lived *right* over in Germany!"

Pointed down into their work, the two men were laughing modestly. They were slightly turned away from me.

"*Laugh,* motherfucker! This boy ain't none a your bossman!" Jones shouted.

"How I know who he is," laughed the man.

"Don't insult me," I said, laughing.

"Who these people?" asked the other cat, pointing at me and Jones, and laughing. We had nearly finished setting up the mold when the rumble of a truck became audible in the distance. Hearing it, Jones stood up and waited. He said, "This is it." The rumble got loud, and a second or two later over the hill appeared USA Builders' big red and silver truck with headlights like solemn gold flares for the arrival of the silver and dark-red building all in pieces chained to the trailer. My mind erected it as it rolled near — the picture from Jones' plans fanned out across the bare ground as beams zoomed into place. There it stood, shining metal shed, with rows of shrubs and walks . . . It was amazing that the thing could be packed onto

one truck, but there it was. Jones started walking toward the
highway. With a hiss of brakes, the truck was pulling off onto
the grass. The white driver idled the motor, head cocked to one
side seeming to listen, absently staring at Jones coming up. But
he didn't wait for him; he cut the engine off, climbed back up
on the load — very thin ordinary-looking cracker, wearing a
white shirt, new blue jeans, and boots. On his belt was a bone-
handle knife in a leather sheath. He unlocked and unchained
the load, and threw the many chains down in a harsh way that
discouraged assistance, like he'd do his work. Jones was standing near. I called, "You want some help?" But he didn't answer. I resented that, and I saw Jones looking at him in a
strange way. We waited at a place in front of the cab until he'd
finished and jumped down. I signed some papers — Charlie
Robertson. "Take her away, boys!" he said, and got up in the
cab, and stretched out on his back on the seat, boots sticking
out. "Wake me up when I can go!"

We rolled out a large tarpaulin on the grass. Jones brought
the crane into position next to the truck. I and one of the workmen hooked up for him, and he dispersed the flat wide cartons
containing the doors, kegs of bolts, crates of brackets and
braces; dozens of bundles of purlins swung over the canvas,
thudded like cannonballs. Next came the heavy steel beams at
the bottom of the load. These Jones drove one at a time to their
places on the perimeter of the site. Then in the middle of the
work, he cut off the engine, climbed down and stood motionless, looking over at the cracker evenly snoring in the cab. In
the air, sharp energy of me and the truckhands totally tuned in
on Jones starting to advance on the sleeper. Gently, noiseless,
he walked to the truck and stepped up on the running board,
and dug the snores. Finding his moment, he reached inside,

lightly struggled with something, and jumped back down, gazing intently at the palm of his hand in which rested the man's
bone-handle knife.

He held it for me to look at and touch. I took it and spit on it
and wiped it off. He laughed a mean satisfied laugh, while I
polished it on my knee. I returned it to him and he slipped it
into his pocket and returned to work. We hooked up for him
and he laid a few more beams down on the opposite side of the
site.

The periphery bundles of zinc-tin sheeting for the roof and
walls were last to be unloaded. When there was no room left
on the tarpaulin, we laid out scrap two-by-fours to keep the
metal off the ground. Without gloves, I cut my hands up plenty
on the razor sheets and the flat steel ribbons binding each
bundle. This made me feel soft. I could've borrowed gloves
but I figured the sooner they got sore, sooner they'd be calloused. Every bite I returned with a determination, looking
forward to when I'd have extracted from the metal an equivalent hardness. Hardness of soul I thought I was achieving by
another process.

When the last piece was on the ground and the USA trailer
clean except some wrapping, Jones got off the crane but left the
engine running. He was going to D. W.'s for beer, he told me,
and time he returned I should switch it off and wake the driver.
I thought: and when he touches his sheath and shouts where in
hell his knife? I guess I say, Knife, I don't know man, what
knife is that? Ha-ha-ha! It felt good like the good (not too
old) days. Knight, who didn't appreciate Jones, would appreciate this. But he'd want to plant in white's mind seed of the
knowledge it was he who'd got it. That would be his mistake.
A little cold apprehension stole into me. Jones *got* the knife —

and damn little *money* in it! — but he's acting like he still has something on his mind. He emerged from D. W.'s looking hot and clutching a bunch of king-sized cans like delicate bombs across his chest. A doubt of his ability took hold of me, and perhaps caused me to see his truck weave nervously on the road. Then I saw an arc of glints out the cab window — was that the knife? stashed in the grassy ditch? Yeah, Jones, that's right! Time for it — that's more like you!

I shut off the crane and pulled the driver's leg. Standing up on the running board, I said, "Yeah, we're all finished."

He checked his watch and, through the windshield, the sun. He looked refreshed. "Not bad," he said, looking back at the empty trailer.

"You want a beer?" I offered him, taking two from Jones who'd come up wordlessly with them.

"Yeah!" he said, and pitched up one more chain. "Thanks," he added — but as I started to hand him his, I noticed neither had been opened —

"Hey man, you didn't get em open — sposeta use my teeth?" I called to Jones who was retreating toward the graders.

Whirling, under a twinkling eye, light leer tip of a tooth, like a mean pitcher, up comes his hand, wrist cracks — the knife was in the air, point up, spinning — Oh *no!* cried a voice that seemed to come from a part of me crawled clear across the site under the shade of the graders' wheels where all that was visible, four little eye flames distantly disapproving. If looks had power, mine would have froze that knife in flight — but here it dropped, I caught it, and quick knelt, punched two holes in each can. I wanted to bury the knife in the earth. But I didn't, I almost stuck it in my shirt. Ah Jesus, I didn't do that either. Rising, I scooped it back to Jones — shining big as a saber — I face around at the cracker, draw myself taller than any doubt, shorter than he but I'm practically looking down at him, getting his beer from me. Incredibly he noticed nothing. He took a couple long cool swallows, and went to one-handing up the chains. I drank awhile and let him work . . .

He finished his beer and tossed away the can. He followed the last chain up onto the bed and locked them together. He was in the final look around before departure. He wasn't moving fast, but steady.

Jones was advancing on us cross the site. The driver saw him. He climbed up in the cab, his face saying there was something he didn't like about that nigger. Now what was it? He gunned the big engine and slammed his door.

I leaped up on the running board as the truck began to move. "Well take it easy — " I gave him that in a friendly tone to think about later and slipped away as he hit the highway. He forgot his sword. I never believed he would pack up and leave without missing a fine thing like that. But then he never could've expected Jones' audacity in stealing it. I extended a hand to him. He slapped it and laughed sly, looking down his nose at the bone blade loose in his palm, glinting medals. I took it and held it in the sun so it flashed rays after the diminishing USA truck, winding through gear after gear, up the hill. I hit the side mirror for some pops . . . Jones carried it point forward as he walked over the tarp. On a beam, he pressed the flat of the blade and set his foot on it, and — snick — snapped it off. He reached down and picked up severed blade and handle — he drew back truly. He threw them high toward the trees — through the air that'll be filled with steel . . .

twenty-one

WITH THE FIRST MONEY I earned working for Jones, I bought myself some clothes. Oh yeah, I felt like I was something on the corner, Jones' partner, and I had to have a gold-green suit, and slacks and shirts, and some hip Italian boots. I felt like I was into something, the best way of life I'd known. I even considered buying a sharp hat, but at the last I decided against it. I'd let Jones wear the hat. He was the boss, but I was way into his game. I figured I was smart. I knew how to listen! I knew more about the operation than Hobshead who thought he knew what Jones was doing. The basic idea to Hobshead was the cheap black crew that Jones could get up, who would do the job for a fraction of what a white crew would demand. But Jones was also stealing from the materials out of which the building was to be constructed. He was carting off pieces of steel and kegs of bolts in his truck and selling them someplace. Beginning in this way, we would set up half a structure that looked like the whole in process. Thus Hobshead couldn't know that Jones was going to leave before the building was completed, and I suspected that from the start, though Jones never put it to me that clearly. When I learned that this was only one of several metal buildings that Jones was putting up for the man, I just extended the principle, and figured Jones would leave when the time was right. He'd find another town or city; he knew his games. I didn't know everything, but I guessed I knew all that I needed to know. I listened carefully. His philosophizing wasn't wasted on me.

"I want to school you how to make it, boy!" he told me repeatedly, in words like these: "In the *States*, sheeit! I'm a con man with thirteen trades an a new face each time. I'm a businessman who knows his business! I got brains to *see* — an so do you. I got patience to wait on my chance, an I keep my cool, which is areas you got to work on, boy. You can't con nobody less in *time* you get close, they let you in. Don't think I built up the confidence a that man in a day! I been workin for Hobshead for some time, I been a mechanic for that ass!"

I didn't have much way of my own, but it didn't scare me. I had the sense to conspire with an *easy* way, I was glad to let Jones do the thinking, it was his scene. But I did a little brainwork on the side, and I knew Jones was getting something out of me, not only the cheap labor. I figured he needed a little sidekick, and I was glad to play that role. The days were easy. I knew my pleasures, which was like having questions, and Jones was the answer.

The concrete was poured a few days after I went to work for Jones. Not more than half what was required went down, just as Jones had explained it to me. Still it took all day and the cats who smoothed it worked under the headlights of the truck well into the dark. It was an eerie sight. The sharp beams cast the shadows of the men clear to the forest. A couple of days later, the floor had set and it looked sound as if it had been of the right thickness throughout. Then we set to work on the basic structure of the shed. We ran up the I-beams, the five of us in a line — Jones, who was shortest, near the bottom and High, the biggest, at the end, and me and the other two winos working for us that day in the middle. We set each one on the bolts that had been sunk in the concrete for it and tightened it down. It was extremely hard work, but it went quickly, and in a half a day the beams were standing up there, and to look at them, you'd never have thought men without a machine could've done it. But it was actually easier that way. The crane came in on the next step. We had spent a day before the concrete was ready bolting together the roof beams. They lay next to each other in pairs, making wide V's in the grass. With the crane Jones raised one up and drove it into position and lowered it down to inches of the I-beams on which it would rest. He locked gears, a shudder passed down the cables into the steel, the ends of the joined roof beams swung in the air. He climbed down from the machine and climbed up the one beam and pulled the roof beam into place. But it wasn't quite right. On the crane again, he dropped it another degree. But the old mechanism of the arm and cables wasn't up to this delicate work. Many times he jumped off and climbed the beam, and had to get back on again to drop or raise it once more. Eventually he hit it right and bolted it down. While this was going on there was nothing for the rest of us to do but sit on the grass and watch and call to Jones when we thought it looked right. But he could see just as well or better himself. It must've got tiring but he didn't let up. For an afternoon he kept climbing and again getting down. It took all his weight to bring the roof beam into place. He let go with his legs of the I-beam and hung on to the top beam, trying to bring it right. When he finally had it, he dangled by one arm while he brought the two beams exactly together with a spud wrench and then slipped in a bolt. Out of the air he kicked one foot over the beam and pulled himself up and, sitting backward on the slant of it, he inserted the other bolts and clamped down on them all. Single-handedly he raised the roof beams. It was good entertainment watching. And it's a good thing it was, he wasn't paying us for this time. But me and some winos, we didn't have anyplace to go, and no way to get there. As far as they were concerned, a few dollars for the morning would buy them something to drink tonight, and they lazed back. And me, I knew I'd be drinking off what Jones bought anyway, it didn't matter to me. I lay back too, and napped and watched.

The only sadness this afternoon was the mild sadness that nothing could be stolen from the project at this stage. Once Jones smacked an I-beam with his gloved hand and said, "Like to steal me one a these mothers an saw it up, sell it for junk iron — but it just ain possible goddammit!" He grinned ruefully and went on to work, to our knowing laughter on the grass auditorium. The way Jones was working — off the crane, up the beam — down the beam, onto the crane — it was a mildly hypnotic show and we all were easily nodding. It was such a pleasant afternoon, and really Jones' problems bothered me not at all. I liked the work and I liked resting too. I could get into either one. I could easily identify, and right now I felt just like one of the winos resting back without a care in the world, and thus capable of enjoying the falling sunshine like no other people in the world. Except other winos. We were as if sprung from the grass itself, so completely were we watching and resting back.

•

On the days that followed, the really tedious work got under way and there was more than enough for all of us to do. Between all the beams hundreds of purlins, smaller beams, had to be bolted and the big beams had to be tied with steel rods, and thus the actual frame of the building put together. Then would come the long job of sheeting the outside and insulating the inside and the detailed work on the doors and gutters, if we got that far. The winos carried the purlins to position and handed them to me and Jones. Beginning at the bottom of each pair of big beams, we bolted them on and then stood on the one we'd bolted and connected up the next. We could work up to a height of about eighteen feet, or the length of one purlin, before we had to use ropes to haul them up. It was hard work that got more enjoyable for me the higher off the ground we rose.

We started work early and quit late. Jones kept a fast pace. By seven or seven-thirty in the morning we'd be in a little restaurant down the alley from the Paradise called Nasty Sally's having our breakfast. Not actually one thing nasty about Sally's — clean cafe with wooden tables and dance posters on the wood walls that was open all day and almost all night. Two or three owners come and gone since Sally, I guess, who may not have been nasty herself. Paradise people gave it that name. We usually had some kind of sandwich that was quickest to make and eat, bacon and egg sandwich or pork or sausage sandwich. If we were late we could jump in the truck and eat on the way. We rode down to the wino section of town and picked up the winos, usually High and Army and Cook, or whoever happened to be standing around needing a day's work to get some money for wine. It was a half-hour's drive to the site through forest and swamp country, and usually the winos would've fallen asleep in the back of the truck and we'd have to

wake them up when we got there. Winter was well on its way
— it was December. We built a fire of scrap wood when we
got there to loosen up by, and then we took the tarp off the
metal and got the tools out of the truck and went to work.

Evenings we parked the truck in the alley behind Jones'
place, walked over to Sally's — washed, ate pork chops,
chicken, barbecue. Sometimes we went straight on the corner
in work clothes, which we could wear on the corner with pres-
tige of wearing, among people in on it, a disguise. That was the
correct notion of what Jones was into that people had on the
block. Every evening we would do some heavy drinking. I
would feel so good, relaxed after the work of the day. Not
thinking of the future or the past, I would get a nice glow on
and sit back . . . and wait for Angel to show up. Or we would
sit in the poolroom and drink. And things would happen. I
remember the night . . .

"Butter, why am I so good?" Jones was shouting and shooting. Four balls left the green in a hurry, each one followed by
chalk sounds. Behind his stroke, for luck, he talked. "Jones,
why are you so good?" Dealer Suitcase chuckled at that, at a
card game at the little L-shape of counter in a front corner behind the ruby-red big glass. Iridescent Jones' suit grainy and
flowing, in the over-table sharp light. No one else was shooting.
Some winos were drinking at the back of the room in deepening dark, in the passageway to the can. Trying to hex Jones'
thing, Butter took a walk over to the cigar box of talcum
powder, and coated his bridge fingers, and vigorously rubbed
down his cue. Jones waited for him. Through the door, I saw a
peanut seller stroll by munching and dip in his hand for more,
not even looking for a customer — too little a boy to come inside, so I ran out. In the street I heard Jones drop another ball

in his run. In the entranceway, opening my pack of nuts, as I watched him sink the six, I became aware of the floor under my feet covered with peanut shells, like crunchy sawdust, and I felt like one of the young cats, dropouts in sneakers and shades, who stand in the doorway to watch, smoke cigarettes, chew peanuts. Or in any little bar, at the edge of the jukebox — jitterbugs — *Knights* Jones might say, "Ain't got nothin on the table but their elbows —"

"Money balls, Jones!" Glum Butter leaning on his stick, head sagged between his forearms, got one cold eye on the table. "Les see how loud you *shoot!*" He tried to put a little poison in those words — but Jones laughed.

"Ha-ha-ha! I pray a blessing on my friends an my enemies — especially Butterball — cross-side Butter! — because me an the Lord, we know how bad he needs it!" Seven ball banked easy — shine of the win in Jones' eye as he bore down on the eight, nearly blocked — and last hope in Butter's eye on the difficulty of this cut; Jones looked up to say, "I ain't gonna take all your money, Butter! — Butter a cousin a mine, he in the family — gonna leave you forty cent, Butter, buy a chicken sandwich!" Then he concentrated —

"All the best things in the world are free," he sang as the eight ball slid off cleanly, and the anticlimactic nine lined up. "But you can give em to the birds an bees, *I need money!*" Nine hit the mark with more force than necessary. "I *love* money," cried Jones, with too large a laugh. He'd been winning steady. Butter's round weight pressing more obstinately against his starched shirt and cotton trousers, face slumped, he broke the balls next rack, but he didn't sink anything, and Jones ran the table. For a long time, the loser didn't move, he just stared at the cleared green field, as if beyond the hopelessness of it rising from pockets in dissolving warps of heat waves, there was appearing a final sign. Slowly his head was being drawn down toward the tip of his stick by his concentrated drinking deep of what he saw. Then he pulled up and packed himself up into a determination with eyes narrowed and back straight, and he strode to the wall and slipped his stick in the rack, turned around and, passing the table, threw a bill on it, just smiling, cool. He walked to the bench, sat down next to me, crossed his legs and leaned on them, and began to nod. I inclined the paper bag his way — I liked to watch Jones or Suitcase almost always winning at nine ball. I comforted the losers — losing plenty because Jones didn't play for less than five dollars a game. I comforted them so he could win more. With an understated motion, I offered Butter some peanuts, so he could look it away —

"Butter shut up like that?" said Jones, without looking. He walked around the table, flipping balls out of the pockets with both hands. "Say something, Butter!" he addressed his opponent, deep in self-pity next to me, who said, *"You win, buddy!"*

"Rack em, *house!*" Jones called indignantly to the slow houseman playing cards behind the bar under the big gold Budweiser watch hanging by links big as horseshoes from the ceiling, showing a tan couple in evening dress with sparkling tall glasses of beer very pleasing to them on one face, the wrong time on the other. He waved once. He was finishing out the hand.

"C'mon, Butter!" said Jones.

The fat man let his nod increase, his eyes shut, lower lip drooped down. "Lord, I got the stomach pains this evenin'," taking his sides in his hands, "got no business to shoot pool feel like I do."

"Rack em back!" Jones yelled. The houseman dropped his cards. He pulled the plastic diamond in figures over the table that collected all the balls, and he arranged them. He rolled the rack around in a circle like a ritual, stopped it on the spot — peeled the plastic form off the cluster.

"Break em, Butter!"

"I don't know why," muttered Butter, sinking down, exploring his stomach that pained him so with little lurches of his fingers. "I *don't* know why," he repeated, suddenly rising, going to the cue case and bringing down his twenty-ounce stick. He broke — like a snarl — crash, two balls went for an opener. Jones took a step back. The skin all over Butter seemed to have tightened. He chalked his cue and took a sight, he had a high eye, he shot: four more balls fell.

"Lady luck, I need you, baby!" cried Jones. "What you gonna do, Butter?" keeping opposite the shooter, "win?"

The seven fell, and the eight, in a rhythm that implied the nine, which was a shot at a slight angle, to the far corner. He let go — almost too light — it rolled . . .

"Jump, honey!" said Butter. "Run, darlin!" he implored the nine rolling. "Fall, baby! —" It stopped short. "Motherfuck you, lazy son of a bitch!" he screamed, as Jones broke into a deep laugh he sucked silent, shook his head, and made the ridiculous straight-in shot, sang, "Your love give me such a thrill! But it don't pay my bills, *I need money!*"

Butter slammed his stick in the case, spun off a bill, and, making no effort to conceal his angry disgust, started for the door. Jones reached for the money. — A dark flash in the doorway: whizzing past Butterball, brushing the peanut bag on my knee, materializing next to the table: it was Leo, who grabbed the bill out of Jones' fingers, that had just grasped it. Jones seemed to be waving goodbye — Leo dashed back the way he'd come.

Jones took out after him. But he didn't catch him. "You see that!" he shouted, when he came back in.

"Yeah, ha-ha!" said Butter standing there. "Leo's fast."

"Fast as a fish," I said; I don't know why, but Leo amused me.

"You *see* that shit?" said Jones.

"Ha-ha-ha! Oh — ! Don't make me laugh! It hurt my stomach!"

"George!" Jones called to the houseman, "I thought you got a rule against Leo."

"Leo, he don't have much —" gasped Butter.

"Much! He ain't got shit! He ain't got *no game!*" complained Jones.

"He got your five dollars! Ha-ha, oh Lord!"

"Jones, it don't begin to compare!" shouted Leo, suddenly reappearing in the doorway. "When I think of all the times you ain't gimme nothin!"

This time Jones didn't move. He pulled a ball out of a pocket — I thought he was going to fastball it at Leo — he started banking it with English into a corner pocket. "Rack em, house!" he called, and each time he caught the ball as it entered the pocket. "I don mind, it don bother me. Cause I love money! I always keep plenty. You other jitterbugs, you like some for liquor or maybe a short. But I love money for itself. An that's why I always got some. Which one a you suckers ready?" He scowled up and down the bench at some solid customers, men who'd been up North awhile. Nobody said anything. They'd come home again too. A few young boys, who'd traveled a long way to this corner from the scarred tables of a country pool parlor, laughed self-consciously. He was too good. He was the best. He placed some balls around a pocket and began trying trick shots. Nobody wanted to shoot him after he'd whipped Butter, who was good. They stared back.

"Look at me! That's right! You can look. I look like a quarter million dollars an I'm tryin to look poor so you raggedy asses won't beg off me! I wish I was Moses for one day! I'd turn all the crackers an every average nigger into toadfrogs — an dry up the pond . . ."

With this speech, Jones broke off and headed out the door. I followed. In silence we walked to the Paradise. At the last moment a big smile burst onto his face. "Hello, Jones!" he cried as we entered. "Hello, Jones!" Right hand high as his eyes, twirling like fire. Case had his forearms on the bar and his back to us, turned his face up to Angel, her lips intense with pleasure — they both burst out laughing.

"Case, I been robbed by a blind lady! Ninety-year-old, carry a cane, wear a black shawl, got a mean look, say, 'Here boy,' throw me back a nickel, think we're still in the depression — 'buy you a can a sardines!'"

"Yeah, I know it," said Case.

A warm energy was coming from them. As I was walking toward her gazing into her face, dark-red lips composed, expectant, open — captivating me with a smile: at this moment when thought of our excellent situation was swelling up in my proud, suave bearing, light grin, Jones asked me, "Say man, go on to Speck's and cop a taste . . . two fifths," showing the thick roll from which he pulled the twenty he shook at me —

Yes, I thought, I'll run and fetch us a bottle like a white boy. Damn, he should have thought of it before we came in, we could've bought it on the way. But since he's buying it, and since he's source of the wealth, I'll be happy to do the running and play that role. Before I took the bill I greeted warm Angel, cool, I carried on, showed nothing. Then I took the money, my head sought into a deeper pride for energy (shoots through my body) of pleasantly slipping it into my pocket, this retreat back through the door to the street: Jones, showing me high and low points of being thief Jones, required of me ironies and dignity that the whiteys from whom he stole required of him. I knew what I wanted each evening after the curiously ennobling work up high (as any work on a scaffolding is good for the eyes and spirit) — with Jones I get it. As I'm not sincere, my agreement's not the last of it. This game I got: these days in these streets, exhilarating cold awareness of it is going to be my private high. — Jones and his boy.

Under paint, decals, neon glitter, the buildings I was passing seemed heavy and enduring like clay cliffs. That's the color of the bricks under the occasional red-orange shimmer — dark gray-purple under the light sky. And the windows were black. A streetlamp ahead of me; my eye is drawn to it because there's only one. Even at this distance I could see big silver moths flying around it. Just a few places were open at this hour, midnight. Speck's exclusive aura depended on his being the last to close of the liquor stores on the block, and I was walking there. On a bench in front of a bar I saw a man asleep. Passing him, I glanced down and saw it was Yellow! How strange to see him curled up out in the open perfectly still on a slab of wood like a pew bench. When I've always seen him next to the stove at Cara Lee's in the evenings. Suddenly I feared he was stone cold, but when I leaned over him, I heard his breathing thin as straws in the lines of his shadows, and his colors light and black like the wood. Cousin Yellow, yeah! The sight

of him put warmth in my cold heart, but I was unprepared for
it, challenging the congealed coldness in me, calling for a deep
or kind response I wasn't capable of. I'd never have expected
Yellow downtown late at night like this. The young men, a few
girls, nobody else from CME. I heard he came down here some
days to shine shoes and run errands in one of the barber shops,
but I remembered no evening when he wasn't settled silently
smiling in the kitchen or in the corner of Cara Lee's front
porch. Maybe tonight he was just too tired and the walk too
much for him, caught by the dark. I ought to wake him up, and
see if he needs me to help him home. But he was sleeping. I'd
let him sleep. Already I'd walked past him. It seemed wrong
for me to wake him out of a sound sleep, though I'm no superstitious respecter of any sleep, and he might catch pneumonia if
there's a frost before dawn. The fact is, I wanted to get back to
Angel and get drunk. Really I was betraying a part of me,
which did rejoice in the strangely whole limp-legged man of no
age. Yellow's happiness and his silence and childlike grin,
which once excited my mind in admiration, moved my brother
love, even mild envy, did not now seem superior to the rhythm
of my own selfish ease, which was stepping on toward Speck's.
Any sense of loss in this, and my whole memory, were wiped
out by a slow rush of pleasant coldness, and lazy hardness. I
would complete the errand and hand Jones the change and the
bottles wrapped in brown paper twisted with a flourish by
Speck at the neck, and I'd drink happily. I noticed a pile of
burlap sacking in the corner of Speck's store, and while he was
getting down the liquor and before I'd paid him I asked him if I
could have it. The good eye of some part of my heart was
struggling to see through the rest of my indifference. It was in
kindness I carried the burlap down the street and spread it over

him. But as I rounded the corner a frightening doubt hit me —
that I'd failed Yellow and myself too. I hadn't really helped
him, nor had I spurned him, I did what I could with second
thought and easy materials. Would I give a starving man a
penny? Insult him! Jones would laugh. With every step I got
more convinced that Yellow hadn't been asleep at all, his hand
across his face was disguising his slight smile, finding out!
Insult him with a piece of burlap when he needed help!
Knight would know. And Deacon and Mrs. Stock. And Cara
Lee. The people whom Yellow valued. Though they might not
hear of the actual test, or my lukewarm response, the next time
I saw them they would be withdrawn in more than the normal
way after long absence. In this way I felt my present betraying
my past, and my sense of the past betraying my present, though
I'd meant to just veer off at a new angle.

When I walked back into the Paradise it seemed a long time
since I'd left it with a clear, if bowed, head. Jones was gone.
Just like that! He had ordered the liquor and then disappeared. Later that night I'd see him, and he'd be saying goodbye for a few days. Now Case had a surprise for me. He said,
"Look a here, I got some grass I'm gonna buy tonight from
Miami. A pound, man! Let's do this thing over at the crib."

That was music to my ears. Marijuana! I hadn't had any to
smoke since I'd been at Harvard, almost a year ago. I was so
glad to hear it. Jones'd be sorry to miss it. I wondered if Case
was planning to make some money off the pound. Undoubtedly
he was. I drank some of the liquor I'd just bought with Jones'
money.

Case made a phone call, and then we walked over to the crib.
I was surprised to discover that the cat making the delivery
was a white cat. Case knew him from the service, a Miami hip-

ster. He wanted $150 for the pound and the trip, which was not bad. Case handed him the bread immediately they had exchanged greetings, and accepted the paper bag containing the grass. He spread a newspaper on the floor and poured the pound onto it, a long mound of green whose beauty I could appreciate, who highly valued even a thimbleful. I stuck my hand in it and let it run through my fingers. Case sat down cross-legged in front of it and began to roll reefers. When he'd rolled about two dozen he was satisfied. He fingered the heap and smelled of it, and let it sit there in the middle of the floor where we could admire it. And he stood up and shook the cat's hand who had ridden the bus up from Florida. I turned on the radio to Tennessee, and we sat on the bed and began to smoke. It was good smoke, not dynamite, but very reasonable grass. By the look on his face, this cat was as curious to find me in on the operation as I was surprised to see him. When Case caught this vibration he started laughing. "You two cats — ha-ha-ha . . . Mmm this some nice smoke ha-ha . . . Only gray boys I know ain gray ha-ha-ha . . . Listen, you both all right — trust me — trust each other!" He took one of our hands in each of his and kept on laughing. "This his crib," he said to the cat, "he live here, dig it?" And to me, he said, "I knowed this boy on a army base in Texas, he was the only hip dude on the place, we was tight, dig?" So we got together, we let our natural racialistic fears aloose, and accepted each other. He was from Brooklyn, he was a musician, and he did this grass thing to help support himself. Now, as if by long-distance sympathetic programming on the part of the station, Mose Allison's dusky voice came out the box, "I'm back on the corner . . ." I was surprised to hear Mose Allison from Memphis, but after all he's a southerner.

Angel came in, bringing another chick with her. Her face lit up, "Mm-mm-mmmm!" she breathed, entering the green cloud that hung from the ceiling. She didn't ask for a joint, she didn't sit down, she closed her eyes and began breathing deeply in and out, finally laughing lightly and walking over with kisses for me and Case and a warm hello for Case's old pal. Now we made room for the girls to sit down. Case got up and sat up in the barber's chair, pointing at it under him and calling his friend's attention to it. It was a funny thing to have in the room. When I was high just the thought of it made me laugh. "I wish I could sell that thing," I told Case, "if I could get a bill for it." The gleaming massive chair must be worth a lot more than that. But nobody could imagine how to sell it, except to approach some barbers. The cat said he knew a barber who was a fence in Florida someplace and that he'd ask him. He said he didn't see why it couldn't go like everything else, but I had my doubts.

Later we turned off the radio and turned on one of the televisions, and laughed at some local shows and an old movie. Mellow and goofy was how we were feeling after smoking most of the grass Case had rolled. I also had a little wine in the cupboard. We cut the sound and turned the radio back on, to hear music with the flickering image. This was beautiful, the random correspondences between the two changed each and deepened the visual image which was so lame with its own sound. Everything got strange and funny.

When I remembered Yellow again, I knew he'd been asleep after all; it didn't matter what my motive was, nor what the meaning in his eyes, because they'd been closed. At another moment in my memory, I saw his arm slide upward momentarily, and the smile that had been under it shone. But it was a

smile in his sleep! He wouldn't rightly dig the little moral
drama I'd built up around him out there in the nice night air.
Probably he'd laugh, in his sleep. And when he woke up, he'd
be pleased in his burlap. Deacon Stock didn't even know him.
— The lights and sounds coming my way dissolved these de-
tached structures of my head — I'm just happily here at the
center of many circles.

We smoked and talked until the news came on, and on the
screen a reporter was interviewing some black chick. That was
extraordinary for a southern broadcast; she must be an enter-
tainer or Olympics sensation. But her face, with a sly smile,
and her natural hair brushed out in an Afro style, and long
swinging earrings, said she wasn't either, she was a mystery.
Angel got up and turned the sound back on, and we heard the
man asking her why she had her hair done like that, and her
saying, well she liked how it looked that way. "That sawed off
cracker," remarked Angel of the interviewer who was bald.
The girl was telling about her schooling, something about
where she came up, up North, and the fun she was having.
What kind of fun was that? I wondered, the point of the inter-
view not yet revealed. She said, really everybody ought to try
it, they'd find out how much fun. Then the man asked her what
she had used to dye her skin brown! I actually don't remember
what she said, because I was watching her face as if it were
changing colors and all sound seemed frozen in the white that
was lighting her face like falling snow. So I don't know what it
was — shoe polish? She was actually a white girl.

"Ain't that disgustin," said Angel.

"It don surprise me," said the other chick.

"At least she's getting some," smiled Case's friend.

And on the tube she was smirking kind of secret and superior, while Case laughed raucously and pounded his leg in a steady rhythm, and I thought, like a minstrel of old America, she had to put on blackface to get her fun. She wasn't bad looking, black or white, I wouldn't mind . . . in my head the sound was unfreezing, she was being asked by the lecherous newsman whether she put it on all over or — No, it *ran,* she smiled, the stuff started dripping off her face and arms before long anyway, she had to be careful. In my mind's eye I was imagining how she would look naked — two-tone! — oh that would be something else . . .

Late that night, or early in the morning, I was writing in Jones' apartment. I was lying in the bed, the paper was shining whitely under my pen, I was smoking a reefer. Angel left the Paradise early, she had other things to do. I was missing her, and writing the more energetically. In the front room the white dealer from Florida was asleep, I'd agreed to let him spend the night. I wrote about Jones. As the night got later, I indulged in a fantasy that writing was stealing, and I wrote down ideas of Jones' and events and occurrences that I'd witnessed and my thoughts about him. In my mind the notion developed that if I sought hard enough and thought long enough and listened to him closely from now on, I might find behind his consciousness or maybe right in his words some secret sense of loss that fired the strenuous efforts of the thief. But this was just my idea, I didn't want to invent it, and I'm not sure I ever discovered anything like it to be true. In my soul for many days the hope of stealing from the thief by writing coldly burned. I tried to trace the path of our partnership: When I first met him, I thought I was getting something from him, drinking those beers while I listened to his endless talk about the angles.

When he offered me work, I figured I was lucky, and I guess I was. Right away I found he had a use for me on the job, he had a use for a white face. Also it must've been hard for him to find anybody who would go up high for that little dollar an hour. But maybe he had a liking for me too, maybe seeing I had nothing, he was offering me a chance. He had seen that I was heading in destructive and self-destructive directions and he was trying to school me toward a better understanding of life as he saw it. — All of a sudden I was thinking and writing these thoughts that were not in accord with my idea of theft. Under effect of the reefer I smiled at myself, as if I recognized my errant good nature.

But from everything Jones had said to me, and from what I'd heard about him, he was somebody who disappeared easily when the time was right. And I was soon to discover I was quite correct. I began to recall images of our days together and write them down. I remembered the night Nub, the manager of the movies, had invited us in to test the cushioned seats, and how Jones had laughed at Jerry Lewis, not in the easy way of laughing at a comedy, but more harshly, as if there was something obscene on the screen. I wasn't sure what I was getting at, or if I was getting at anything at all. But I felt I was back on the right track again; I was testing Jones' coldness, seeking some part of him that I hadn't yet discovered, that I might steal with my pen. What kind of dream was all this? Who was dreaming? Why had Jones handed me this dream? And suddenly I was certain that's all it was, and I felt deflated, bad, but clear. And another incident popped into mind: One day out on the job, Hobshead had come by to check on our progress. We had the purlins up on the front and one side and were working on the other. Naturally Jones wanted to fix up the portions of the building most visible from the road first. On this occasion Hobshead gave Jones a large level — a beautiful dull silver instrument about two and a half feet long with several little glass cylinders filled with a light green liquid and the little air bubbles that ran up and down and side to side. This was to help putting up the tin sheeting that would go on top of the purlins. Hobshead left, and five minutes later so did Jones. He drove in his truck to a nearby town and sold the level to somebody he knew there. I asked him how we would put up the sheeting, and he said he didn't need a level, because he didn't care if the shit went up straight or not. And he told me not to ask stupid questions. Yes, I had my doubts about whether this building was going to go up even halfway. And Jones was pretending to me there would be others after this one.

I started to get angry with Jones. Sometimes he talked to me as if we were really partners, or even friends. He passed on his ideas to me as though he thought they might do me some good. But I sensed a contradiction beneath the surface, as if he were telling me about how to live in America, about his ideas that everyone was a thief, in order that I should think that at least he wasn't stealing from *me*. But I knew something else. He was undermining my dignity for one thing and I was having to seek or create new levels in myself in order to hold on to it. I was glad to be Jones' sidekick and even his errand boy, but I wasn't going to be his fool. The more I thought about it, the more I felt insulted and disappointed, and the more I felt I was right in these feelings.

In this way I finally tired myself to sleep that night. But I woke early; I had slept for a few hours. Jones had left the night before for Savannah. He hadn't said anything and I didn't ask. His last words before leaving were: "I have no doubt you can

outsell Hobshead himself. If he brings his ass by the site tell
him I'm gone to Charlesville for the day." That was where another of the buildings was to go up. I was excited by the pros-
pect of going to work on my own. I dressed and ran down the
stairs and jumped on the truck. I threw my hard hat on the seat
beside me, and took off for Nasty Sally's. I had Billie fix me a
bacon and egg sandwich and put it on the bill, and I chomped
it down on the way to wino corner half a mile away. What a
broken block this was! In the distance, beyond the last dusty
crossroads, fields of coarse grass gave way to a scrub pine
woods overtopped by great oaks that rooted above the banks of
the river. Silhouetted against this view, on that last street that
must've had its hopes one time, a burned-out old hotel seemed
to barely stand, with its rooms and staircases exposed. I
stopped in front of the bar where our winos usually waited.
Tensely, I was picking out details. On the door of the next bar
down, I saw a big police padlock and wondered what had taken
place in there. Under the eaves I saw High and another man I
didn't recognize sitting back and drinking. And then Army
came out of the bar also with a bottle in his hand. As if they
knew Jones was out of town, they had already started in drinking. They climbed up in front with me. I asked High if the
man he'd been sitting with would like to work today, but at that
moment he fell off the bench, dropping a bottle which didn't
break but clanked loudly on some other empty bottles. He
swore and picked himself up and walked into the bar, and High
didn't bother answering me.

I liked High a lot. He had a strange kind of fat man's slow
grace and ease. He was the brother of a prominent funeral
home director in Meansville, and had the broken face, laughing
eyes and self-knowing good humor of the fallen brother. He

drank openly in front of me, and he would've hidden the bottle from Jones. He offered me a taste and I didn't refuse. Before we got to the site I was half drunk. Maybe it was the wine, maybe the fact that I was behind the wheel: the swamp country through which we passed seemed strongly morose and lush, the tar road was blacker and shinier in the sun, the pitch and rattle of the truck I felt all through me. When we got to the building, I jumped out and climbed up the purlins on the front side of it and sat on the topmost where it joined the roof beam. It was a clear cold morning, and there was ice on the steel that was melting in the sun. Below me the winos had sat down in the grass and were slowly drinking. Everything in view was quiet, the forest was quiet, nothing was happening at D. W.'s Good Eats, at the far end of the pasture some cows were standing perfectly motionless. It was just beautiful to sit up there high in the still chill air and think of nothing. High got some scrap wood together and started a fire. From above it was the palest orange dancing gas. After a while I climbed down, and the fire was hot and good and I dried off by it. There was a certain amount of work that the three of us could do close to the ground. It would be impossible to do anything high up because I was the only one who would climb. We carried purlins around to the back side of the building and laid them out in position. Then we moved from one end of the building to the other bolting in the lowermost ones. This took half a day. I bought some lunch meat and bread at D. W.'s and we ate on the grass and drank the rest of the wine and rested awhile. After lunch we put in the second row of purlins all across and that was it. Without anyone else who would go up even to the height of a man, there was nothing else to be done. It was late in the afternoon but not as late as we usually worked. I took a long look at the work we had done. It seemed very good. In the straight rows of purlins I sensed my ability to build something better than this structure for theft. It was a very vague sense, but it filled me with pride. It was a feeling apart from any that belonged to my partnership with Jones. It was my personal relationship to the work on the building that I'd done. When a feeling of sadness started to overtake me, I walked away to the truck, and we all got in and drove back to town.

I paid High and Army and dropped them off and drove around to the corner and parked the truck. I didn't want to change out of my work clothes, I was too proud of what I'd been into this day.

twenty-two

JONES RETURNED from Savannah late one night. When I came in he was asleep in his clothes, like he'd sat down and fell out. Not looking very rested, he woke me early the next morning, and by quarter to seven we were in Nasty Sally's drinking coffee and eating sausage sandwiches fixed by beautiful Billie, who made them big when we got there before the owner. The only other one in this early was Old Head, sitting at the other table, nodding over his cane, in a long gray topcoat covering his shoes, 1930's zap hat too large, he elbowed a fresh stack of newspapers. He glanced at the papers like they were his and politely looked away when Jones slid one off the top. Headline: RIOTING CONTINUES.

"I wish I was there," mumbled Jones. "I'd be right in behind them niggers, arrangin an exchangin."

Plenty of goods must be floating after a few nights looting. I pulled his paper — there were two riots, in D.C. and Alabama. "One of these days'll be some shit right here on this street," I said, thinking: right here in Meansville, Georgia — a successful exhilarated riot I'd be proud to be in, ranging into the white zone — plate glass crashing from store windows, shrieks of laughter, Molotov orange bursts — yeah, I'd like that, my white hands causing what damage I do to glisten just like all other — everybody mingling and delighting, touching in flight, and after, by memory of unique sensations —

"These law abidin niggers in this town!" A cold judgment from the thief — specially harsh like hearing a preacher say, "The devil take them!" He gave me the paper and finished his sandwich. I was drinking my coffee. I'd read enough, the bold print expressed everything. I lit a cigarette. It was Friday — the day he paid his bills, which included mine this week he'd been away plus ours for the week before. He walked out the door saying, "Okay, Billie." Okay what? I refolded the paper and put it back on Old Head's stack. Billie was looking after him, an ashy tone appearing in her skin, usually a rich black lighted by reds or blues —

"I don't know, baby," I waved to her and left the cafe. He was revving the truck across the street. I got a long squint at him as I climbed into the cab. He looked bitter and hot, and I'd ask him what the fuck's wrong! if I didn't know better. He didn't like a lot of questions. I guessed he'd explain when he got ready. His face relaxed when he popped the clutch, but he glared straight ahead with his eyes narrowed. The town dipped down. The street turned to clay as it dropped toward the river and he raced down it leaping the pits. Wino scenery, desolate and repetitive. The hour of the day only one of many. Nobody else could've got up a crew of Jones' winos. He found them in the cracks. He swung the truck in a circle and stopped in front of the bar doing daybreak business. From a wooden bench in the eaves, the very big cat, High, and the lean one, Army, in faded combat threads, rose wearily and headed through the littered Red Hurricane bottles. "Where is every-body!" yelled Jones. Where was the bunch of cats needing money to start drinking again, so he had his choice? "Where's Cook?" Three was the minimum. With High and Army in the back we drove around to Cook's aunt's house, and he yelled for High to go in and get him. Like he knew what he was having to do, the big man lumbered up the porch stairs and rapped the front door before he went in. Five minutes later he came out alone shaking his head hopelessly. "The way that man is this mornin, Jones! Cain't see me to cuss me, lookin roun the bed—" Jones flung open the cab door which creased the front of High's overalls; he tilted back, and Jones flew by. In a minute there were screams and groans from inside the house, and I knew Jones was tickling him and forcing him up. Finally he came out with wasted Cook by the elbow, with some lopsided red eyes! Every other step thumped the ground that was closer than it looked. It really hadn't hit him he was out of bed for good, and we'd have to wake him up again at the other end. I saw he'd already forgotten where he was going — zzz . . . The idea of a full day's work wasn't available to him. But by eleven he'd know where he was, sun dry and working fair — stiff, dazed, and resentful. It didn't matter on the ground.

I dozed off myself before we'd hit the outskirts. But out on the road, somebody in back woke me, pounding on the little window behind our heads and shouting, "Stop!" Jones slowed down and stuck his ear out in the breeze.

"Ten minutes! That cow is birthin!" High was yelling this.

"You country ass!" cried Jones.

"Stop or we ain workin, Jones! For ten minutes."

Ahead and to the right of us, moving at the edge and just inside the yellow woods at the bottom of a hill, hundreds of

cows and vague segments of spotted cows could be seen
through the trees, gently tripping away from the road. I could
smell them. We were going faster than they, and I could see
their eyes rolling back at us, not yet in alarm. Jones pulled
over, almost where the woods began. "Winehead always find a
way to delay . . ." Through the truck we could feel the two of
them jump off. "I'm too quick already," he said without a smile,
"I don't need no cow charm!"

You don't? This morning sure don't feel right to me, I might
need some luck. Do I believe that? I dropped out the cab and
took out after Army and High running in a diagonal toward the
animals. I could see her — speckled slick baby head hanging
down from her, slower than the rest but not left behind by
them. She galloped almost straight up the hill, ducking
branches, and we flat out after that radiant rear end, slightly
bowed legs churning in sudden ferocious leaps interrupted by
tense freezes behind trees. I was afraid for the fragile luck
baby, that seemed to have dropped a little — so shiny, should
really be some luck. I was afraid it would whang against a
trunk or be whipped by a branch, popping between her legs —
what if it flew out? My foot caught on a root and I took a dive,
landing on my shoulder in a bank of pine needles. I didn't have
the calf. It wasn't around me. I hoped I hadn't missed it. The
chase was too fast — it was all over for me. I lay listening to
the pursuit grow dim, on the dry winter ground so soft, and the
smell of piney resins cool and restful, shadowy, far from anything —

Crack! — "I got her!" — Faint piercing yell of High, jubilant
up the hill. Wood crashes — "Oh yeah, I touch her!" Maybe
the luck'd spread around. I'd like to touch the wet calf itself
where luck must be centered. I was falling asleep, I was

dreaming. I hoped Army was still chasing her up there so I could sleep —

"I was afraid you broke your leg," Jones woke me up talking about me. "Or your neck. How you fall asleep when we on our way? You getting lushed up like these winos! You can't get up in the morning!"

"Look I tripped an fell down," meaning to imply a little of the broken leg in it, getting to my feet and shaking off the needles.

"Most people fall down they get up for Chrissake."

"Ah Jones, you know how I love to work up high for you an endanger my life," I said bitterly. His mood was getting to me. It wasn't my decision to stop for the cow, I managed to think. If we lost a half hour, I felt a lot stronger for that blank. Anyway we're on our way. Speed was one thing that mattered to him, hours and dollars — he loved to steal. Sometimes I lost enthusiasm for it. Thieving had turned out to mean long days and nights because Jones couldn't have just one or two things going. We sweat erecting the metal shell so he can steal from it, from the crew, the buyers, USA Builders, and *me*. I know your heart, brother.

Up on the steel, he was very graceful. He put all his talents, backs of his knees and his teeth into connecting it up. He got where he wanted on the steel that appeared everywhere around him allowing him astounding leaps and slides. After lunch he would take a nap on a roof beam, as that made him rest deep. "I don't sleep after lunch," I said. "What picks *me* up, a short z an hour after I first get up."

He drove along, very sullen. The road fell and began to wind. We entered the swamp, weirdly reminding me of the risk of the work up high, murky sensation of the dirt-streaked

height over the red concrete I never felt while I was up there.
The work itself was clean and lofty. I lacked the southerner's
humorous affection for the dismal swamp, where he could
never starve, full of strange fruits and roots. — A rise, and suddenly — always suddenly after the swamp — sharp red skeleton of our big shed loomed up in the flat distance, and I felt
happy adrenaline pride, workman's joy in tall erection. Jones
laughed joyfully though a little forced, "Listen man, till our
next score on this shack I'm busted."

"Busted!"

"Damn, brother, I've wasted my last dollar."

Oh no! I don't believe it! For months he's been tutoring me
there never was no last dollar for Jones Jones. What'd he get
into over in Savannah? Three hell of a sore ground men tonight, needing money for their wine.

"You did?"

"I'll tell you later — with a fifth of rum."

Even the fire was cold which he built out of scrap while we
unloaded tools and equipment and got Cook awake and forced
coffee down him. That was a cold thing to get a man out of bed
for a job you can't pay for! I glanced at him for a sign. No, I
couldn't believe it — he could sell some of the stolen shit in his
crib. I wanted to slap his arm — "Say *what*, man?" But I
wouldn't rank his scene. Right now he was gingerly getting the
work operation under way. What a sweet bearing! He never
made the fire — I did, while he consulted the plans. Now he
was coiling the ropes. Leadenly, nobody picked up on the new
vibration — like every morning, colder and brighter as winter
deepened, stiffening the fingers and mind. I feel like I'm going
to get burned — but not by this slow fire. I shifted the wood,
receiving flame kisses. The winos set out tools, the bolt kegs,

the welding equipment. I filled nail aprons with washers, nuts, and bolts, and kept the fire rising to loosen up by. I loved the work up high, and wouldn't quit. What are you telling me this lame shit that you're broke, Jones? You can tell it to some wineheads!

Ropes on our shoulders, full aprons advertising A&B Hardware around our waists, spud wrenches in our belts, we shinned up the thirty-foot I-beams, and then walked up the roof beams to where we left off last week. All moves were amplified by the red grids shifting their huge patterns. In the early sun, ice was melting off the metal like sparkling cages, and on the ground, shadows intricate as blueprints flashed. Day after day creating this mirror motion — I respected the steel with a behavior, like earth or water. My gloves were soaked and heavy after the climb and I laid them out to dry, preferring my bare hands. We lowered our hooks, and Army connected up the first purlin. High and Cook were laying out the purlins under position in the roof structure. All three were wearing yellow hard hats and not looking up much. Hook-man backed off in a quick arc as, hand under hand, we hauled it up. At the last Jones pulled faster and swung his end over the beam so I could clear mine. With the spuds capable of spreading the big beams an inch or two, we bolted it down. On the roof purlins we put in only two bolts instead of the required four, and I tightened down hard on it to make up for the kegs he's sold away. It took a few trips to get us together, aware of the other's work by rhythms in the ropes and metal sounds. Occasionally I smoked a cigarette for alertness and exactness, and watched the horizon for inquisitive strangers. It got hot before noon and the bitterness left the steel. The purlins seemed lighter though endless, the lift automatic and satisfying . . .

Army waved when one was ready. I watched the hook which turned in the bolt hole, the angles showed we were even and level — but not halfway up, Jones' hook slipped out! glistening point of it floating sideways! Before I could let go, his end of the purlin hit concrete, and the rope burned my hands, and my legs' grip broke. Fear snapped my mind, and I was flung forward and down. Somehow I caught a fleeting hold of the beam with my right arm, as the long still concrete loomed up like a white slab or last wall in the acid surety I was going to fall. But old right arm hung on. I've never seen it battered or thinner — had I ever seen it? Incredibly it was saving me. The shock of the stop seemed to require everything. On the concrete below my shadow was swinging. My bruised right held tight as a shiny hook until I got a hold with my left, and some part below my fear swung a numb leg over, and dragged me up on the beach. I heard some birds clear across the meadow. I was so grateful. Everything was at peace, throbbing. I heard the sound of hillbilly music as D. W. and two other white men came out of D. W.'s Good Eats, and even that was soulful. The Ford pickup and the Impala and the three white men watching from the gravel patch around the gas pumps, and the wino workmen watching near the remains of the fire next to Jones' truck — the bright woods, white sky, empty road, seven or eight cows camped out in the middle of the pasture. I was digging everything and hanging on for sweet life.

Jones took half a dozen steps on a purlin before it was wobbling too hard and he pitched over on his hands on the next, bowing the purlins, on his way over to me — in his eye, like a snake in an egg, a coil of fear: like it was him almost fell. He was taking the danger now — in the middle, with the greatest spread, he was just treading air and looking at me — and I felt fear again in his body-bridge over the drop. I wished he'd leave me alone. I was tightening up again. Below me the floor dropped away, and bubbled and sweltered. How was I managing to stay atop this wire between vast opposites? I'd slip to one side and be clinging upside down again. Jones seemed to be looking through me to the accident I'd been spared, or to some other disaster in the past or future. No move! Body has no imagination for delicate move down the roof beam from the slippery balance owed to luck. But he got in front of me, and helped me down to the edge of the roof, and slapped my head a little, and got my gloves for me. He told me I had nothing but the straight slide down now, he had hold of my shoulders like he saw I was dreaming. I woke slightly and got a grip as I slipped over. How amazing that we were caught on the corner of this lace steel — like gnats invisible at the top of a corridor, and in his eyes was reflected yet another distance, as if his mind was fastened to something else, not here. When he let go he held his hands out above me for a steadiness sign, that grew small as I dropped fast. I didn't lose the idea but my feet slipped away and I had just my hands for brakes which were weak and shocked. I hit too hard and rolled twenty feet, and would've hurt myself if I hadn't been so numb and lank. He slid down, too, and walked over to me, shaking his head.

"Dig it, I'm resting," I said, gazing up at the firm still sky.

"Have a rest!" he said. "Hey Army, you wanna go up?"

The helpers were standing in the slight shadow of the truck, with their helmets in their hands. Nobody else was going up there. Jones begged Army to go up, since he used to be able to before he was a wino, but his voice was unreal, until he got angry — "You can't even hook right!" He feigned a kick at him, "Chocolate Chinaman! — You owe me some time on top."

What a game.

"No!" To illustrate his unwillingness to climb, Army fell over on the ground next to me and threw his arm over his eyes.

"Damn useless nervous winos," muttered Jones. "High — come on help me out!"

"Oh no! — I need a big flat space to walk on," laughed High good-natured.

It was too much for poor hung-over Cook to resist. He took a couple steps and settled down beside us.

"Oh Jesus God," yelled Jones, "look at this shit!" He began throwing tools and metal parts up in the back of the truck, like he was quitting. None of us moved, digging the utter stillness of the clay, only deepened by the crashes of heavy stuff hitting the trailer. — Jones, looting by building — that's what holds it up! He hasn't thieved extravagantly, he's put in minimum credibility at every stage because he wants to steal off the top. A prefabricated job that's coming up in his image — it's patterned to suggest that the missing parts he's sold have not been attached yet. He has the skill but he's no builder. It's not the factory shell Hobshead (who imagines he's hired him) and the buyers anticipate. In my ear, a musical suspense was created by the absences of standard parts, because they may be ignorant really, but certainly they got specifications of the final product. In my inner ear, I heard a crescendo of metal crashes — an evil image of the big shed toppled over. — I sat up. Yes, I sometimes wondered when it would fall. Man I was getting morbid. *I* was fine — Jones was into some shit, over in Savannah, no big surprise — why was I so down? I jumped to my feet — I had to kill this cold wave. I wanted to go back up to prove myself. I went over to him, "Look, Jones, I'll be ready to go back up in a while, let's take a break." But he didn't stop packing so I climbed up in the cab and relaxed. I lit a cigarette and turned on the radio and got the thermos of coffee from under the seat. The cats would have jumped up in back, Cook with relief, but he was ferociously pitching up hammers, and wrenches, and metal worth anything. Every day when we left he had to have everything under lock and key. Some sounds from Nashville were nice. Where's the Pontiac, now? Riding cross-country, knowing and spending . . . But we weren't to make it.

He hadn't got everything in — giving no sign, he suddenly slid in the cab, gunned the engine, and threw her into gear. I was staring a hole in the side of his head as we lunged forward. — "Slow down, brother."

"Don't slow me down!"

This cold motherfucker! It's ten miles to town! In the side mirror, beyond his hands high up on the wheel, I saw High chasing us for more than luck, Cook and Army too far behind, waving, supplicating, looking for something to throw. High made it to the trailer with a daring dive, but the others faded as Jones kept topping gears. High began banging on the welding tanks with a wrench or something. After a while he hit a beat and I turned up the radio. We were entering the swamp.

twenty-three

JONES WAS BROKE, but I had enough for a little bottle. Seated in a booth, drinking rum and Coke, he cursed Hobshead, and the winos that he'd left behind out on the site. I wondered when they would find us — that would be a soul meeting. On top of the walk home, they weren't going to get paid. But they must have something like that already figured out. Jones was cursing the building itself, that was recently cause for gladness, that I had almost fallen off of, as if it had delivered *him* a threat. He didn't talk about other buildings or our future in this business. After he'd got some rum in him, he started talking about the coast and how we'd ride out there in the truck. He said he had a grandmother who lived out there, who had raised him: we would stay with her and live easy. "She taught me to count to a thousand before how to sign my name. She was generous, like lavish, but she couldn't stand me losin nothin. But she paid those liquor bills for me and my so-called friends, and put or-chids on the little girls I brought home. Oh yeah, it's been many years and she'll welcome us, man. One of the first sights looked lush to me, and rich — after the beaches — her liquor cabinet. All them labels, seals, colors of glass. Yeah, man, we'll stay high on her liquids, float out on the ocean. She has always lived dead on the water. Her mother was white as you —"

We soon drank the last of the rum. We needed something else to get high on. We walked to the corner and stood there awhile. If Case were around we might get a reefer. I checked in the poolroom but he wasn't there. The air was calm and loose, unlike Jones, whose face showed a constant change of expressions as if he were thinking a lot of things very fast. A breeze started toward the river. We walked in that direction, and the glass storefronts soon ceased, and little gray shotgun houses began, with cane fishing poles hung under their eaves. The land was dipping down. The only thing I knew of down here was the block where the winos hung out and we didn't have money for even a bottle of cheap wine. We were walking directly away from Speck's and the other liquor stores. "You got to be ready," Jones was saying cryptically. "You never know, unless you watch . . ."

When he was ready to leave, I'd stay here, I knew that. Even if I had a choice, I'd stay, without there being anything much for me to stay for. I didn't understand him anymore and I didn't trust him. He was muttering phrases in an almost furious voice, like, "Some sorry sonofabitches in a jail . . . can't get high, ha! . . ."

We turned down a side street, and before we'd gone half a block, music started up. Yells and light voices could be heard. In the doorway of a small building was a speaker, on which two little girls were sitting, and it was from this speaker that the music was playing, maybe in advertisement of the place. I saw a sign: LITTLE JOE'S MUSIC HOUSE. Glossy record covers were taped into the windows. Kids were dancing inside, and in the doorway.

As we cut between the record store and the house next to it, a boy on the fringe stopped dancing and looked after us.

"Gimme a quarter," said Jones, stepping closer to him.

"I ain't got no quarter."

"Get a quarter from one a them girls."

"This is the Music House, man. They don't got no quarters."

Jones rapped on the back door of the house next door. It was twice unbarred inside seconds later. "Ah, it's Jones," Jones had announced resonantly. The door came open a couple inches, and a man's head appeared in the slit a foot or two higher than you would have expected. He said, "Ha-ha, Brother Rat! Welcome! Ha-ha!"

"What you say, Slim?" said Jones.

"Ha-ha, you hear how I call him?" Slim asked two ladies at the other end of the kitchen as we entered, and turned to a wiry black middle-aged workman with some dignified gray in his hair and a handkerchief in one hand, and pointed his thumb back at Jones, as if the man might otherwise miss him. He gave me a sober smile, shut the door, and replaced the long bolts through their rings.

"Yeah, that door used to fly open at the sound of my name!" said Jones.

"Yeah, been a long time since your name been in that door, hey Rat, ha-ha!"

I began to understand that I was in a stump liquor house. Jones made it to the sink, spat in it, picked up a small jar and washed it off with a quick burst of the faucet and dipped it in a wide-mouth gallon jug of very clear corn liquor. There were a lot of little jars around the kitchen — I saw they were the basic unit measurement, little jars just like baby food jars. I got one and filled it up — the whiskey exploded through my mouth, strong and clear. There's something handsome about this simple way of drinking, I thought. There was pineapple juice on a table to drink behind the whiskey. I enjoyed even the nice way the jars fitted in your hand. Without their labels, they were stark common elegant items.

I had never been in a stump liquor house before. Except for the little jars and the five open-mouth gallon jugs of stump in a row on the sink counter and the bolts on the back door, the kitchen could have belonged to any house on the block. There was the regular array of kitchenware and eating utensils on all the flat surfaces of the room. Everybody was friendly and easy just like in any kitchen. Knight used to drive stump liquor across this state; I remembered he told me that once. But he preferred to drink wine. I never would have thought to find Jones who enjoyed the glitter and flash of places like the Paradise in a drinking place like this one. It didn't seem the proper setting for him, even in his work clothes. But he was broke. He didn't have any money even to pay for this cheap homemade liquor that we were drinking. The names for the stuff rolled through my mind: *stump* was a good blunt designation. And *shine* was fine, like how it made you feel. I liked *splo* the best; it could be the essence of the verb "explode." And *splizzo,* to seriously or facetiously further disguise the nearby or hoped-for existence of the illegal juice. It amused me that I knew lots of names for the stuff, but this was the first time I was drinking it. I had just picked up the names in hanging around. I admired Jones. He knew how to get high under any circumstances. A man who has as much bread as he has sometimes, I said to myself, doesn't need to have *any* all the time. He knew this cat Slim; he'd drink up a nice loan, and I'd be glad to help him. Sounds from the Music House were penetrating the thin walls of the kitchen. It seemed like a dance hall or nightclub out there, though I remembered it was just a bunch of kids in a record shop, and we sat in a kind of backstage or afterglow, with those associations.

"Well ain it always the same," said one of the ladies, resuming a conversation that our entrance had interrupted.

"Well it is," said the other one.

"Huh, yeah," said the gray-haired man, wiping one side of his neck and then the other with his handkerchief, "if it didn't want to get done in the first place, he could only do it if he could think it through, which he couldn't."

"Yeah man, he wasn worth shit was he!" said Slim sarcastically.

"Naw Slim, I didn't say *that!*"

"Yeah you did, you said he couldn't *think*," said Jones, who didn't know who they were talking about and had no stake in this.

"He can't," said the lady, toying with a button on her blouse. "Too much a temper!"

"A bad man!" laughed Slim, "Nigger stone from the woods — "

"Which he didn even make out there," softly laughed the man with the handkerchief, and he threw the square of cloth out of his hand, and caught it by one corner, trailing down between his legs, where he stared. It was either all too true or completely unfair, because Slim didn't reply.

Jones said, "There only so much brains to go aroun in this here world."

"Jones, you know who we talkin about?" Slim smiled. Staring at him, he slowly started to laugh. "Red," he said.

Mention of Red's name made Jones' eye soft. When it immediately became hard again, it was blank, shining slightly with smug *splo* luster.

"I'll tell you a story about Red and this man here," said Slim, pointing at Jones. Slim had the type of face that always looked pleased, and he was smiling and his eyes were sparkling as he started telling the story. "Red an Rat here were working with a crew put up some kinda warehouse on the road out to Dalton, that was four, five year ago, I recollect. It musta been a real hot day, type a *bad* hot day make any man feel kinda evil, and it sure enough had Red feelin mean, hey Rat? Now I wasn there, I don know what start the argument, but Red he get into it with the man. He have Red diggin somethin — an Red a good mechanic, can't none a ya tell me no different bout that. Maybe he jus damn tired a that shovel. Anyway, they jawin at each other — all of a sudden Red let loose with it, he cut that man all to pieces with that sharp spade an *run!* — An when the man try to get up too, he gon chase Red, this man here — " Slim pushed his open hand at Jones — "this man fall down on him an start screamin, 'The wound, the wound, it too *bad*' — an he raise the alarm an some other white boys come runnin an carry him to the hospital. Red, he got away, lef the state."

"An *still* runnin, ignorant fool," said the man with the handkerchief.

"You know what he done?" said one of the ladies to Jones. "He done put his wife in the hospital this time."

But Jones was staring straight at Slim. His eyes, almost shut, had not left Slim's face, and now he said, "I never save Red's ass, but what I did, I kept that man from gettin his revenge . . ."

Something very cold was emanating from him. It was so cold it was a little warm. I had the feeling everybody was going to break into laughter, but we all sat in silence for quite a while, drinking. Jones must know what he had done, nobody else could know really; but the effect of it, undeniably, was to help someone. That reinforced this idea I'd been developing about him, that someone who tried so hard to be bad and cold, who kept at it with such purity of intention, couldn't help doing good on occasion, and helping certain others out now and then. Like me, this evening. He might be pretending to be broke for some reason. And I had to believe it was a pretense, because only recently he'd had so much, and I knew nobody was going to beat him out of what he had. I was probably going to continue working for him without pay, he wasn't ever going to straighten with the crew, what he owed them, but he might even get them to work for him again. But he was helping me to a good evening right now. He might think he was deceiving me, but I was high and pleasant, and how he was going to pay for the liquor was his problem, and for me this was enough. Because when I'd had something to drink I was quite capable of losing any conception of tomorrow, and it wasn't that the future, or what I might lose in the future didn't matter — it didn't exist. And the best was yet to come, though I didn't know it. I poured some pineapple juice from the can with pictures on it of a tropical beach and a nice clean breakfast.

"Where your box, Slim?" asked a lady. "That little music I can hear out there jus about make me thirsty for some music."

"Ha-ha! Ain it nice! Naw, the damn thing is busted."

Outside, Gladys Knight was singing, "Giving up is so hard to do . . ." Reflected in the shiny tin of the can which I still held in my hand was a vague picture of this room, with Slim over in the corner, with his drink between the tips of all his fingers, shoulders hunched against the wall. But his face was blurred, I couldn't see the smile I knew was there. I liked the man a lot already. I felt warm and mellow in this kitchen. But Jones was standing up. This is where I would have stopped for a long while, but he was drinking feelingly, like it was his last jar. He pulled the shade slightly and gazed through the crack, through the window; he kept looking out for quite a long time, like something he saw was spinning his mind. The colors of the room were turning golden. The big liquor jars looked cool and nice as water coolers on a hot day, and I sure did like this way of drinking. When Jones turned around, he headed right for the door. "Slim, my man," he said — I was waiting for this moment — "I got to owe you for this, but don worry about it, a couple a days an I be right again."

Slim's smile remained, but it dimmed a little; like it was still there, but it meant something else. "Okay, Brother Rat! I *know* you, an maybe I'll get it. An you know that I know that you know I know you real well, an I know you hold some long money sometimes, so I'm glad to help you out when you in need — everything work out in time I know . . ." said Slim softly watching Jones slip the bolts out of the door and taking them from him. I gulped the last of my jar, and smiled goodbye and followed Jones out, thinking what a nerve he had, he would just play on anybody and think nothing of it when he wanted to.

We cut back between the houses. The music got louder. A line of kids dancing made a strangely beautiful sight. The snaking line extended into the Music House and almost to the street. On this side of the dance, near the doorway, stood a thin figure, a head above any of the kids. As we came near, I saw it was an old man with keen features and little sprays of white hair on his head like phosphorous in water. His eyes were filmy and bright. He was chewing or mumbling lightly, his lips were curved in not quite a smile, the simplest statement of satisfaction. Then I saw he was saying something but I couldn't hear what, possibly little jokes to himself, he burst into soft laughter.

I could feel his joy. This was my thought first seeing him; I could see his happy facility —

Something embarrassed him at this moment when we arrived next to him. He stopped laughing — Jones said, "Tell me, Feelgood!"

He regarded us silently for a long moment. Finally he said, "Nope. You wouldn't dig it."

"Dr. Feelgood! Doctor!" shouted Jones, with a jovial meek grin on his face, "I'm doing poorly."

"You live wrong, Jones," said Feelgood, turning back to the dance, moving a step away.

"I'm down, an wanna be up!" said Jones. He looked at me. I don't know why he was looking at me.

"I know you're bad," said Feelgood over his shoulder. "What I mean, you do it wrong."

"Nobody wronger, Doctor," said Jones, glancing back at him, "but I'm down on my luck and I need some help."

"You need a new direction, Jones —" he laughed, walking away and motioning for us to follow. We caught up with him as he hit the first trees. He was lighting a reefer, he passed it along.

"Sweet Jesus," said Jones, smoke bursting from his mouth and nostrils — "at the right hand a the Lord!" It was wrapped in straw-colored paper, which was my favorite, the kind they had in the warning exhibits the police showed us back at high school. Round as a milk shake straw. Health director used to say, *Don't smoke at all,* and you can never be fooled. Who could not notice they were being handed an aromatic delight? I would jump up and accept it, and thank the giver with all my heart, as I did just now, by a thankful look, and packed in the good smoke.

"Don't burn your fingers," said Jones, taking the roach from me. "Be careful how much a this you smoke, it'll go to your head."

"Where else it gonna go, Jones?" I asked him.

Feelgood lit up another and smoked on it. Jones offered him the roach. That cracked me up — Feelgood traded with him! "Roach is what you smoke for," he said, coughing and wiping his eyes — he passed the sticky tit to me. I smoked on it awhile. It didn't seem to burn up — collected resins bubbling rich brown smoke, billowing around me.

"It'll wipe out your mind," said Jones, stopping so he could smoke harder. "This ain't none a Suitcase' reefer."

Stoned as I was on the corn whiskey, I concentrated on one thing at a time, and now it was the smoke. The tiny coal didn't hurt, and I burned away the roach to nothing in my fingers. Suddenly my lungs gave way — I had to cough; I coughed and coughed and couldn't stop. This was some coughing reefer, as they say. And it was starting to go to my head. Very soon I could tell this was no ordinary shit, this was some extra power-ful smoke, and the night began expanding and the stars began popping and the air became softer than soft.

"Let's make it!" said Jones, swinging his arms like he was al-ready striding.

"Where to?" I was moved to ask, and the question echoed in my head, where to, where to? I couldn't get any more stoned than this, and I was more than fascinated by the old man who'd just passed us this wonderful smoke, and Jones was hurrying on again.

"They somebody thought a time, make no mistake, it was in-vented like shoes. An you a slave to that man, Jones," said the old man, beginning to walk himself, though at an easy pace.

"If you don know the rules, you can't play," Jones said, and began to laugh real hard. "I need some help, Feelgood! Ha! Put some luck on me, I ain got a dime!"

The old man Jones called Dr. Feelgood laughed a little too, with a straight face. But he didn't reply — as if Jones were too distant from him for a reply. He got out one more joint and lit it and immediately passed it to me. We entered a grove of trees that was the last shelter before the corner, and stopped to smoke this last one. Damn, I felt like my head would explode and my body flick away in the breeze. Or I felt so heavy, I felt like I'd just stay rooted to this spot, one of the trees. If I had been uncertain about why I was following Jones around, now I might be a blade of grass under this grove, following only the sun. We were all brushing ashes off our chests and laughing in our separate fashions. The corner was aburst with light, rainbows of yellows, greens, and blues of neon signs, and the moon and stars were powerful and clear above the open intersection. "The light!" I exclaimed.

"Them orange bricks, an the people inside," said Feelgood, "the sand."

I had never actually noticed the sand that surfaced the secondary road at this intersection, reflecting sand that strengthened the light that hung in curved growths through the air. A glimmering in the light, as if water were near, was perhaps also created by the sand; or perhaps it just gave me the idea of water. At this moment a sense of gliding and of currents filled the air, and it didn't surprise me to see the old man suddenly moving fast away. Now I look back on it, perhaps in his easy voice I had felt the river, perhaps the smell of the water was thick on him.

"I'm goin to the show," he called, gliding irrevocably away

like a leaf falling toward the water. I had glimpsed it when I first came to town and for some reason I was thinking of it now.

"Hey Doctor!" I called. But he was already too far away. He waved once but didn't turn around. Then he was buying his ticket — I would have hipped him how to get a free seat, maybe cushioned.

"C'mon man," said Jones, "he ain the las man aroun here got reefer." Well I knew that, but this stuff, it was true, this was some exceptional stuff. I watched Jones stiffly cross the intersection, and frowned at myself, remembering hoarding little stashes back in college days. (Gold, shit, careful little caches of the grass with many nicknames.) Squirrel! But it wasn't just that. There was something about the old man — Water, air, earth, smoke . . . I wanted to let go, and let it come easy. I wanted to stop following Jones and let go of everything and everybody and drift and float. The Doctor was gone. But even that wasn't significant. I'd float into him again someday I was sure. I started off on my legs which I didn't feel like I controlled. And his legs carried him off with them! — That metaphor came out of somebody's real experience, and now it's mine: this perception gave me pleasure and I laughed. Riffs and runs of the mind that I don't remember made me laugh some more, as if a lake of mental laughs had been located by the reefer, and I'm going swimming, in the smoke. My legs were walking behind Jones, veering off slightly in another direction that I wasn't choosing, but up in my laughter I was riding.

"Damn, you just go crazy," said Jones, as I went by.

"Hey look!" I said, seeing ahead of me in a pool of white dust in the concrete, a small shining object to which my steps were taking me. I walked faster — I could speed up, but only in this direction, I couldn't break out of it and I couldn't stop, and I saw why: feeling great desire, I reached down — and picked up a cigarette cellophane; it was glittering in my hand. Surfaces of buildings swelled out into the street, perhaps under pressure of the life packed inside. The painted windows glowed like your fingertips over a light. Jones took off his hat in the doorway of the Paradise, called, "Hey brother! Be cool," and went inside.

The cellophane was beautiful as a seashell of the street. I cast it back on the beach. As if he were gone already, Jones' words of slight concern filled me with sorrow. But it was me who was going, I was walking on and I couldn't stop. I was leaving the thief, whose work was so vain and lonely, and somehow I felt sad for him, and sad for myself, because I didn't know where I was going. It didn't feel like freedom; it was starting to feel like being lost, and momentarily I felt afraid. I couldn't listen to my legs with amusement any longer, I was afraid they were being drawn on by something hidden from me in the dark spaces up ahead. If I could've faced the other way, I would've seen the light in the Paradise door. I tried to stop, I managed to walk slower. At each moment I had the sensation that at the moment before I could've stopped but that now it's too late. This made me dizzy and sick; I felt knee deep in the sand. But it didn't stop me. It was true that everything that had ever happened to me now placed me right here, and brought me to this realization of nothingness.

Then I heard an organ sound, one note sustained, with a voice spread over it, rising to a cry. Moving away from the bright lights of the corner, this is what I found myself approaching: blue bright awesome sound of the singer and the organ. When I reached the next street, I could see the church, with a little crowd around it. And I kept walking. When I got close, I could see a young boy at the organ, through the open double doors. And in the doorway, a huge old woman in a white robe was singing into a microphone. In front of the low unadorned wood church, people included me by warm changes in their eyes or by not noticing me at all.

Oh will the circle be unbroken bye an bye . . .

Her voice was husky and somehow comforting; the boy's wispy flitting hands, blowing deathlight pipes, focused attention of my soul on the unified loneliness of the congregation, and the sense of falling away into a bottomless pit from all I'd known so far in life abruptly left me. Jones and I were parting. I'd be forced back on myself again for direction. I was losing my way again. But standing by the church and listening, it began to feel less strange and sad. A touch of freedom crossed my heart, and again I felt how good it would be just to float for a while. Somehow the church service had released me. I thought, I've lost my way but what the hell! I walked on. It occurred to me that nobody knew where they were going anyway, and I walked faster, springing slightly off my toes. I was enjoying the sensation of it growing darker all around me — for a while it was smooth black ahead. This didn't last. I was approaching the edge of the white side of town, with streetlamps. I had the exhilarating feeling of somebody going to look over the edge of a cliff. When I hit Lee Street, which was the racial dividing line, I didn't cross it, I walked down it. Like all the big streets of the white area of Meansville — and like the main streets of many larger southern towns — Lee Street was planted with palm trees: the Florida look. I passed a few, spaced about a hundred and fifty feet apart, eerily bending up out of little dirt holes in the sidewalk, and then I climbed one. The trunk was dry and cold; the fronds, in which I propped myself, were winter brown and brittle. Oh it was very peaceful up high off the ground, over the empty night street. Sitting up there, I realized how much I liked to be up high, and I thought that was what I'd miss most about my partnership with Jones: the being up high in the air.

Two cops, wearing blue and white uniforms, spinning their clubs, came into sight. One of them started picking his nose. I relaxed, and kept from laughing. I stayed very still and held my breath while they passed beneath. Without too much effort, I resisted the effort to spit. But I felt invisible, and practically invulnerable up in my perch. Through the frayed big leaves, I watched the street. In a line with the street, a nearly full moon was shining, down low in the sky. Everything was quiet, and the air seemed finer and colder up there. But I wasn't cold. As if warmed by the light of the moon, I clung in the tree and enjoyed my unusual vantage. A bus marked Jacksonville barreled past. Carrying black and white — the bus was like birth or death: they came and went together. Way up the street, I could see the Trailways Bus Station. With nothing else to do, my mind easily took on the feeling of a long bus ride someplace. I'd sit in the back, where black people would rather not sit next to me and white wouldn't stray, and I'd get a nice ride alone. Up in the tree, I watched the scenery roll by. I glanced up and down Lee Street, but I couldn't see another soul. It was a street of small insurance companies, farm supplies' stores, tractor showrooms, big old boardinghouses. Right beneath me was a clothing store. A single bulb burned in the window and lighted up a wooden torso sporting an old fash-

ioned gray jacket with wide lapels and the gray material span-
gled with little crisscrosses of darker and yellow threads . . .
At the next corner, a traffic light never changed from green
. . . I lit a cigarette and arranged myself more comfortably.
It required a good deal of effort to stay balanced up there,
there wasn't any kind of good limb like on a pine tree or an oak.
When Jones appeared out of a side street, I was hardly surprised. I almost called him, but I didn't have anything to call.
He turned and seemed to gaze in my direction. His look was
smashed, eyes pointing not quite in the same direction. They
seemed to be loose in their sockets and his stoned mean expression was a long way from his old popeyed invulnerable stare.
He looked across the street like there was a river to cross, and
paused a moment. Smiling in a lopsided way, he began to walk;
and then he was on the opposite sidewalk, and speeding up, he
headed into the white section.

I had to wonder where he was going. I couldn't make much
sense out of things; thus it might seem agreeable to sit up in a
tree and watch the night pass. But when Jones had come and
gone, I climbed down from my heights and started walking. I
was feeling pretty nice. After the changes of the evening, this
was where I wound up, feeling free and easy. I didn't know
why I had felt so suddenly scared earlier, and I didn't know
why I was feeling all right again now. I guessed it was the
powerful reefer and didn't think any more about how I was
feeling. Passing the traffic signal, I suddenly wanted to take a
closer look into the light that was still green, like an unblinking
green eye. I climbed, laughing: once you got into climbing,
you could see things at levels never seen. I hung there quite a
while, gazing into the green light that was big as a plate. The
spaces inside it were immense, with many shadings. I saw a

lush green forest. It seemed to move and grow before my eyes, in a moist green air. Somehow this mechanical and electrical contrivance of the traffic system was affording me a view of thick grasses, tall waving plants, matted bright green thickets, and vibrant-leaved trees perhaps on the banks of a river. Summer life was mine and all around me as long as I clung to the metal casing, with my nose pressed to the glass. When I got down, for many minutes everything carried this green luster. It was very pleasant. I felt happy. The street seemed soft and alive, the cars like shiny bushes. The only way I knew was straight to the Paradise to see if Angel was there. Thank heavens she was, and could be persuaded to come up to the apartment. Now I felt in a strange fine mood. But when we got there, men were pushing into every room, and carting down all the goods to a big van in the alley. So Jones was selling out to somebody, he was dumping everything at once! I sat in the barber's chair, and Angel lay down on the bed. When the men indicated they wanted these items, I objected. The bed was a necessity, and the chair was my favorite thing. They let it go, they turned to carry out other stuff, but I felt they would insist later. When they were all out of the room, I got one of the pistols and set it in my lap when I got up in the chair again. Later, they made a definite move for the bed. It was a rather handsome piece of modern furniture, but still it wouldn't bring all that much. Two of them were looking it over, to take it apart. A third was trying to pull Angel off it. I pointed the gun not quite at anybody and told them to leave it be.

"It's been paid for, man," said one, but they were all backing away.

"It's not for sale," I contradicted him. "Send the man who says he bought it."

The man came right away. He had been down in the van waiting. He had a good-humored face and was showing a slight ironic grin. I told him I was Jones' partner and that the bed and the chair couldn't go. He acted very genial, and said of course the items could stay. I could tell he doubted I'd ever use the gun, and of course he was right. It wasn't even loaded. Probably he didn't value what I wanted to keep. He must've appreciated my stubborn gesture, and he responded with style. My face felt like it was reddening slightly. He grinned: "Fuck it! What else you want?" — I said, a radio.

When they'd all gone, and the apartment was practically empty, I enjoyed a triumphant laugh and a glass of whiskey from the cupboard. But in the morning, I felt strange and kind of lost again. I wondered how long I'd live here before I got evicted for no rent, and what I'd do then. I wondered if there would be any heat from the unfinished building that'd turn my way with Jones gone. I could sense that my relationship to everything was about to change but I couldn't tell just how. And a new day was beginning. It was with a certain surprised relief that I heard Jones let himself in the front door. He announced he wanted me to work that day, and more from not knowing what else I'd do than anything else I got dressed and followed him down to the truck. High was waiting; somehow he'd been persuaded to come back to work too. We drove out to the site in silence. With High hooking up, Jones and I continued laying in purlins on the top. Jones received money a piece at a time, and I gathered that the next installment would come to him when all the purlins were in and the tin had been started. Naturally, he was looking forward to this new money, and again I became certain that he'd be leaving as soon as he had it. I suspected that it was only because he was near to this new money that he was staying. He already must have quite a pile from the stolen goods sold out of the apartment. These days it was altogether like my apartment. He was staying elsewhere, and I didn't know where. This made me uneasy. Like some of the heat I kept on expecting might be centering on the target of these rooms. On the job I tried just to enjoy the pleasure of the work up high. At night I got as drunk as I could and tried not to think about any of this criminal business with which I was associated. I didn't do any writing at night, I didn't think at all about stealing, or Jones' ideas, or my counter-ideas. There was no way for me to trust Jones anymore, he had tipped his hand — he'd dropped the damn thing on the floor, and I knew he was going to split. Yet he went on acting like the completion of the building was in sight. On two different mornings, I saw him optimistically talking with Hobshead, who looked happy with the state of things. I couldn't help calling him a fool in my mind. There he stood, near the highway, taking in some general impression of our progress. He could have walked up close and climbed up a few yards for a better look. Maybe he would have had to kick off those expensive shoes he wore and stain his pants a little at the knees, but he could have found out. Fool! There he went, gunning down the road in his little Ford, content that we were doing the job and his extra profits based on nonessential thefts and cheap black labor were very well protected. I knew something else was happening, though I wasn't too certain what it was.

Then came this very last day. The tin sheeting had got started. I'd begun to think Jones was going to finish the building and make that final money. It looked right, as long as no one looked too close. We were up on top, putting in tie rods between the beams. We crossed the long limber steel rods, they made big X's under the purlins. It was tedious work; it would take a couple of days to put them all in. They made the structure *look* a lot more solid anyway. Ironically, this is when it happened. A fluttering of the beams could be felt, a ticking someplace in the joints could be heard. I could hardly be certain I wasn't imagining it. I looked up — for a moment, all seemed the same. And then I could see the building moving, all the beams shifting, and I grabbed hold as we traveled through a short arc, maybe several feet. Then it stopped. Tensely, Jones said, "Wait to jump! If this shithouse goes, wait till I say, last ten feet, jump ahead of the beam . . . "

I felt weird stresses around unknown new pivots. The steel felt very cold, and dangerous, and insubstantial as the small white glare of sun bouncing in the sky above our heads. We paused several moments. But the building held its new configuration. Jones started sliding down the beam, and I followed. Nothing happened. Our movements did not start anything, we were allowed the escape. On the ground, Jones said, "We got to get the crane again, we'll pull her back in shape." We got right in the truck. High came running from the highway where he'd run to, out of range. Jones rubbed his hands and squinted at the thing, standing up over us. When High had got in, we stayed in its shadow another moment, while Jones cast it a hateful look. Then we drove away. As we topped the hill, I looked back and it was still standing.

On the way into town, Jones talked about how lucky we were, and High swore he was never coming back. I was silent. Jones insisted all could be set right again with the crane. His talk kept coming, with a cheerfulness that sounded forced to me. We dropped off High, and then Jones let me off at the

Paradise. He nodded seriously, and said he had something to take care of, and he'd meet me inside after a while. I waved to him as he drove away. I had a few dollars in my pocket that he'd let me have, and I bought a beer. It was early in the day, nobody was in here. I took the beer and sat alone in a booth. It didn't surprise me that after a few hours he hadn't showed up. I had several beers and played a few songs and enjoyed the lighting in the place and the parachutes hanging from the ceiling. I never did see him again.

twenty-four

"HELP ME," said Leo, sticking out his hand, "gimme a joint."

"For a dollar," said the man selling reefers.

"Shit cat, all you want is to con folks, you never help a brother! This is *me*, man!"

"I don play that shit, fat boy!"

"You jive country nigger! You jus like every other loud-talkin Georgia country — This here is the only soul man on the street," said Leo, turning to me. "Lemme smoke some with you, brother . . ."

"For a dollar, Leo," I said, laughing. "I'm so high I don want no more to smoke myself!"

"You cold motherfucker whitey, you ain no good!"

Jones left me a friend in Suitcase. He left owing each of us money. The arrogance that was practically his trademark had not endeared him to many around here, and though the reaction against it had never been much expressed while he was around, I sensed it now, and so did Case. But he wasn't so much affected by it; I was often dependent on the goodwill of others, but Case had his game together. For one thing, he could cer-

tainly shoot some pool. For another, he had his drug connec-
tions, and there was a market for good things to get high on;
there was a need to be satisfied here on the corner, and he was
one of those who tried to profit by meeting it. Besides me,
there were several others who sold reefers for him.

After a while Leo walked away, disgusted as usual. In my
mind sounded Betty Everett's song, "You're no good, you're no
good, you're no good, baby you're no good!" I loved that song.
I laughed, enjoying the fine descending sound and watching
Leo, whom I couldn't help liking, searching for a sucker. And
for Leo it'd have to be a stumbling and bumbling backwater
sucker's sucker, no lie. He never did have anything, but he kept
looking. But one thing about Leo, he could make you feel
mean and cold, if that tickled you. Like me, I rarely had anything to feel bad and selfish about, I was usually on the other
end of it, and what I had now was no big thing and even to say
that is stretching it. In a strange way, Leo didn't really bring
me down. His clowning and begging was oddly designed to
make you feel good, in hopes that would get you to give him
something.

I expected some trouble after Jones' abrupt departure,
though I truly didn't know what to make of it myself. Hobshead came by the corner one time, and sent somebody in the
Paradise looking for him, who came to me. "White man lookin
for one of you — either one a you — outside," this cat said.
Me? I nearly lost my head. Just what I'd been expecting — the
heat. I tried to get my liquory self together to go out there and
talk to the man. I was walking toward the door, but I was
scared. Of course, my worst fear was that one of the buildings
had collapsed. Though I didn't know anything, I knew too
much. But it was only red-face Hobshead, to wonder where

Jones had gone and to moan about the jam he was in. I said, too bad: I obsequiously told him I wished I could help him out, but it was a mystery to me, and so was the construction business. So he was going to forfeit a side operation, I thought, he might've gotten burned for a couple thousand, and we're sitting there in his brand-new T-bird, which he won't get out of on this street. Why was he crying like this? I wondered if he knew the half of it yet — missing beams! Finishing those shacks was going to be a strange trip for some white crew. Hobshead was still hoping to avoid paying any wages, hoping I could get the crew out to work. I wished him luck, but it was an impossibility. We all lost something just like him, I explained. "I could get you for this," said Hobshead — "Not me," I told him, "Robert, your partner — not me."

Getting out of the car, I told him we were all going to put labor liens on him in the morning. And that was the last I ever saw of him, but it wasn't the end of my apprehension about him and even the law, whom I hadn't forgotten. I was reckoning, Jones didn't leave for nothing, did he? His ability to hat quick was his lifeline, his sense of time was his saving grace.

I dreamed about jail every night and lapsed into far daydreams in which the street where I stood was apparent to me only through a wonderment that I was free out on it. Somebody was standing nearby, saying, "When you are gone . . ." And wherever I was, I felt vulnerable, like it was an open place easily penetrated by the police, whom I had every reason, so it seemed, to smell nearby. This was nowhere more true than in our old apartment, which was nearly empty of items. But my fear wasn't rational. My sense of losing hold on the outside was nothing thought out; it flowed from a laceration in my brain I couldn't close, and my sad guess was it never would heal. In fact, I hadn't known one day free of the possibility of jail in the past year, though I'd apprehended that in different ways. Now that Jones was gone I knew what I'd been risking the last six months and only the confidence he'd inspired had kept me from thinking of it much till now. For one thing, if I ever got busted it would be difficult getting bail together, which Jones would have put up. I often wished for my old African thumb piano, that was stashed up North, to quietly play . . .

Suddenly Leo had his hand in my pocket, which was empty. He's tireless like a clown or a madman, but he's not crazy and he's not stupid. At the last moment I tried to check his strike by walking into him. But he walked with me: "Gimme fifty cents, Leo, I'm hungry," I told him, to put him off. He's fast, though he doesn't look able. His eyes move like water over the surfaces of things, and suddenly he's on you, got his hand in your pocket. I should've walked in the poolroom where he's barred, but I was afraid of tearing my best pants.

"Don play with me man, don come on to me like that brother, I'm in trouble!" he told me. I gave him a blank look which was difficult under the circumstances. "My mama is very sick, she at home in bed an can't move, an don none a her damn people care bout her but *me*, an all I'm tryin to do raise enough for medicine, I ain askin no one person for all of it, could I hol bout two dollars cat?" With his beret down over one eye, and a mean mischievous glint in the other that he didn't bother to hide during his story, he didn't deserve any answer but a mild expression of amazement, but really I wondered what was he doing and why was he running this line. At all times, not deep behind his sly face, he seemed to pose an insult, like, "Some people are the problem, and some people are the solution like

you, sucker!" Ever since I heard him say that to somebody foolish enough to have lost a dollar in his little game, I heard him
thinking it. More than anybody else around here, he held his
memory of Jones against me. He drew his hand out of my
pocket but let it linger, loose, in the little air between us, like
I'd said yes and he was politely waiting for me to get out my
wallet. I said nothing and didn't bother moving away. He
looked out in the street with his eyebrows up, cool expression
that he kept a few seconds. Finally I couldn't resist it, I stuck
my hand in his pocket, and quick pulled out some change,
"Man you're holding out on me," I accused, righteously, because I never expected him to have anything. I was going to
grab him on the leg and ask him how he liked it, but my fingertips struck silver.

"Say man, I thought we was tight!" He grabbed my hand,
and I let him get his money back, but a quarter. "Lemme hold
a quarter, Leo — a little quarter!"

"You don have no respect for the sick do you? I thought we
was friends. I don ask these other suckers aroun here, they
don have no feelins. I ask you, cause you — I thought, you
know . . . " Gazing at me sorrowfully, like a friendship was in
danger, a terrible mistake being made — with that same crafty,
haughty light in his eye just the same. The contradiction made
me laugh, which seemed to be his subtle aim. Too bad I really
was broke because I might give him a dollar if I had a few
thousand, he had me laughing. Since I didn't have a thing, he
was going to get hot and curse me. He took a few steps away in
a huff, and turned around and glared at me. "Look here — tomorrow I'm a pay you what I owe you an we finished, hear!
You stay outa my way an I stay outa yours. I don wanna hear
nothin from ya no more, hear?"

Case came out of the poolroom and waved his stick in a direction up the street, "Hey Leo, that woman up at the movies say she wanna talk to you —"

Leo grabbed for the stick and missed, pushing against Suitcase. "Get away from me sucker!" he shouted at him. He ran back at me. "Gimme some money, whitey!" and he got my wallet. I was cool. I did have a wallet. Case was laughing to himself, but wearily. "You ain right," said Leo, tossing it back to me. It was so light it almost floated in the air, containing nothing but my license to wheels, and draft card, which I liked to have on my person at all times. Leo sat down on the bench at the curb and began to throw his cards, the old game.

Incredibly, a drunk came around the corner and began to stare at the movements of Leo's hands as he jumped the three cards around and around on the bench. He put down fifty cents on the game and Leo moved the cards. Just as he was about to point to the card of his choice — he was making a tentative selection with his finger about two feet from the card — Case started laughing. He had been watching and knew the drunk was making the proper choice, and his laughter caused the man to bring down his finger with finality. Leo jumped up. He ran at Case. "Nigger, don't you peep me!" He started walking away. He strode back to the bench and picked up his cards, and walked away. He was shaking his finger at Case. "Why you wanna rank *me*, nigger?" The drunk was waking up to how he was being cheated and began to protest. But it was useless with Leo, who was a special kind of super-cheat. But the drunk was persisting. He ran after him, and caught his arm, and Leo wrestled with him for a moment. When he'd pushed him aside, he came storming back to where we stood in central spots on the corner.

"Gimme a joint!" Leo cried, standing a few inches away from where I stood. We'd been through this before, but Leo was going to start over again.

"No, goddamit!" I cried.

"Don't you goddam me, whitey! What you doin on our side of town? What you doin anyway?"

Leo hurled this ultimate question at me and stood still, glaring into my eyes for several seconds. When I didn't respond, but only returned the glare, he took a swing at me, which I evaded. He went wild and began swinging wildly. I backed away, I ducked. He creased me a couple times. I was about to lose my temper and get into it, when somebody hit him from behind. It wasn't Case, it was somebody I didn't know well. I could tell by his expression that Leo's racialistic outburst had offended him too. Nobody wanted any fighting on this corner, which was a peaceful place. I could hardly believe what had happened. Leo had gone over the edge. I took a walk.

About halfway down the block, I thought I glimpsed a familiar figure in a doorway farther on. It took me a moment to make the recognition. I was suddenly sure I'd seen Cousin Yellow, and I realized I'd missed him for months. He was standing in a doorway down the block — I couldn't be sure which doorway. As I continued to walk, I decided I wasn't even sure it was him. Something in the soft posture and the yellow-brown glint of the skin made me think it was, and I walked more quickly, not really knowing why, nor what I would say to him if I found him. How few words had passed between us in the hours we'd spent in each other's presence at Cara Lee's! It was beyond him, it seemed, to talk with somebody white — it was frightening or plain impossible. But it was my pride I could talk to anybody in the world, with the exception of most cops,

and anybody in America for sure, where we all spoke English.
I'd gone about it wrong with Yellow, but I wasn't sure how, or
what the nature of my mistake. Nobody else seemed to talk
with him much. Knight took him for granted, he treated him
like one of the real young kids. Cara Lee was gentle toward
him, but their conversation had to do with practical matters. A
lot of cats couldn't even notice anyone with so diminutive a
vibration — in their world of lightning, and dollars. To have
learned anything about such a one as Yellow back at Harvard
I'd have had to take a course on psychological disorders, and
that would've only made the chance of communicating with
him more unlikely. Anyway I didn't want to tell him anything,
or help him. Such a soul, who smiled so much as he drifted
here and there in the town, had a simple secret, I thought, and I
wished I knew it.

As I neared the end of the block, I began to look in doors,
but I didn't see him. I didn't hang out down here, and I hardly
knew the lay of the shops. I knew he shined shoes at a barbershop, and I kept searching for one. I could sort of use a trim
myself, I reflected, running my fingers through my very long
hair. I crossed the street and headed into the next block, but
the next corner, after a vacant lot, was white, and that would
put an end to my search. I hadn't got another glimpse of
him . . .

I saw a barber's — a little slot in the block of shops, a two-
chair setup, but neither of the chairs were in use. The barbers
in white jackets were playing checkers with two gentlemen.
Nobody was shining any shoes. I saw Yellow nowhere in the
place. Considering the possibility that I'd only imagined seeing him in the first place, I turned around and looked all
around, up and down the street. For the middle of a summer

afternoon, there were a lot of people walking on the pavement and idling in the doorways. But up and down the street I spotted no one with Yellow's aura. I gave it up and started back to the poolroom to see if anybody had showed up who was a worse shooter than me, from whom I might win the price of a few beers. Such individuals were so few and far between there was little point hanging around all day. But there was some percentage in checking in now and again. Sometimes I wished some of the guys from the movement would get up their courage and stop by for a game. But maybe I didn't really, on second thought, because it was kind of humiliating to win money from somebody whose lack of any skill put my own minor talent in an even poorer light. And suppose I ran into a collegiate sharpshooter down for the summer vacation! Some cats wouldn't let me forget about that! It would put an end to Suitcase's plan to train me for a certain game. As soon as I'd got good enough, he wanted to drive to other towns in the state, pretending to be SNCC workers. He'd borrow some overalls for the trip, and I'd hesitantly walk into the hippest local pool parlor, pretending to be a "movement sucker," and let myself get sucked into something. I would have no trouble playing the "sucker," but I'd have to be sure of playing the winner . . .

twenty-five

THINKING THESE THOUGHTS, I was headed back down the block toward the corner when I suddenly saw Yellow across the street entering the cut between a dry-cleaning establishment and a liquor store. The physical mystery of how he could have arrived up there without crossing my path disappeared into the greater mysteries of Yellow's soul as I caught up with him, still not knowing how I would allay his natural fear of me, or even greet him. Then I saw that around his right hand were wound fishing lines, and sure I felt like throwing a line out in the river.

"Hi Yellow," I called softly. "You going fishing? Could I go along with you man? I sure would like to check out the river . . ."

What a surprise when he turned around and, saying nothing, took my arm and guided me through these back lots as if we were in a crossing. After a while he let go and formed his lips as though to say something and smiled. Several roads led to the river, but he followed a route of his own. It was a way I never would have taken, and we slipped beneath people's windows and walked through their backyards, offending no one, I'm sure, because Yellow was offensive to no man. When someone appeared, he took my hand or my arm. Rapidly my ideas about him were going through a change, though he hadn't given me a word to change them. Had he always accepted my friendly feeling toward him? In my earnest desire to confound all stereotypes, had I mistaken his silence for fear that was only mine and the "times"? What did he see? Where was he leading me?

The tall oaks that overlooked the river came into view on the horizon of shacks and scrub pines. His steps quickened, and then relaxed. Soon we stood on the top of the bank in the shade of the trees and looked down at the bluegreen water. "You see where she stop," he said, pointing to a pool on the near side of the main current where all ripples and twigs and indicators of the river's speed seemed not to move at all. I knew myself that there might probably be fish at a deep spot like that, down in a hole where the water was dark and cool, and the shelter undoubtedly fine. I was beginning to feel very happy. We started down.

"River my girl friend . . ." Yellow laughed. His forehead and temples and ears were smiling, and his lips were drawn back in expectation of the moments that were coming. Chuckling and whispering on his way down the invisible path over roots and clumps of moss and rocks and prickly grasses, that he knew so well, even with his limp he forged ahead of me, on my two good legs, tripping and stubbing my toes as I misjudged mounds and drops, eager to reach the soothing waters. He was seated on the ground straightening his lines when I arrived, and passed him by, and kicked off my shoes and put my hands and feet in the river, in fresh cool water, in the brown bottom muck

that was soft and smooth, that sucked the hot day out of my
fingers and soles, and charged them with mineral and vegetable
ease. I squatted down and threw scoops of water over my face,
and soaked my head repeatedly. I thought to myself: today I
can appreciate this river, I can give it my undivided love and be
refreshed. I'm going to get wet and clean, and I don't want to
go anyplace else, I want to stay right here and catch some fish.
Turning around to Yellow, stepping out of the river onto the
small grassy field at the bottom of the bank almost as steep as a
cliff, I saw somebody else, an old gray-headed man seated leaning against a big rock: the Doctor!

Not knowing what to say to him, I didn't, but I couldn't
help smiling with pleasure and surprise. That night with Jones
when I first met him, in the spring, his silences had seemed
strange and powerful, full of secret thoughts, and meanings
that were not appreciated by Jones and were beyond me. I'll
never forget how he vanished so suddenly down the street, in a
quick irrevocable glide toward the movies. And I was remark-
ing to myself, Now here he is again, just as sudden, and I kept
myself from laughing at the marvelous, I don't know why, because with these cats, laughter was very free. But I wasn't free
yet, to laugh on the least impulse, not having to explain myself
to my companions. Yellow handed me a line. I did like he did,
got a stout twig and tied it on for a bobber about eighteen feet
above the hook. He extended his fist toward me, and I cupped
my hand around it, and caught the cricket when he released it,
and baited my hook. And then I coiled the end of the line
around my left hand, took the bobber and cricket hook in my
right, and saw that nothing was snagged, and my rig hit well
out in the pool, I was happy with it, settled down maybe
twenty feet from Yellow's. I peeled out some line and walked

out of the edge of the water, and sat down on the bank, and lay back.

"River time . . ." called Feelgood.

After a while he got up and came down to where we were sitting and squatted down between us. And he had his good pipe in his hand! Yes indeed! My mouth began to water, and I forgot all about my line as my eyes hit on the thin column of smoke rising up, and my nose tuned in to that most delicious smell. We each took a turn, and then he handed me the pipe once more, and moved back to his comfortable spot against the rock. When I leaned to pass it over to Yellow, he waved the back of his hand by his smile, and I was left with the big live cup that was packed deep and running over with a breathtaking view! It was that same smoke I'd tasted once before. This was no street smoke, but something else. It was the best I'd ever had the honor of tasting. Back in Cambridge, I smoked some *black* brought home from the Ivory Coast by a Peace Corpsman, that was something. In the City I scored an ounce from a GI home from Vietnam, and that *jungle green* was out of sight. I've heard of one-puff smoke, but that didn't mean too much to me, because if you can get high on one, I always did want to smoke up a cloud and lose track and *see.* So I partook greedily of the Doctor's offering, and behind me I heard him laughing. Or was it in front of me that I heard the river flowing? And above and all around the leaves were whistling lightest notes pitched higher and softer than the insects! And there was no wind, so that the rustling of the leaf-skins together did not obscure this fluting, as if some gentle god-musician were blowing the pores of the plants. And I was slipped down into the grass, down into the earthbank, past any desire, with the line in my hand through which I could feel the meaningless and beautiful subtleties of the pool . . .

Bap! Somehow I felt it. Out of the corner of my eye I saw
Yellow's twig tilt straight up, and at once he was scooting down
the bank, and hand over hand hauling in his line that was
cutting the still surface of the water and spattering droplets in
every direction as he easily but surely brought up the fish. And
as the rainbow creature spent its fury in the shallows, another
hit mine! Gently I set the hook, and set to bringing in the prey
that had jumped to eat my cricket but was going to make my
dinner. In a few moments we had them both on shore, almost
exactly the same big saucer size, and I asked Yellow what he
called these fish. He said, "Sunnies."

"Yellow time . . ." laughed Feelgood. "Ho ho . . . Yellow
time . . ."

Yellow killed them quickly, he rapped their heads with a
short piece of pipe. He broke off handfuls of thick grass and
made a bed for the fish and covered them over with a blanket of
grass, almost as if he were laying them to rest, and then he
made many trips to the river and poured handcups of water
over them, for freshness. After the myriad leaps of the last moments — they peacefully slept in the earth surface and readied
themselves to be eaten by us.

Feelgood was wearing his same dark suit. With his hands in
his coat pockets, and his head tipped back on the rock, he
spoke, he let words go, like puffs of smoke, occasional, light,
and rising. "River like a window where you meet, you an the
fish . . . an you don know it, but that fish try to pull *you in!*
Ha! Time! Ha! . . . Yeah, time! . . . Hey son, bring me that
pipe . . ."

While we were catching the fish and preparing our lines
again, the pipe had gone out. I found it where I'd dropped it in
the grass and took it over to him, leaving my line in Yellow's
other hand. He didn't knock it out or clean it, but reached in

his inside pocket and took out another nice pinch of grass and packed it down with his thumb, and lit up. He smoked vigorously, with a cloud curling around his ears and hiding his face. I leaned over and got a breath of it going by. "I like to build a little fire, an let it die down, throw a heap on the coals an ev'body gather roun put their heads together," he said.

"Yeah!" I said. Wouldn't I love to see that day! Me, who was used to spitting on the tips of half-smoked joints, so as not to waste any, and hoarding roaches for another day when I didn't expect to have anything!

"But a pipe is nice when you travelin . . ."

I sat at his feet and smoked with him. I let Yellow take my line. When I got up once to take him some, the Doctor touched my leg, "He don want much," he shook his head. We sat there together and watched Yellow pick up a few more of the colorful "sunnies." Once, when he had two on at once again, I helped him pull one up. I had it at the edge of the water and was reaching down to grab it in my hand when somehow it broke free, and fluttered in the shallow mud, and sort of sidled away from me as I stabbed my hand at it, and finding a few inches of clear water, shot away, on its side, like a flatfish. Yellow was howling with laughter. He had his that he'd just caught in both hands, but I thought he'd lose that one too, he was laughing so hard.

"*Fish* time . . ." called Feelgood.

I looked at the several big smackers that Yellow was rearranging to make a place for the new one, and I helped him carry water. He always watered all the fish each time he caught another one. "Yellow, you sure are lucky when it comes to fishing," I told him. That seemed to please him. He looked proudly at me, and I was happy to've been able to find some-

thing to say to release me from my embarrassment at having
lost my fish; and I was even happier to've said something that
got *to* him what I felt. Because I never really met anyone like
him before I came down here to Meansville; and I never hardly
knew him, it seemed, before this day. And I admired this cat, I
was proud to be next to him.

"Now you right . . ." Feelgood had sat up straight and was
regarding me with a sharp eye. "Yellow lucky yeah! . . . He
luck cause he on his own way . . . He a luck cause he in his
own time an don know nothin bout it . . ."

If he was listening, he didn't have anything to add to this,
and he sure had no dispute or other idea about it. He was setting out the lines again. I didn't mind letting him do the work,
because I saw his fingers were so nimble. With but one good
leg, I bet he could handle half a dozen lines.

"Doctor, is a cow ever lucky?" I asked him, as I remembered
Jones' ideas about luck, and how the workmen had interrupted
us on the way to the site that day last winter in order to chase
the cow and her calf into the forest.

"Cow!" he said, glancing past me down to the water. "You
got some feed for her, you lucky," he smiled.

"No, Doctor, a cow havin a calf! I remember a time some
cats were chasin this cow with a baby calf half outa her — I
was chasin too, but I fell down an gave it up."

"Ha!" He peered at me closely. "Some get a force, if they
can lay a hand on. That mighty hard, less that cow know you.
An en you already lucky . . . What you think? *Birthin* . . .
for the baby it ain nothin *but* some luck! . . . Me . . ." He
puffed the pipe awhile. He handed it over to me, holding his
last full breath . . . He held it a very long time and shut his
eyes. When he opened them again and let out the breath,

didn't any smoke come out with it at all. "Me . . . all I need for some birthin luck is *think on it!*"

Yellow fell back on his neck, and his good leg shot up in the air. "Ooooh-hoooo . . . !" His foot twirled and he gave this kind of hoot of beauty or coo of triumph, and all three of us were thinking of nothing other than a baby calf being born and feeling good about it. And I can say this about luck: It all depends on how you measure it and what you want from it, but for me it's how I *feel,* and I must be lucky, because I damn sure was feeling fine! I was feeling so good, I was so high, I wanted to take another look at the fish, because that's always been a pretty sight to me, a mess of fat colorful good-eating fish. I crawled down to where they were and peeled the grass back. These were true pan fish — one for each pan. I peered closely at them and dug their coloration. The main markings were blue and green, but there were shapes of red and yellow, and their bellies white and silver, and there were browns and golden rims to the scales near the gills. And around the eyes, little streaks of pink and amber. And their tails examined from just inches away were like the tails of peacocks, mottled like feathers, the purples and browns and blues, with odd circles and numerous irregular bars. Yellow had alternated the fish so that they were head and tail and head and tail. They fit together best that way, in an almost solid row, overlapping. He'd caught seven or eight already — with my finger I counted them —

"One–two–three–four–" said Feelgood, "five–six–seven — eight times seven–fifty-six — seven–eight — ha-ha! Oh you count em, you can dive in the river — count em for the record book— put a number in your stomach! Ha! . . . You count stars in the sky from now on an skulls back through time if you had the way!" I stopped counting, I spread some grass back over the fish and looked up at him, but he didn't seem to be talking to me, he was looking in the sky. "Nothin wrong with that, till you fallin tween the threads a your handkerchief . . . Kings, presidents, earth swindles, boat rides . . . Time you see a man who seen too much for him but can't quit! Eyes like they in water, got his head stuck in it an lookin at you through . . . the ripples. He don hardly move no more — he order the fish! — 'Swim behin that weed!' Ha-ha . . . 'Bring me a crab with an armor on its eye!' Ha . . . Wipe his nose, fall through the kerchee with the salt drops . . . *Five–four–three–two–one!.... . two–three–four–five*.. . . In the grass, yeah, under the aerodrome now it ain hurrin . . . cross a white lye strip — make that . . . fall down, fall in a hole an climb out again — some kinda moth . . . A lot! Yeah, can't put no number on her . . . You wouldn't count the grass now — you could name each one separate . . . Too much . . ."

I couldn't completely follow what he was saying, but I must have picked up on a wave, and I started to think: if I could only lose the habit of counting and measuring! If I could get ideas of control and all the words out! And the stray crumbling syllables, that filled up my ear with all the phrases I've heard like alphabet soup on the brain that's been stirred too much. I might be able to relax and enjoy the world. I lay on my back, next to the immeasurable fish (you could count their scales!) and looked up through the long grass at the blue . . . Into my head now came sounds from my childhood — word-sounds from a private language I spoke as a child and made rules for and taught my friends — TEELEEPA-HONEE! DONUT AYN-SWER TA-HEE TEELEEPA-HONEE! NOBO-DWY HOMEE! — Everything pronounced phonetically with vowels long in this way, over the vacuum cleaner tubing we pretended was a walkie-talkie net-work, while we crawled through the rooms over the carpet-ing . . . I thought of speaking a few lines for the Doctor. I opened my mouth and shut it again. He didn't need any more evidence . . . I let go, I tried to let go and forget it, but the pages of textbooks filled my head with hieroglyph graphs and diagrams, and blackboards crammed and half erased and scrawled on again before the afternoon cleaning which was to be my punishment for talking and joking during lessons, the blackboards sliced through my brain with the scre-e-ech of a careless lady teacher's long fingernail. I washed the boards with a moist rag: and what a pleasure to watch complex mathe-matical theorems disappear under my hand! — The teacher had stepped out; I grabbed the globe and pitched it out a window. I took a match out of my pocket and lit the edges of a map of North America! But I heard her coming, I stepped out one door as she entered the other, and ran like hell! If I had time I would've taken care of the U.S.S.R. and north Asia, on the other wall . . .

I had somehow turned from my position straight up and down the bank, and suddenly I started rolling. I didn't try to stop, it felt so good and easy. I rolled and rolled until I hit the water, and there I lay, on my back in the cool sweet mud — so close to the blue sky I could take it in my arms, I could kiss it. I reached up my hands . . . When I was a kid, back in school, I had some questions that seemed so silly and childish to my school-sense that I never dared ask them. Like, why do people walk, why don't they roll? I mean, why did they get into this thing with their feet? Later I discovered the mysteries and pleasures of long running, but I never forgot my desire to roll . . .

The Doctor was standing next to me in the water. He'd taken off his shoes and rolled up his trousers, and every now and then he wriggled his toes making a small splash. He glanced down at me, solicitously I felt, but he never suggested I get off my back out of the muddy water. I think I really recognized his strange wisdom when he smiled, "I like to get down like you, but I jus ain that high . . . today . . . I got my damn *suit* on!" he went on, looking vexedly at the cloth that restricted him.

We weren't disturbing Yellow. A little action in the shallows doesn't bother the fish down deep. I had the feeling that if I just lay here long enough, as no straight-up-and-down-man ever would, some realization might come over me that in my "right" mind I'd always been denied. The Doctor stood next to me and splashed like he was a little kid. Nothing appeared in my mind but old memories and notions, around the awareness that he had some way prodded me to get beyond them, that included my times in Meansville right up to the present day. He hadn't exactly been speaking to me, he'd been riffing to himself, or something else, no man. And I'd cut him off with my own thoughts, he hadn't stopped talking, he was mumbling softly right now, I couldn't quite hear what he was saying. There was no reason to get up, and I didn't. Now and then I picked up another word or phrase, that I might only guess at or approximate now because I was someplace else, at the edge of my mind, and anything I heard had the effect of shooting me off near my own thoughts, faster and faster, until I fell out and in a flash, that quickly dimmed, perceived the water lapping my body and the sky. Finally I stopped listening, or he must only have been moving his lips. All I had were the simplest sensations, and I was in a very pleasant place. What I felt was nothing like knowledge, and I didn't think it was wisdom because I didn't think I could carry it with me to envelop other situations. At this moment I glimpsed the possibility of a time of my own. Simultaneously I was aware of the astounding lack of it. Perhaps the truth of the moment was that times only partly my own had led up to it, and now river time, grass time, green time surrounded me and my time that seemed fragmentary, always rebounding off and seeking inspiration from others. I lay in the mud and considered what I saw. Where did it lead? I saw that my future depended on luck more than any idea or ambition of my own, and this was not terrible — it was only slightly troubling — because it seemed to be true. I could see that my time was fragile and precarious as a fish's — and I thought again, what if it could be all my own? There was just no plan I had a desire to pursue, and so this relaxation by the river could appear to me as my fate. And how happy I felt, easing away from the right to keep up with Jones. But I had just gained some hope. I didn't move, I didn't think of rising. There was nothing to think anymore, no interpretation of what I was doing. I lay in the warm mud and looked up.

It was strange when Yellow caught a fish. Being half in and half out of the water, I understood both sides of the battle, and I could easily imagine there was as much chance of him being downed in the river as of the fish being upped into the air. And I felt indifferent to the outcome as if I was a fallen tree, and the tugging match that was going on around my roots and limbs affected me only very slightly, physically — but if the line caught on my hand or toe I might snap it just like that! An old tree in the water can't move, but it'll cut a line in a second, and so a fish always tries to snag a fisherman. At the last moment, this fish sought to escape by burrowing under my ankle into the

mud, but Yellow's careful hand removed him. We smiled at
each other, me and the winner, as many an old log has smiled at
other fishermen in their moment of triumph. Watching him go
up the bank with the fish, I smelled the good dinner that was
practically cooking and hoped I was going to be one of those
who would enjoy it. It occurred to me then that I wouldn't be
here in this wonderful, comfortable, and promising place, cooling off and looking forward to supper, if it hadn't been for
Yellow and his willingness to bring me along. A surge of gratitude half lifted me up. I sat up like to do something — and an
idea came into my mind: before the lock was on the door and
the landlord had confiscated every last thing in Jones' old crib,
I wanted to give the barber's chair to Yellow's friend the
barber. I never had heard anything from Case's friend in
Florida, and I'd rather give it away. I said, "Hey, you know I
got a barber's chair that Jones left behind. That was one thing
he couldn't sell, but it's in nice shape, it's a really nice chair.
Hey Yellow, would your friend the barber like another chair?"

"How you get here?" asked the Doctor, fixing me with a look
like he was surprised to see me.

"I rolled," I said, standing up.

"Ha-ha-ha-ha!" he laughed, and when I walked out of the
river so did he, and we walked up to where Yellow was pouring
water on the fish.

"How you arrive here in this here . . . Meansville?" asked
the Doctor.

"With the movement, Doctor — you know?"

"Huh! The movmen . . . That how you firs came?"

"Yep."

"I thought maybe you come here with you frien you call
Jones . . ."

"No — I was one of those freedom riders, remember?"

"Remember? All I do is walk in town an see em . . ."

"Oh yeah . . ." I didn't really think of the newcomers as good old freedom riders.

"I see y'all got your black policemen like you wanted," he said in a grouchy tone that I'd never heard before. "I don see why no movement want to get more *polices* — an a Negro police worse than a cracker, cause a cracker don know nothin bout no smoke, an a Negro know what us folks like to do, an he might jus be bad enough to snatch me . . . You all movemen ever think a that? . . ."

Well I never had. That was one of the main demands, and I never did think about it, or why it was one of the only demands that was ever met.

"Spies . . . Shit!" And I hadn't imagined Doctor Feelgood capable of this anger I heard in his voice now either.

"Be some nice fish for Miz Boket," said Yellow, passing by on his way with some water. "An some nice fishfry tonight," he smiled, coming over next to us. He began to coil his lines. He must have enough already. He untied the twigs from the lines and wound them up around his hand and hooked the hooks tight. And then he sat down by the fish that were under the wet grass, and Feelgood sat down too and breathed a big sigh. As I sat down, I felt obliged to say, "Well I'm for the movement, but I couldn't go along with it forever."

"If you like the river, you stay by her," said Yellow.

Feelgood lit his pipe and passed it. "Son," he said, "you been a movemen, but I'm gonna tell you somethin: the Negro peoples *is* free! . . . You don see that, do you, but they free just like you! . . . What you got there?" He was pointing at me . . . He was pointing at nothing but my balls. In a deep true voice, he said, "I know I'm free! . . . Can't nobody — can't no leader — can't no president tell me this man *here* ain free! . . ." He opened his arm and put the back of his hand on Yellow's chest, who smiled. "If you think you ain free, then you gon try to do things to *get* free, an the more you try, the more set you is in your way a bein not free . . . Don you see that? But now if you *be* free, then that is how you gon act, cause you ain think a how you act, cause you jus *walk on out!* Like the river here — it don ever stop — it stay so still . . ."

The sun was drying out my clothes. I stretched around so it could get at all sides. Yellow had pulled a heavy string out of his pocket and he was winding it through the gills of the fish. He had a lot of fish there. He laced about a dozen on the string, and piled the moist grass over them again. "These here I carry to Miz Boket," he told Feelgood. And he pointed to about as many that remained, "An these here we gon fry tonight an eat em, I hope you come, suh."

"I be happy," said Feelgood.

"I know you come cuz I know you like some fish," Yellow smiled at me.

"Yeah, I'm stickin with you, Yellow," I told him. Every time I puffed the pipe, I started laughing, because I felt so good. And I was going to eat good tonight, thanks to lucky Yellow! We were all chuckling and puffing, and even Yellow was having some more to smoke. I told Feelgood, "Doctor, I don't know too much about anything except how I feel, an I tell you, with you cats, I feel free."

"Thank you," he said.

"When I left the voter drive, I felt kinda free, an I got into this construction business with Jones, you know . . . Pretty soon I felt tied up again — plenty money, but I can see it now, I didn't usually feel too good . . .   Lately man, I been feelin *bad* . . ."

"You sposeta feel good when you got somethin, an also when you got *nothin*. If you gon worry bout how to get somethin, when it come your way you ain know how to enjoy . . ."

"Yeah, I woulda sold this barber's chair if I knew somebody to buy it — an I love to sit in it too, just sit and relax, but I woulda sold it . . .   But I'm glad I didn't! If your friend would really like to have it, Yellow."

Feelgood said he knew a man with a truck if I wanted to give it away right now. Yellow said the barber had two sons who'd help us get it down. Suddenly we were all in motion, up the bank. Feelgood ran back down again and got the fish on the stringer, and smoothed the grass over the rest to protect against another couple hours sun and air. He was going to send these right out to Mrs. Boket, he said, and not have to worry about it later. After we took care of the business of the chair we'd come back here and clean these others up and head on over for dinner.

We took a path that led to a road that paralleled the river, and we walked down it together a ways. Soon Yellow and I took a cut that led straight away toward the downtown section, and we left Feelgood headed down the river to his friend, the owner of the truck. We made one stop at the barber's to tell him the good news. It pleased me terrifically to hear Yellow tell him in his direct few words, to see the man's mouth drop open with nothing to say but some stutterings of wonderment. I saw how he looked at Yellow, such a look of astonishment and faith confirmed, and that's how I felt too, and that was why he was going to get the expensive chair as a present. He got on the phone and told his two sons: Drop everything. I told him which project it was and which apartment. He wanted us to wait for his sons to stop and give us a ride. But it was only a few blocks from here, and we went ahead and walked. I would've liked to ride Yellow in the elevator, but I never went in the front, to avoid a confrontation with the landlord's rent man. In the pad that was barren now of everything but the chair and the bed, I paced the floor and just looked at the walls, thinking this place was soon to go out of my experience. I sat in the chair and enjoyed it for the last time — but Yellow stayed glued to the window. He looked and looked. And I thought, this may be the highest up off the ground this cat has ever been, because he can walk miles with that bad leg but I don't think he can climb a tree. I went over and stood next to him, and just being near him enjoying so much made me savor the familiar view too.

"You ever think a flyin, Yellow? Not in an airplane either, no sounds an no *glider*, nothin! Free flyin! . . . You're in the air, look all around . . . Look at the people, so little, look at the patterns that the ground makes . . . Everything you feel around you is air! An you're warm as toast because the sunshine!"

His eyes gazing down out that window looked like behind them was some kind of rush. The effect of the idea I gave him was like he took off. Reflected in his eyes was a veinwork of light as he floated through the glass and revolved toward the sun. The young men sent by the barber came, and we carted the beautiful chair downstairs and out back. Feelgood showed up, driving the old truck himself, and we set the chair up on it. We didn't tie it down, as it was only a few blocks. I walked around to the side of the building and looked up. Pressed against the glass up three stories, Yellow's face showed a kind of rapture. I waved at him, and he waved back, but I couldn't get him to come down. Feelgood said leave him be, and we piled in the truck without him and drove down the alley to the barber's corner. Now he was sure he couldn't believe his own eyes! It was in a better condition than either of his two old chairs. We set it down inside, and he sent one of his boys running to a mechanic who would help him drill the floor and bolt it down. It looked nice already, just leaning up against a wall. The barber told me, "Anytime you want a cut, you know where to come. I useta cut some white boys' hair in the service, I know how." He was peering at it right now, but I was liking it long, and I didn't have to please anybody these days. I thanked him, but walked out of the shop, while he worked his scissors in the air. "You got any frien need a cut, you sen him over," he called after me. "You sen the whole movemen to me! I'll trim em nice!"

Well, the movement was going to get a little credit out of this too. I was happy. The Doctor and I drove back to Jones' place, and went upstairs. Yellow hadn't budged.

twenty-six

THE FISHFRY was in CME, in a backyard on the very block where Knight's mother lived. Cara Lee was there, and she was surprised and embarrassed to see me. Mine was a delicate position. But I was just as friendly as I could be, having not been by to see her in so many months. It wouldn't have surprised me if she'd been cold and aloof, but unbelievably as the evening passed she warmed up. I figured I owed everything to Feelgood and Yellow. Mae was there too, and even she was pleasant. She looked from me to the Doctor as if she couldn't quite understand how we had ever come to know each other, but she accepted it. Yellow and the Doctor were favorites among the people gathered here, and the fact I showed up with them cooled out any tensions that might've got started, owing to my past in this community. I saw some people I recognized — a few kids. I tried to get some news of Knight, but nobody seemed to know anything. A few boys were glad to talk about him, and his famous exploits that were legend among them. But when I said something to Cara Lee, she told me right away I'd better forget about it and I'd do better not mentioning him or those times, because they'd had some peace since he'd been gone, and nobody wanted to remember trouble. The way she said it — her eyes flashed and her lips pouted for a second — I got the message, and it might include me too, if I was the same person I used to be. I never said another word about him, hero of the CME drifters and angry young boys. I didn't refer to the past, but to the fish which we'd caught that afternoon. The firm, flaky meat was good in our mouths; it was all in my favor, that I'd come with the contribution. Plates of fish and fried potatoes and pitchers of tea were set on two long tables right back of the kitchen door. Empty vessels were quickly replaced with filled ones by Mae and the other ladies in charge. A stout man in a T-shirt was sweating over an open pit, frying the fish in three big skillets. I saw a couple preachers, and there were a lot of old sisters having the best kind of time, and dozens of little kids darting and flying. At the peak there must've been a hundred and fifty people jammed into the yards, under the trees. I was as relaxed and happy as I'd been in a long time. I was so thankful I'd found Yellow, or he'd found me — I was no longer sure how in the world we had met, but the day had changed all around since I'd been in his company. The feeling at this picnic was so easy and friendly — it was as if his calm, good spirit prevailed underneath, like a root, that allowed it all to happen so peaceful. At first he was seated off to one side on a folding chair. The Doctor was mingling with people, mostly the ladies. These cats had connected me to the sweetest strain of my past in Meansville, and I was reveling in it, laughing with the kids, and following Cara Lee from place to place in the rolling party scene. There were dozens of fine-looking chicks, all ages, and some were shy and some were not. The feeling of the church was here, and the movement spirit. I was noticing how my presence put some off and drew others near, but mostly no one paid me any mind, as I kept trying to talk to my old girl friend or at least keep my eye on her. There was at least one other cat with the same idea, and I didn't miss the hostile looks he was giving me, but I was so high, it didn't get to me. So it surprised me, it brought me down when she suddenly whispered to me that she had to go, that I should come by and see her sometime, but she had something to do tonight. And there she went. She'd disappeared before I could think of protest. And I should've known it, but I was disappointed. I stood there near the fish tables, and couldn't get my mind together, to do anything. But I found my cool — I just stood there, real cool, with my natural hopes, like the climax of the fine day, shattered.

When I went to look for my friend Yellow and the Doctor, I got another shock. They were nowhere around. I asked Mae, and she told me Yellow was likely over at somebody's house, she named a name, but it didn't mean anything to me. When I asked her about Feelgood, she gave me a blank look. I realized she didn't know who I meant, though I'd seen her talking with him. He must not be named Feelgood. Where did I get that idea anyhow? "You don mean Doctor Simson, do you?" asked Mae. "He gone on home, I reckon." I didn't know. That must be him, but strangely I didn't ask her any more, I didn't make sure. "You done put us down in CME," she said. No, I said. I wondered what she meant — I thought she was glad I'd gone away. She was looking at me kindly. I remembered the Mae of my first days in CME, trying to give me good advice about survival. I was getting sad — it was time to go. I told her I'd probably be by sometime if she didn't mind. I started walking, I hadn't decided where to go, it was already late.

I was tired and I felt bad. I found my steps leading me toward Jones' apartment, and I guess I didn't feel like anything but sleeping. The old crib was the one place where I was sure of solitude. But I couldn't get free of my thoughts, which began tending toward the memory of my time with Jones. Strange, but the events of the afternoon hadn't so much relieved me of consideration of thief images as they had reminded me of them and catalyzed new ones. I found myself trying to recall what I might have learned from the Doctor this afternoon, that is what profit I might have reaped. That wasn't right. Under the night sky, I felt cold and mean, not good enough for the likes of Cousin Yellow and the Doctor. (Oh yes, Mae knew the Doctor, the church was here.) With Jones, I'd become cold and contemptuous of people. Like him, I'd come to feel that I could even do without people, I was that strong, or that bad. This afternoon I had felt good and comfortable by the river, but now I couldn't help suspecting that all I'd been doing was trying to bum something off somebody. That it would be impossible to steal anything from the Doctor I didn't realize; that the afternoon had been as open and friendly as it had seemed at the time, my depressed mood couldn't remember. I didn't take the elevator, I walked up the backstairs. There was always the chance of seeing somebody, although most of the apartments in the building were unrented; and I didn't want to see anybody. I'd never much thought about the fact that there were few people to be seen around this building. I guess it had been built in advance of demand. But since Jones lived here, it had seemed natural, like his steel structures that might fall over before they were put to use by anybody. When I did see anybody around the place, it was always a surprise. But I didn't want to chance it. I walked up and entered the apartment, and didn't turn on any lights. I sat down by the window and looked out over sparsely-lit night Meansville. Memory of the afternoon stung me like thought of a lost heaven. In reality, of course, the time had been pleasant and at moments profound, but now in the despair perhaps caused by losing my friends at the fishfry, I doubted I would ever achieve such fantastic green peace again. I caught sight of the empty space by the wall where the barber's chair had stood. Had I only been trying to win them over with a solid gift when I'd let the barber have it? But I'd felt just plain generous. — Who? Jones' boy generous? — I couldn't believe in myself. I thought all I wanted was some new friends with some good smoke and knowledge of the river. That this didn't affect what had happened, where I'd got to, or what I'd been given, I didn't see. In a way I guess, I felt worse than Jones, who didn't pretend. I remembered the sketches I'd done of him and my life as his sidekick on the job, on the corner. They were hidden right here under the mattress. I got them out and examined them. They might not have been bad. They might have contained humor or even love, but all I could think of was my intention in having undertaken writing them. And that was to get back, to steal from Jones. Perhaps I'd compromised or desecrated the possibility of my writing anything for real, or even writing itself. For a moment I felt slight exhilaration as I quickly read the evil document I would destroy. Then I put a match to it. I burned the pages on the tiled floor of the shower.

In a frenzy or a dream I got up and went downstairs, outside. Dazed by my own furious destruction, I walked clear back to CME to compound it. Of my relationship to this part of town and to its leading citizen, Knight Collins, all I could remember was that I'd tried to get something out of it by writing it down.

And I knew it was better than that. It was real and inimitable, the rebellion of Knight was unwritten history, to some extent a part of the folklore of the region, at least among the youngest generation. Without waking anyone, I crept around Cara Lee's and Mae's house in CME and found my notes of my early days in Meansville that I'd written during my strange wait in this home while Knight settled his business with Jack and in effect took the blame for the burning of the car and the Coca-Cola factory. Somehow I'd escaped from that time. I couldn't re-read these notes, it was too dark. All I could think was that I'd profaned those brave times and tried to steal from them. I knew I had a book in my mind and that would be a multiple larceny. With a light, good feeling in my heart, I walked to the alley with the papers in my hands. I found a little hidden place where the bushes were dense, and set fire to them. I felt better as I walked back to the apartment. A nice drowsiness was over-taking me and I knew I'd sleep well. But in the morning I felt worse.

With my back against the poolroom window, I waited to see what would happen. A light inside made the glass glow. I was in its red aura, along with Joe China, smoking. Like others on this street, leaning on parking meters and parked cars, balanced on the curbstones and stationed in doorways, sustained by neon figures in the air, the music floating everywhere and the hope-giving traffic of the purposeful and fortunate people, I was counting on a blessing from above that could come out of any-where — cold and ready, scorning modesty —

Above the broad red band in the poolroom glass, there were painted advertisements for King Edward cigars, with little pic-tures of the King, and Red Rose Snuff, with a line of decorous roses; and below it in a maroon strip, Budweiser was claimed king of beers with a few gold stars. It was a beautiful window, a picture for my idleness or patience. The stoplight at this corner was always fierce dark red when my eye crossed it. I felt like a young fish under a log, almost motionless, in wait for the smallest particle on the surface of the water. Looking to beg, Jones would say understandingly. His memory lingered, separating me from the others here who admired his successes but resented his hostile jive. He could have been a hero on the corner, outwitting and bleeding whitey, if out of the same cold heart he hadn't despised and defrauded his own blood (never admitting that's who they were). From Jones I learned hardness of spirit. It was just barely equal to his arrogant legacy I had to deal with now. When I first came around here, considered to be with the movement, I would often drink because of the generosity of some rich hustler. Many people buy liquor having nobody in particular to drink it with. I enjoyed my poverty. All I wanted to do was get high. That was how I met Jones. When you don't have anything, you know it, and I knew it by my lightness of mind, digging ease, on a windowledge, anywhere.

> Say "It's all right!"
> It's all right!
> Say "It's all right!"
> It's all right!
> It's all right to have a good time,
> Cause it's all right,
> Woa it's all right!

Jones seemed just like one of a generous crowd, as if there were plenty of others who were waiting to be friendly. But now I was always waiting. The wait might be long or not.

Then there was another. If I couldn't sell a few reefers, I might not eat. I kept thinking I should be able to fill up the spaces with a better mood, if not a more ingenious game. Without Jones, I didn't do so well. I was just on the corner, without the edge of being a newcomer or an outsider anymore. It seemed like there were less people on the street.

Angel came out a door, and beckoned me over. I went to her to see what it was; she wanted to know if I had a dollar on me. That's just what I had; what a day, I thought, as I gave it to her. But she wanted me to come back in the bar with her. In the little bar, we drank a bottle of wine. She wanted to sing. The bartender was a friend of hers and appreciated her voice and style. So did I, and I liked her stories too. I liked it when we were high and she sat there said nothing, just smiling. Angel and I had an understanding, that may've been love. Her flavor was always there, in my taste for this place. When I was really down, I would find her, and she always wanted to help. But we had our lives to live, she with more zest than I these days — and she had her living to make. And as long as she did that, I wasn't going to starve, was I. With her looks, I was okay, my crafty spine was thinking, but it saddened me sometimes. About the time I might see her drinking with somebody I didn't even know, I felt bluer than cool, but that's the way it was, and she never confessed any pain on this score, and neither did I, only need of money or some loving.

I walked her partway home, to the motel where she stayed. She was going to have a bath before supper. That was Angel. She enjoyed her leisure. Without Jones, this life was getting dull. Without her, I thought, it might turn to ice.

Then, on my way back to the corner, I saw the old man, Dr. Feelgood or Dr. Simson, whatever his name was, my friend. He was walking down the street in a direction away from the movie theater, and I figured that's where he'd been. I ran after him.

"Hi Doctor! Was the movie any good?"

He recognized me and smiled, but took a quick look behind me, as if to see who else might be with me.

"Same," he said, starting to walk again. But he didn't seem to mind if I walked along with him. "How I watch, tilt my head any way, run the soun backward — crack the egg — let the colors spill roun. Story soun to me in letters you ain ever heard. But I can turn off my hearin . . ."

I couldn't, I knew, and I was silent. I wished I could turn it off sometimes. Even in the silence I heard sirens and distant shouts. We walked in the darkness downhill toward the river. We passed Little Joe's Music House, and I saw a light coming from Slim's through the cut. We passed the burned block of wino bars where we used to pick up the crew in the morning and walked down one of the forks in the road into the wastelands. I thought he must live by the river here. No light from the sky tonight, but the stillness was big and hollow and I could barely hear the sound of the current itself. The road was curving beside the river, which could only be felt. Small houses appeared. I never knew anybody lived down in these lands where the dump started, and auto graveyards filled the air up with wreckage. I never walked down this far to find out. Here were seventy or eighty houses on the river side of the road and half a dozen cross streets, sending the woods back a hundred yards, and as we walked along they thinned and soon they were just a scattered few shacks on the edge of the vast cleared claylands, in the center of which was the dump. At one of the last ones he stopped. He told me to go stand by some trees across the road. A dim light showed at the door, and he went inside. Minutes passed, and now I wondered what the hell I was doing out here on the edge of the woods, waiting in the dark for this old man Jones had taken as a joke. Yes, Jones missed some things. Softly I laughed to myself. It was a taste of that oracular smoke I remembered him by, that's what I was waiting for, and I'd do well to be honest with him soon's he came out. But immediately I knew that wasn't quite it, or it wasn't all of it. Cries of kids playing night games in the long valley playground of the dump carried to my hiding place. In truth, I didn't know what it was I was waiting for, and I had the feeling this had happened many times before. I was always waiting for people and then following them into things. This was my way. But waiting for the old man made me think these thoughts . . .

When he came out, a lady took a step out of the doorway with him, she waved and then called something to him while he walked to an old car parked beside the next house on the road. After a while he got her cranked up, and as he backed out the woman returned inside. He had some trouble getting the car out of reverse and kept backing up in little spurts four or five times. Then he got into first and rolled slow up to where I stood.

"Sorry to leave you stan out there," he said. "Some folks take a compliment I bring a white man by they place, others don mind — an some leery . . ." I got in. "Ride you anywhere?" he asked.

In second gear we were moving down the road behind some weak headlights. Quickly I said, "Doctor, I wonder if I could get some a that smoke a yours that was so good — I got a couple dollars." More than that I wanted to listen to his talk again, like the afternoon by the river. But I couldn't quite say that.

"Hmm!" he smiled, "I don sell no smoke . . . But I sho do like to give some away . . ." He laughed a little while, more to himself. "C'mon with me an we'll smoke some," he said. I was immediately happy. He gave it like a true present. I never met anybody friendly as he was with smoke. We were on a road out of town in a direction I had never traveled, a river road. I sat back a bit and found myself enjoying the drive. We passed some big decaying mansions, their massive grandeur all falling in with time. Somebody was living in them though; I saw wash strung up on a balcony and, glancing back, I saw, behind one of them, cooking fires. And beyond them lay the dump; in the darkness, the razed claylands stretched on and on. I guess they figured their town was going to grow and grow until one day it's big enough for this fantastic empty hole here. When it finally did stop, woods took up. And then a small cemetery; and after that there wasn't much else to be seen on this road.

"Yeah, we get a smoke when we get home," said Feelgood, coming out of a reverie that had his head drooped down to the wheel, eyes narrowed, picking out the road. "In the *swamp* I get it," he smiled, and with a twinkle in his eye added, "I know you probably think it gotta be from New York, New Orleans, to be right . . . Shit! Some folks don talk bout it they know where to fin it. Yeah . . . I go in the swamp!"

When I thought of a swamp, I thought of a lot of mud and bad bog. I remembered passing by those gloomy marshlands to get out to the job each day with Jones, and it only made me look forward to the heights on the steel. I remember hearing someplace about good grass growing on hillsides in the good air to have best head qualities, and it didn't have to have a Mexico-

New Orleans label on it, no, that wasn't what I looked for, and
it sure didn't have to have a New York City-Maf smell on it — I
gave it *my* test, ha-ha! Now I was laughing to myself and
I thought, Now how did I know where good grass grew? And I
thought, Even being with this old customer gave me a high. I
said, "Doctor, I never been to a swamp, I just looked at em from
the outside. But I remember that smoke of yours, yeah, I *remember* that smoke!"

We laughed that good laugh. We were quite a ways out of
town, and the road was growing thin. I didn't know he lived
way out in the country. Suitcase said he lived in a shack down
by the river, and I had a picture of that in my mind. But I
didn't know anything about this road that was curving and
twisting beyond my sense of geography. The night air was cool
in town, but it was nicer out here. It was refreshing to ride
away from the neon lights, all that fast walking of the street,
and idling at the coolest and the hottest spots. I'd always
wanted to get out in the country with its grasses and shade
trees, and here I was, on that slight road, even if it was almost
the middle of the night. But as quick as I felt happy, I wondered how I was going to stay. And that made me angry at
myself, and I thought, Oh yeah, Jones, already trying to figure
out the scene and how to hang on! I coughed, and spit out the
window, and breathed in the fragrant air, and breathed out,
coughed again, had a little bad coughing spell . . . and got
out my handkerchief and wiped off my face.

Dr. Feelgood stopped the car, and got out, and I followed
him. He went and sat under a big tree that hung over the road
right before us, in its deep shadow. "Look here — sit down, I
like to sit by this tree, cause it keep some good air under it. I like
to smoke and breathe, you know?" he said; and I sat. "I taken it

in my hand a handful an lit up, an breathe! Anytime you want some smoke, boy, jus tell me — don ask . . . I don come in town too often, you may have a walk . . . That a be good for you too. I like to make a stop or two for a rest, drive that ol machine," he explained. After a silence, he said, "Look here, I love to give you some plant — you can give somethin back . . ." He half closed his eyes and he brought his hands up together, so the index fingers were together in front of his eyes, and then he had a good stretch as if to clear his mind. "Don see me wrong! Firs I gotta try to tell you somethin . . . Ain gon be easy less you let your min travel, turn a turn with me . . ." With his finger he drew a circle in the air, and then with his other hand he drew a complex shape with many angles and curves, and then he stood, and drew his hand in the air and found a branch that dipped low and ran his fingers through the leaves. "Here the power. Baby know that, watch a baby, how he look at a leaf. He see the . . . termenda plant, power . . ." He sat again and looked closely at me. "This ain gon be easy cuz I know who you are . . . but I see some other things . . . You don know what I do, but some cats probly tol ya — *me!* root man! Root doctor! Naw, they lots a fakes. Ain too many old enough to know! See a doctor — he drive some fine car — he *big!* I'm little, see how small . . ." Running his hands in the forest loam beneath the tree that caked the road right to the middle, where a little moist clay showed, letting the tiny berries and slivers of the soil fall off the backs of his thumbs — he picked one. On his hands and knees — on the tip of his finger he held it out. I had to look close to see, I got my eye to about one inch away, and I don't know what tiny fraction of a measurement would size that split seed, of a fine wild grass, that he showed me. "The power here, but us human peoples . . . in a

funny shape . . . man! I try to help, an I do . . . Times, you
gotta be *like* folks, if you wanna help em, an folks ain got sense
a where the power, times you gotta *help* em to feel! You see?"

I was following him in my way, but I couldn't make too
much of what I followed, and kept quiet.

"Naw not yet . . ." He looked at me. "It don matter.
C'mon, it time," he said, and rose. In the car again he said,
"What I do, I got fame, cuz I help a woman to have a
child . . . Some people comin clear from the coast tonight,
from . . . near Savannah. You can help me help em."

I'd do anything I could to help. But what that might be I
sure didn't know. What he was talking — no, I was ignorant,
and humble. In the dark — we suddenly pulled up in front of a
bus!

A *bus!* A big old rusted orange school bus parked perpendic-
ular to the road and back from it a ways. He got out, and I got
out too, and astonishedly admired the long vehicle that looked
very strange there in the woods. And behind it was a house of
unpainted gray wood. In my amaze — I walked away from
Feelgood to the side, to the extreme of the cleared indentation
in the woods in which the house was built. The bus was rolled
right back on the house where a porch, maybe, should have
been. The house was a shotgun house like many, three maybe
four rooms in a line without a hall. The Doctor was going in
the bus. That made me smile, seeing him go in the door of the
bus like the front door of his house. I walked right after him.
"Watch ya step!" he called and laughed. I saw I did have to
watch it, the landing was almost rusted through. I jumped up
inside, and made my way down the aisle between the seats. I
sat down in the last one in the corner by the window. Looking
out into the dark clearing, I felt wildly happy. I got up and

walked through the back door of the bus over some boards into the front room which was furnished with a small bed and several chairs and a little table by the bed. There was a fireplace, and on one wall was a picture of a lake and some forest, and one little boat on the lake; and a plaque with an inscription or a poem scripted on it that I didn't stop to read. In the next room was nothing but some blankets and thin pallets strewn around the floor and an open closet with a few clothes hung in it. He wasn't in the kitchen either, the last room back, so I walked out on the back stoop. He handed me a glass of water and dipped one for himself from a wide wooden bucket, and replaced the round wood cover, and pushed the bucket back under the house which I realized was set on short stilts, solid chunks of wood that raised the house two, or two-and-a-half feet above the ground, like Cara Lee's house on its cinderblocks. Then he sat down on the step and lit up the pipe — his same good pipe I remembered from the day by the river. He got a couple good puffs on it and handed it to me, and I smoked with love of the weed and pleasant expectation . . . Ahhhhhh! Haaaah! Yes it was! Ha-ha! Yes indeed, the same! With the fine wild perfumey taste in my nose — I jumped up, though I didn't have anything in mind.

"Sit down," he said. I did, I back-jumped onto the porch and sat there swinging my legs off it. He got up and went inside and momentarily came back with a black bag which he set on the porch by the door. He motioned me over — he handed me a couple kitchen matches, said, "When I call you . . . bring my bag, all right? And light this here candle an bring it." On the kitchen table was a tall white new candle in a metal holder with a little finger grip on it. Something was about to start. I didn't know what. I listened to his simple instructions, and

nodded that I understood. If that was all there was to it . . .
"Walk real slow, with dignity, when you come," he said. He
went inside and returned with an old dark suit like his own and
handed it to me. "Put this on," he said. Smiling, he
disappeared into the house. Through the doorways I watched
him proceed into the front room, and then shut that last door
behind him. Finding I still had the pipe in my hand, I began to
smoke again. A little coal was still alive and I puffed it up to
strong life and savored the good fumes . . . And the gardens
that began to grow! In the back of his house, taking up the
clearing, row upon row of leafy vegetables and strange plant
shapes receded into the dark and the trees. Pipe in hand, I
went for a walk amongst them. I could recognize cabbages and
tomato plants and in a corner a modest stand of corn; the leafy
tops of the rest I just enjoyed without naming. I took off my
shoes and threw them back toward the house. The lines of the
greens weren't straight at all, they were gentle curves, undulat-
ing toward the manifold forest like mottled snakes at rest. The
leaves were dry and cool against my ankles. I opened a small
head of lettuce, and peeled off a few leaves and munched them
as I walked out of the garden along the woods to the side of the
yard and got another gaze at the whole setup — bus, house,
and garden. The bus was just that type with the snout-nose
hood, like the old high school track team used to travel in. And
those were my old high school colors! — the bus and the house
— orange and gray . . . and the green of the fields we ran
. . . What a space I'd traveled since those days! No, *drifted*
was the better word. As always, it best described my movement. But if chance had got me out here, I liked where I was
more than anyplace in my memory, and I hardly knew where I
was. But I may have never known where I was, and if this

place was strange, it was warm and green . . . and orange. Yes, I'd seen a bit since I'd ridden to track meets in a bus like this one. I'd been down different paths, and seen different ways, and been somehow captured by them and carried along within them by an energy they'd released. But I kept hitting walls, dead ends . . . I kept spending the last of a certain energy or enthusiasm, or coming to the end of an idea. I wanted to get *through*. Where was *I?* There was something about the Doctor, and Cousin Yellow too, that made me think they might help me find an answer . . . I was pondering such thoughts when I heard a car on the road. For a moment I almost felt like running.

Sticking close to the trees, I quickly walked back into the garden; and then I cut for the back porch. Without wasting a moment, I jumped into the suit, which was too big. I could hear the car stopping out in front, and the doors softly close. I had to light one of the matches the Doctor had given me in order to find my shoes. As there was flame left, I relit the pipe. But it didn't affect my nervousness. It felt like nothing other than a play that was about to start, for which I'd received a terse briefing, but there'd been no rehearsal, nor had I even seen the stage. The trousers were way too long, and it hardly mattered that I'd found my shoes. This was no play! I picked up the Doctor's bag and went into the kitchen. I sat in a chair, breathed deeply, and tried to settle down.

The bag was old black leather with a flap that buttoned down like a medical doctor's or a professor's. I wondered what was in it, but I wasn't going to look and mix up the vibrations. He'd show me if he wanted to show me, I thought, as I realized how easy it'd be for me to open up and inspect. But I just sat there, and a lot of time went by. I wondered what was going on up in front, and what I'd walk into. I couldn't hear a thing but the insects in the night.

When the door that I was keeping my eye on opened, Feelgood called softly, "My bag please, and a light . . ." And shut the door again. With my fingernail, to be as quiet as possible, I split the phosphorous of the match head, and the flame I let explode around the wick. I picked up the bag and the lighted candle, and walked very slowly and soberly through the middle room, praying the flame wouldn't go out, worrying how I was going to open the door — with my foot? I hated the thought of having to call for him, I might just make it through this thing without messing up if only I didn't have to think too much or say anything. Because I felt kind of unbelievable. And the Doctor had explained it to me, I knew, and in the effective drama of the fertility blessing, I had my role — and yet . . . I didn't feel real. Maybe the next one of these I'd be better — but to my relief he pushed open the door for me, and stood aside. He had put on a tie to go with his suit, and some tinted spectacles. He pointed to the bedside table and I walked toward it. I was staring right at the candle flame so as not to catch anybody's eye, and with my peripheral vision I was staring at this delicate chick laid back on the bed. If she opened her eyes she wouldn't catch me eyeing her. I placed the bag down on the table. "Hold the light please," he instructed me, while he opened his bag. The dim light I was adding a candle to came from a kerosene lamp by the window. She hadn't opened her eyes yet. She was light-boned and very relaxed. She hadn't moved a muscle. For my part, I imagined her giving birth to a son, and in my strange dream he was mine. I was holding the flame perfectly steady and not breathing. The shadow of the burning candle on the wall didn't move. But my eyes were creeping over. Out of his bag he selected a bottle of an amber fluid, and taking a few drops on his fingertips he anointed her inner parts. He spread the rose skin, and gently rubbed in it. He took a few drops more and soaked her good. He went in his bag again and brought out what looked like a little round berry, golden brown in color, and this he carefully set right above the tiny bump where it stuck. Now her head tipped back, on a sharp angle on her thin neck, and then it came up and she flashed her eyes. I was glad I wasn't looking at her, but at the flickering shadow of the candle on the wall. He reached out and shut her eyes with his hand. Out of his pocket he pulled an old black Bible with markers in it, and began to read about olive trees, and the bearing of the fruit, and the oil, and he read some beautiful lyrics about a woman. He held the book in one hand and took her hand in the other. Expressions flowed like water over her closed face, memory's configurations. "You the receptacle, an the bowl a creation woman *you*," he named her again and again in a voice growing more forceful. He seemed to seek to caress her with identity of the words. She gave a little gasp when the berry started slowly rolling down, straight down, adhering amazingly. Feelgood leaned over and blew out the candle. "Thank you," he whispered to me, and I went out with the smoking wick.

Maybe because my eyes weren't blinded by the candle and by the need to keep it alive as I walked, on my way back through the middle room I saw a man seated in a chair next to the wall. I saw him with the side of my eye and I didn't stop staring straight ahead as I strode through the kitchen out onto the back porch and into the land. I took off my shoes again and left them by the stoop, and rolled up my pants' cuffs and headed through the greens. I sat down at the edge of the corn

patch, partly in it, in my dark suit, and laughed a little. I
wished I had my handkerchief to wipe the sweat off my face. I
had to use my hand. I laughed for joy — that that cat didn't
follow me out to fight me. I guess he believed in the Doctor
too . . .

It seemed like he knew what to say to make somebody feel
good. It didn't take much for himself, so he had a lot of energy
for receiving other messages and making his reply, hoping to
free a body from a fear into its own time. I guessed that when
she left, possibility would have changed to likelihood, or probability became certainty in her mind. I thought of the berry
rolling down — and I knew she could do it and sent her my
luck through the air. Yeah Jones, old buddy, look at this here!
I addressed one side of myself: How'd you get here if it wasn't
by the luck of your life? Not by any cleverness that's for sure.
And damn if I didn't feel good, sitting in the garden, with a few
stars peeking out of the clouds now, and the greens growing
and glowing all around me. In my world . . . with my dream
. . . I tried to help her baby that would soon begin to live,
and I sent my luck to her man in the waiting room. Soon they'd
step out of the Doctor's office and start home to Savannah, but
they wouldn't be alone.

Later he appeared on the stoop, and I walked the forty yards
to greet him, and I felt fine in the old suit and my bare feet on
the new land. After the curving garden ended, I kept walking
S's and Feelgood laughed. He'd taken off his coat, but he still
had the same tinted specs on. He had refilled the pipe, and he
sat there with it between his teeth. "Well, you did your part.
Them people is all right. They trustin folks to begin
with . . ."

"I know *I* feel good," I said, nevertheless getting a hit on the fresh pipe. "Yessir! Doctor Feelgood!" I grinned at him.

But he scowled back, and then his light laugh broke up the scowl, but it hung in his eyes and even his smile. "You call me that! That name took some routes since it was a good old name. I *use*ta have that name . . . Well I see you mean right . . . Ha-ha! I see you like some good smoke . . ."

I was amazed at his embarrassment. It was a beautiful title, to me.

"Well . . ." he rose and stretched, "well . . ." he walked out in the yard and regarded the ground and the sky. "You make y'self at home an rest if you like," he gave me that good night, and walked inside, and on into the front room. But I had too much energy yet to sleep. No, I felt like running some! I walked around the house, unpainted country temple; I passed the bus and began to jog in the cool dust that ran down the road. A breeze blew at me, which is one of the fine effects of running. And I built up speed, and my brain plied the air humming with the speedsounds of the rocks and streaked with the pictures that the trees gave out. Sky wind my way as long as I have breath! . . . And when I'm ready, I top the lope that can't get any faster, sprint — what surprises of angle and pain the road throws my way! And it's hard not to laugh as it jokes me and pokes me and threatens a fall as I burn. My lungs rip the air, and trust grows, my jaw loosens, and like the noise of propellers I hear my arms chopping, and the wind blows my head off, and all the controls are in my legs, and the lower centers of my spine are doing the thinking . . .

Coming down at last, no arms left at all, my whole feet flapping the hard clay, my rays slowly lost their horizontal thrust and resumed vertical balances and I walked in my breathing . . . The ample night! Sweet water waiting in Feelgood's bucket back behind the stoop . . . In one moment I'd run a thousand yards, but the way back seemed endless, and the faint orange of the bus refused to appear up ahead, and in my mind, gasping the air and cherishing promise of drink, doubt appeared as space and time. In the aftermath of the run, the special satisfaction drained of thought, I felt increasingly lost. If only I kept walking I'd arrive, I knew — until the road forked. Running down it, I had noticed only the unitary road. Wishing I had more matches with me, I examined the pair for my marks. Was I flying so I left no tracks? But I could find none in either. At other moments I believed I could see foottorn places in each. More by listening and touching I made my choice. I waited and let it pick itself. Very tentatively and slowly I started down it, not knowing why it seemed friendlier than the other, each step confirming the last. I was still feeling lost, but it didn't feel bad, as if I'd made the right decision. When I became sure the land was sloping downhill, I knew that Feelgood's house couldn't lie in this direction. Looking down a straight decline of a hundred yards or so, I couldn't deny I'd now walked much farther than I'd run, but at this moment I smelled water. I loped down through the piny woods. Under a few oaks, a dense thicket took up the ground, and the road became a trail, and branched into many paths that zigzagged down the sharp brown bank to the river. Jumping roots and parting vines, I made my way to the water's edge. Everywhere tangled gray moss spilled off the big branches of the oaks, here and there splashing the ground. Where it touched the water, little wakes were caused that parted the smooth flow. I stepped out on stones to a flat boulder where the water swirled, and sat down. When the mosquitoes started getting to me, I stripped off my clothes, and made a flat dive that took me far out in the river, and I began to swim against the current. The water felt so fine, I began to laugh. I had to stop laughing or I'd be washed downstream by this current that was stronger than it looked. Already I was thirty or forty feet below the rock. I got serious and began stretching and pulling. In a few seconds you could be carried away. I swam hard, but I was getting winded. When I had enough I headed for shore, and waded back in the shallows, good ankle-deep in the muck. Weeds on my legs and the water running down my back protected me against the marauding bugs whose drone was bad, lovely and ceaseless as the water's. I made another dive, flat out at first and then down, to the dark green bottom, where fossils and pearls are born, and rolling like a stone — diving up for air — when I emerged, I had a hard-on. I wished for a woman for my rock. The water would open and caress you endlessly, but you'd never come. I was high! But I didn't want the sweet soft mud. I thought of Cara Lee, my water woman, to whom it seemed I'd always wanted to return. Tomorrow I was going back to see her, I promised myself, and I'd have a speck of Feelgood's smoke, and I'd bring a bottle of wine, for a sweet morning or an evening. Up the intricate bank, using my fingers and toes, I climbed. On the road I hollered and tried figures of my voice against the sky. I was not lost. I'd taken the right fork all right, and when I turned into the other, it was right too, and soon the bus loomed friendly as a pier. I went in by the back way, and lay down on one of the pallets, and rested soundly as a sodden log.

twenty-seven

IN HIS BAG were polished roots, birds' bones, light-gold berries, marijuana, a few jars of a red oil. One day there was a pile of speckled brown feathers on the table in the kitchen. He gathered the things he needed and food to eat on his walks through the country. Once I carried a sack while he and Yellow hunted Indian potatoes and other edible tubers in the swamp near his house. Yellow and I had more difficulty with the bog and mats of roots, tangles of vibrant bushes, and shallow water. I took off my shoes to save them and carried them in the sack. My city feet were soft. They laughed or hooted every time they found something. It stirred me up too. Feelgood brought us into favor with the swamp and recognized her gifts. Each potato cleaned of muck and passed to me glowed a moment at the mouth of the bag as I realized the friendly spirit.

"Lucky they ain got down in the swamp much yet," laughed the Doctor. "Too ugly for em, in the wrong direction. — Feel so good! — This ain but a little piece off the edge a the *swamp*, but a nice sample."

Often we passed flourishing patches of thick reeds, growing

in the mud, with white-green skins. When Feelgood broke a stalk, and broke off sections for me and Yellow, I was pleased by a sweet, euphoric taste that was completely new to me, with a quality of saturating the tongue and lasting, like honey. It was something like small sugar cane, but had a bigger taste. A few pieces went in his pocket and mine, and we walked on, chewing the candy fiber. "You know who specially like this?" asked Feelgood. — "Babies," he said.

In the fall he cut a lot of flowering smoke, to last the year, and he showed me it growing on lush hillsides and in wet sunny places as far as we traveled. He didn't waste a seed. Every one went down in the ground, which to some extent he tilled with the help of friends. The wind helped. He was doing everything in his power to spread the seed. It was late summer, a little early for smoking but it hardly mattered. He didn't have his pipe, he pulled a plant and stripped it and made a little bonfire and we breathed off that. "I don cut none yet but I don min a taste." He smiled at the bright tall grass. "She so sweet!" The presence of the marijuana next to us was beautiful, feminine and abundant. I walked back in it a ways, parting the delicate plants. By the hundreds the peaceful rings and swirls of the leaves surrounded me and passed me, in deepening constellations, closing above my head. The sun was glancing down among them, and bringing up the resins that lightly gilded my hands and sleeves as I brushed through. And it seemed like the good aroma was rising too, or was that just my smoky breath?

When I came out again into the clearing in which we had rested and smoked, I couldn't see them at first. They'd walked far away to a stand of pines at the edge of the thicket, but left the potatoes. Since I understood our direction to be through the field of grass at my back, I decided to leave them too.

When I walked over to Feelgood, I noticed that they were staring at the skeleton of a large bird, a little disarrayed by a predator or scavenger. The feathers were scattered all over the place. He was picking them up and discarding them, finally selecting one. Knowingly he stripped the feather hairs from the quill, and to my amazement he got out his pipe and stuffed them in it, and lit up. He passed the bad-smelling bowl over to me, saying, "Here somethin to get high if you ain got no grass, this'll do it," smiling like he knew it must strike me strange, and he wanted me to get past the strangeness to the high. There was a little rush felt in my hands and the backs of my eyes, and it added pleasantly to my already mellow sensation of being in the most fertile jungle, in a green treasure-house miles deep. "Course ain nothin like the number one plant," he laughed. "Yellow, get us some moss —"

"Naw I ain gon walk that far, they ain none aroun here," he sat down and got out a little pocketknife, and started to laugh, "but here, this a stone ya . . ." While Feelgood and I laughed with him, he carved a strip off his pants' cuff and unraveled it good with the tip of his knife and stuck that in the pipe when it was passed to him. The strange part of it is, in the expanding moment, it got me higher . . .

"You see, there be lots a times you can't get no good smoke. You a young man, got a lot a travelin front a ya, don't forget this lesson. If nothin else jus breathe deep," he said, tapping his head. "Now les go get Mrs. Boket some fish," he said, and we walked down to where the thicket was bordered by some scrub woods, and entered those. Yellow found some crisp beans, like a sip of water as we made our way a mile or two in this wood, and the ground became boggy, the trees gave up. Over fifty feet of the sharp green bog I saw open water. It was a small lake, very still, with the sun blazing perfectly on its dark surface. Stuck in the bog was a small wooden boat, that we dragged to the water, leaving a wide scar behind us. I was afraid it would start giving way on us like quick-bog. We were mucked up to our knees with algae and bogshit, and in the flat-end boat that was really a one-seater, in the heat waves of the mean afternoon sun, the floating boggo with a hint of its depths revenged itself like a skunk. There were no oars, but it was so quiet our hands were enough to pull us slowly to the center of the little lake, where the dead calm and expanse of elements absorbed all sound and motion. Yellow unfolded some earth-worms from a paper, that were lank and easily quartered. I feared the fish would be like alligator gar, or maybe blind and pale like cave fish, like potatoes, but they were nicely colored little bass. They fought briefly fiercely against the hand on the line and made as much noise as they could in the bottom of the boat. The first three we caught almost at the same time, within seconds after lowering our hooks, but our luck quickly dropped off, and when seven or eight tails were loudly slapping the wood, there was the end of it. So we paddled ten minutes, let the energies of the fish ease away and the waters still out, and stopped and hit another spot — and did this twice more, wind-ing up with a heap of little guys. On the way back, when we passed over the grounds we took them from, they started jump-ing! Every fish got a jump or two at least, long after we'd subconsciously heard their last silences. At first it was eerie, then it was beautiful and not strange at all. We pulled the boat up and Feelgood got a section of vine and bound the catch to-gether, and we took the walk back through the woods; and in a few minutes, while they waited at the edge of the clearing, I got the potatoes up on my shoulder again, and rejoined them, and we headed for Mrs. Boket's.

By the cuts through the forest Feelgood knew, we were less

than a mile from her house. When we got there, he told me to leave the bag near the rear end of an old black Cadillac, but he carried the fish inside to her. She never dreamed of a fat string of bass! She told him there was some sweet corn outside we could have. He thanked her for that and inquired if she'd like to go to the show this evening, and she said she'd love that. Now things were very mellow in the front room. Did anybody want a little taste? she wanted to know, and returned from the kitchen with a quart jar of light-gold corn whiskey. It looked fine, further mellow influence on the coffee table, with a can of apple juice. We drank an inch or two of that, except for Yellow, and Mrs. Boket didn't much more than wet her lips, but Feelgood and I sat awhile and sipped and listened to her. The lovely lines of her face as she talked moved quick as water. She admired the fish a lot and made us promise to come back to-morrow for a fishfry, to which these bass would make a nice addition, she made clear. "Be a quite a lot a people," she said, with a warm smile at me, that made me wonder if there would be any chicks there. She looked that good. I was thinking, lucky Feelgood, she looked fine for a woman of forty or fifty. She had a matter-of-fact, secure but not heavy, sexy tone, and she glanced my way a lot, most friendly lady. I know what my mind did, it was a matter of simple division. I modeled chicks after her, younger and younger, in the air. With Feelgood, she delivered babies here in this house and around this territory. She too was root enough to help keep things going. She told about a pregnant woman in Meansville who was almost ready. Feelgood was nodding, saying nothing, but smiling, always ready.

Out back Yellow and I cleaned up the fish in about half an hour. Their small scales were tenderly fastened and their fiber was soft and sweet to the touch. To scale them, he had a short board with bottle caps tacked onto it. An easy job. A nice platter of dressed-up fish sat on her table that'd taste good tomorrow. I took it in my hands and gently shook the stack solider. I was so stoned, I could gaze at anything, circles of raw fish, the fixings and appurtenances of the lady's kitchen, whose order, economy, and tasty look were putting me in mind of Mrs. Stock's. I noticed a sweet potato pie on a shelf under a cloth with a V already cut out of it, and I got a slice of it, washed off the knife, and enjoyed it while Yellow gutted the last bass. She was going to take the pile of them over to the store where there was ice, she said, when we came back in the front room. She mentioned to the Doctor that she had high hopes of a line of *big* bass, for a church fair later in the month. — Don't taste too much better after a certain size, he laughed: but a few eight-pounders, baked, in the middle of a row of deep-ribbed fives, would look awfully nice. He said we'd go back in the sloughs sometime, and he could almost promise we'd get all she wanted. I began to look forward to this immediately.

Tonight the Doctor was taking Mrs. Boket to the movies. This was a lucky break for us; it meant a ride into town in her good-looking car. We sat around and sipped the corn whiskey for a while, and they talked off and on, and I silently enjoyed myself. Then she put on some clothes and we rode the two miles to my favorite house in the world, with the bus in front of it. We were mucky from the swamp, and though it had dried, I sat gingerly in the back seat, avoiding any unnecessary rubbing against the upholstery. I carried the sack of potatoes into the kitchen. We had to wait a few minutes while Feelgood changed into some clean clothes. Walking out of the house through the bus always put a new shape on the first moments outside. In the aisle, I felt pleasure of a fresh arrival like a breeze from the road. I sat down in the driver's seat. I liked to stop here for a minute, to lean on the wheel and observe things from the high point of the driver. The wheel was a shiny old circle horizontal above my knees. Being connected to nothing, it spun easily under my fingers, like a strange prayer wheel, producing images of the road on its way back into town.

twenty-eight

OFTEN WE GOT HIGH out at Feelgood's house. I remember an ordinary day with those cats, the Doctor and Cousin Yellow. Various business could be taken care of, relating to staying alive and continuing life. But none of it was pressing. Everything could wait until tomorrow, or the day after. So we were smoking and taking it easy, enjoying the sun high in the blue sky. I think there was nothing I enjoyed more about the company of my friends than their capacity for silence. On the corner, cats would be getting high and rapping and chattering. Sometimes I would hear them running their lines on each other — I'm the baddest, I'm the hippest! — and in the tones and rhythms of their words would be the sound of truth and certainty, and the usual and certain unique symbolisms, and I might be drawn into that and sound off too, or I might be silent and inside myself I'd smile at it all. But that was a knowing smile, remembering Feelgood's, and in no way related to the silence of nothing, when a laugh would signify joy, and might or might not be followed with a word, which could only signify the sun or the sky or the friendship or the silence.

I was discovering a freedom from worry, and woe, and even ambition, that I'd sought for years it seemed, and used to think I'd found — for a day now and then anyway. It was a matter of course with these two, and I was picking up on that. The Doctor was always together. Life moved on. But my own ways intervened sometimes, and on this day, when I'd smoked, from out of the blue came sensations of jail, and distinctly I heard the sheriff taunting me, saying, "Don't worry boy, you belong in jail, you'll be seeing me again!" I began to feel stifled, and scared. I began to be scared of the grass that was illegal, and at this moment the smoke of downtown that shook me occasionally, the way it was smoked by careless cats under the noses of the law that did sometimes patrol the street, and the black law now that was hip, at this moment the red-brown smoke of the swamp was affecting me no different, and the flame of life was clouded. Feeling this, and beginning to enter this badland of the mind, I breathed deep and experienced the loosing of my hatred of the man, that caused my arms to search for something I might strike. When you're stoned, sometimes you can tell the passage of your own nerve energy like that, and I almost watched my anger build. Suddenly — because I was in the habit of acting without thinking in the presence of my comrades — I began to smash my fist into my flattened palm. Again and again — and now I see clearly the despair in such anger at the past — I delivered and received the blows. The burn of adrenaline felt almost good, as if printed on my open palm was a certain smug and vicious face, and here was some release. I sensed my friends' concern, but I didn't see them. I was quite content I guess to sit there in the sunshine raining venom on a bad memory; I was accelerating the tempo when a violent motion caught my eye! It was the Doctor raring back to throw his pipe high in the air — straight up, my God it sailed, it was grabbed by a breeze up there and made an arc and came down and he had to run to catch it. This stunned me out of myself, and I laid off. I slightly wondered where I'd been. The Doctor was walking away into the garden, slowly, quite slowly, his head nodding forward. Yellow gave me a look and started after him, and I followed too. Soon we were walking together. "That's nowhere," he commented. After a moment he added, "Smoke is smoke." And for no apparent reason I was feeling all right again, and almost relaxed, and we were ambling along. With Feelgood we didn't walk down a row in the garden, but many curved rows, and then a diagonal through the rows, but never injuring a plant or even a weed. I thought I heard him say, "Now we goin somewheres." The silence was growing. We entered the forest.

I'd never been back in these woods, though they encircled Feelgood's homestead. They were a lovely green piny woods, not so dense, so the sunlight fell through in many places, and made a marbled green and golden effect that was a pleasure to walk through. We walked something less than a mile, I judged. We passed a strange burned-out patch, a kind of square in the forest just the opposite of a pleasant green square in a town. We walked beside it for only a few minutes — perhaps fifty yards on a side and extending blackly off to our right. It was eerie — I asked Feelgood how it happened. He replied he didn't know, it had always been there in the woods since he'd been around. He stopped and gazed into the wasteland and I looked too, and sure enough I could see places where young trees were growing and some grasses were spreading. Life was good. We were drifting to our left, and knowing the curve of the river, I reckoned we'd be meeting up with it soon, so I was surprised to feel the land begin to rise. The trees got fewer, and very soon we were on a grassy hill that was as high or a little higher than the forest that surrounded it, like a sea of green, so there was a view of the countryside, stretches of river, narrow roads, the tops of little houses here and there. On the hill we sat and rested, and moments after I saw the Doctor shut his eyes, I began to realize what was wonderful and remarkable about this place: what a vista for the ear! A world of sounds. The nearest and loudest I heard first, the intricate play of the insects, the warm voices of birds, the moving air and the responses of leaves and grass. And then I *heard* the river, the gently tumbling, smooth and merry sound of water on its way. Or did I imagine I heard it? I asked myself that question and heard the answer: Is there any difference? Murmurings of voices at a distance so that the songs of the people were heard and not the words: dying and living again, the forms of the people on my ear. Momentarily I heard an indefinable complex of human and metal noises that might have been a wave of the town, too far away in the air. I could hear a truck on a road, like a little hum. With eyes closed and ears open, immense space became apparent, the sky and the land could be felt and not just flatly seen, and I felt like a blind man who had long been perfecting the range and possibility of his good instrument. As time passed, the sense of time passed too, and life alone, in its very musical ramblings, became immanent. And then I *smelled* the river — clean perfume of the water that is the drink of life. I had to laugh, that made me feel so good. It's a simple lesson, I thought, to shut off one sense and find things anew with others. Now I shut off my ears with my hands and just sniffed the air. Lappings of light odors on the air defied any definition or knowledge I might have brought to them. I glimpsed a dance of life smell, long ago forgotten by nameless ancestors of mine. I knew the smell of the earth, and damn it was good, and who can describe it. It can't be heard so words won't do; it can't be seen, but in the mind's eye a certain transference is possible.

I opened my eyes and the colors were bright and the day was fine. How I had polished my vision by resting it! Yellow was lying on the ground staring into the sky. The Doctor hadn't moved or changed his attitude, still nodded out. I lay down on the ground and ran my hands over the soft grass. It was not a large hill and in the spaces that my hands could reach the gentle curve of it could be felt. For minutes I lost myself in the feeling of the earth in my hands and the smell of it in my nostrils. Like on a woman's breast I was in communion with the beautiful world; and when I next had the pleasure that a woman can offer, might I be reminded of this infinitude of life on the hill? I knew I would. I was ever making associations, and life is increase.

It was on the way back to Feelgood's house that I remembered the angry changes which had maybe led to our trip over to the hill of the senses. This is what I'd call the fine hill that was the good thing of this day. Back at the house we had a smoke. It was extraneous. I hardly noticed it, I couldn't feel any nicer. I thought of the bad changes and the palm of my hand was still a little sore. When the arrogant face appeared to me, I easily flew it away into the sun, where presumably it burned. The light was a little brighter. When, in a little flash, I wondered if it hadn't been the face of Jones Jones, I laughed. A recognition. My laughter blended easily into the silence, and my friends were doing other things.

Now I couldn't take the streets so seriously. There was often something amusing happening on them, and they were no longer completely necessary to me, because I was familiar with the Doctor and the river. In all the old man's words I heard the hopeful sound of the ceaselessly flowing waters, and I was affected by it, and at moments even the streets seemed timeless. In a happy way I felt connected with my first days in the town, that I'd felt cut off from while I'd been working for Jones. A sign of that was my desire to go out and visit the Stocks sometime. Or if I ever met one of them on the street, I knew I could speak honestly and easily. Maybe I would appreciate them even more. Everything seemed new again.

Across the street from the poolroom, among other small stores, was a grocery. Covering its window, printed in red, were the names and prices of dozens of foodstuffs that could be bought inside, and with nothing else on my mind, I absently studied the lists. Fresh peas, pork chops, rice, red beans, collard greens, chickens, thin-cut tobacco . . . Mothers, and old grandmothers, and young kids sent by the women entered the store, and left again with bags of these substances in their arms. Through the openings in the letters of the signs on the glass I seemed to see the moments of eating, the happy faces in motion, taking nourishment. In a light moment, I imagined the southern spirit being created and sustained. The slow process of life supported me, even if tenuously. If I was hungry and waiting for a chance to eat, I made up some soul recipes and ate them in my mind. Every day I saw this window, and my attention always lingered on it, I spent my leisure hours examining it like the sky. Sometimes the lists blurred, and the letters mingled, and I got a strange good mood, like a strange flavor stew, and an idea of my connection with this place seemed almost to appear to me, the distances and hardships seemed the shadows in a moving form I couldn't quite imagine. Now if I felt bad I knew the mood would soon change. I never stayed in the apartment morosely staring out the window. I'd go out on the street and meet Angel and the early summer weather would warm things up. Under the new skies, time on the corner would snap and fill; the breezes were bright blue. The promise in the air was undeniable. Everybody was standing outdoors, and wearing new clothes . . .

Looking for the Doctor one day, I walked down to the river, hoping to see him by its side. Near the pool where we fished I had a momentary hallucination. I thought I saw him relaxing on a part of the bank the afternoon sun flooded through the trees. He looked up out of one eye to see who it was, the eye shone for an instant in the shade of his hat. But when I got near, it was only a shimmering of the grass and rocks. I walked down to the water, in a shady part, and found a comfortable spot to lay back with a stone for a pillow. I decided to wait awhile before thinking of the long hike again. I was happy to watch the changing river in the peace of this shore, and to listen to its drone. Though I hadn't found him, the search had at least taken me off the streets, which were tiring just to look at sometimes, when they were empty and not flowing and turning up new expressions. In the evenings, with the lights turning on and everybody out walking and talking, to be on the street could be refreshing and heartening, even lucky, but the river was the place I really enjoyed the heat of the day. Over my toes I could see the circles and ripples constantly forming. Through the earth that cupped me I felt the deeper tumbling of the water over the curved river floor. Since I'd met the Doctor, my senses seemed sharper, though the distinctions between them blurred, maybe an effect of the good smoke we'd been smoking. The place where the senses came together, that was the feeling, that created what you sensed, too, and the better you felt, the more subtly you might perceive. If you could free the chamber of feeling inside, certain occurrences or music-noises or sliding states might be apprehended that were usually clouded or well hidden. The beauty in appearances depended on something behind the mind. Just relaxing down here by the river so easy, with such possibilities rolling by my head, and the music that I can't describe, it was naturally soothing to enter a realm where the beings and the glistening air entered one another and the roots of the trees made a butterfly configuration like almost human nerves binding the earth together, and the schools of fish under the water, hovering near the mouths of small green caves, listened to each other with their spines, and breathed, and would sweep through the curving water in rays, together, unlike any dancers. Suddenly I heard singing, some sharp city blues, I was hearing so closely, maybe it was carried down the water by a current of air. It dimmed, died, came on again, shrank, and then began to grow steadily in volume. It must be coming from the road above the bank, I thought, envisioning a convertible approaching with its top down and radio playing. When it was right behind me, I sat up and saw it was Feelgood and Yellow, stepping down the bank, with a transistor radio tuned to Memphis. Yellow had the radio near his ear, though it was loud. The Doctor had a package in his hand. When they sat down near me, he unwrapped it and it turned out to be some big juicy barbecue sandwiches. The wonder of it was there were three.

I wasn't surprised to see them, I was profoundly glad that out of the peace so deep and green, they had showed up. Anyone else would've disturbed it, and they multiplied it. Feelgood was telling me about the lady who gave him the barbecue, who ran a soul foods kitchen in her house downtown. It was the best food in Georgia, he said, and she fixed him the specialties out of love. He'd take me by there sometime, but I was happy to get this taste — a delicious sandwich, a bellyful. When I was done, I had to wash my hands and face in the water; it was that nice a sandwich. Blues of preacher Joe Tex, Betty Everett, Otis Redding jumped out of the small box at Yellow's side. It was a beautiful picnic. Doctor Feelgood got out his pipe after lunch, and we passed it.

"If you high, you feel a volume a the air, that curvin on your shoulders an the topside a trees, but it don weigh on ya, it connect ya. It don matter how you die, if you in your figure." The Doctor rose. "Maybe you climb out on a high limb." He walked up the bank to the first tree and shinned up it with startling facility while he talked. "Get a look through the air — don worry bout the groun — a new soun come in your head. You make your reply. You jus don know if you be heard, maybe you stay silent — that hard to hear. But you listen to your new soun." And now he was sitting on a limb of the tree, fifteen feet above me. "Now down below there be a man, lookin at a crack in the earth, whether to jump it. A man shape like a snail, you see that from above, but he travel different. An the crack hang out a sign, say 'Too wide!' — so he walk on down till he catch up, where he can step it. Now you look at the crack — you marvel on the tree, but you talk to it. Talk to the sky, you feel good. You right in that pattern that you recognize. Folks always waitin on an answer! But the sky ask you a question, why you wanna worry bout the ground that you free of? What to do, what to do . . . By a sign you might know what . . . Stay up in the tree . . ."

I was feeling pretty good, I loved to listen to the Doctor talk though it was often too much for me. When he stopped I searched for a question to keep him going, but my mind might be rolling in and out of his words, in too many directions, and the highest expression I could find would be silence. He appreciated that, he was a silent man who loved to talk. "In a silence," he once told me, "you can hear the things that don have no noise, cause this air is full of em." But in my head a question was now forming, that expressed a keen ignorance. He didn't always like a question, he didn't ever answer it direct, but he didn't mind. When I walked up the slope to find the pipe, I asked him. I sat down near the foot of the tree and lit up. "Doctor, how do you know a true sign?"

"You jus have to stay in your way," he replied. "Don look for it, you might see it, you never know it, but you under the best influence. Forget it — don listen to me! I might tell you, 'Boy, don smoke no more a that jus now, I ain explained you bout the rhythms!' — Might see a sign say *stop!* — now you sail on through cause what you care about that? Ha-ha! But if I hand you some seeds, you gon plant em, ain't you! Ha, you ain gon smoke em, you plant em in the best spot so you gon have somethin to get high on next year . . . If a man ain amazed at this world an this body — well all right . . . Sign how you feel, see, how you feel by what you see. Who mistake that? I know it, some folks like to look at some bad shit quite a bit . . ."

A voice inside me was saying, If you love the coating, if you haven't put any sadness on the colors, you flash: I'm in this place, this terrain, watch the sun reflecting and deepening the coating . . .

Up in the tree, Feelgood was saying, "I can see a lot more a river . . . I see a boat comin . . ." I wanted to be up there too. I jumped up and climbed on up with the pipe in my pocket, which I got out and relit once I was sitting next to him on the limb. The view was terrific. Though the river was lost to sight now and then as it twisted its way through the wooded land, it reappeared bright green-blue at distances of a mile or more. The banks were high here, but much smaller up and downstream. For minutes, I couldn't see the boat, but I could hear its little motor. Then it came into view in the clear stretch of river in front of us, with an old white couple and their fishing poles in it, the woman in the bow and the man operating the two- or three-horse outboard. It was moving quite slowly upstream, with such a small power propelling it. As they neared our spot, they caught sight of Yellow sitting on the grass and his bobbers out in the pool, which they avoided, sweeping toward the opposite shore like polite fisherfolk. We were passing the pipe and waiting for one of them to get a glimpse of us. It was the woman whose gaze was free to swing over the shores, whose lower jaw dropped slightly, and who signaled her husband. I thought they were going to strike a rock for sure, because he couldn't take his eyes off us and the boat was veering off course rapidly. We waved and grinned, and pointed to straighten them up. Once the man got his eyes on the river again he didn't look back, but the old woman watched us with an incredulous smile on her face until they disappeared around a bend. Minutes later, we saw them again, a half-mile upstream making their way to one of the town docks perhaps, with a story to tell. They were talking heatedly, the woman was leaning toward him out of her front position. Of course they didn't know we could still see them, and that if they'd looked back, there we'd be, flickering through the trees.

twenty-nine

WE'D BEEN on the corner all evening, and nothing had come up.
We were not in a bad mood, it was more of a blank mood.
Case couldn't turn the few dollars he had into more. It was an
empty time — but as I think on it, not so far from average. I
was fairly happy. A Pontiac pulled up to the corner and
stopped, and the driver leaned over to talk through the window
to Case. It was a schoolteacher, a gym teacher, I think he was,
at Lincoln High School, who had a reputation as a lover and a
playboy. He had a steady job, money, a nice car — all those
things. One time in the Paradise, he sat down next to me at the
bar and drank a beer with us. "See that bitch?" he asked, pointing at a girl with some fine legs gazing into the jukebox, "I
fucked her night before last — See that one over the corner," he
nodded at a light-skin woman sitting with two men in the
corner booth, "I fucked her all *day* Sunday!" He went on like
this through every woman in the place, sometimes letting his
voice get loud enough for all at the bar to hear, sometimes
dropping it down kind of sly, until there were no women in the
Paradise this evening whom he hadn't had. He leaned back and

slugged his beer, and sighed, and was silent for a time, with a very well satisfied smirk on his face like he'd just finished a seven-course meal. I had to laugh, in appreciation: I enjoyed my laugh, mellow as some after-dinner brandies, I was sweetening my tongue, and setting up this man to buy me another beer. Hell, I was an expert audience! I could listen, I could respond to somebody's pride and polish and reflect it, when I felt like it. When I didn't have anything I just naturally felt like it.

Now on this off night, the man was motioning us into the car. Case took a last glance up and down the street, for the windfall might even now be approaching. Then we got in, Case in front, me in back alone. The cat began bragging about his women, he was talking down some bitches. The intense rivalry he seemed to feel, not with other men, but with the women, was boiling up in his voice. Verbally, he loved to slam some around, and talk about how easily he'd gotten to them. Me and Case were a snickering, appreciative audience, because we'd've given our eyetooth for a shot at all those pretty women.

As luck would have it, we were pulling up at a club called the Playground in the Pines, and I was immediately uneasy. When I first came down here to this town, in the days before I'd even met Knight, I came out here to the Playground one night with some friends in the movement and was turned away at the door. No whites allowed. I was hurt. I felt like I knew how blacks felt, turned away from some place they had thought of entering. My friends explained it: the man who ran the place was tight with the sheriff of the county. It was a big business he did out here, thousands of customers on a weekend from Meansville and the smaller towns for miles around. This type operation was not possible without the goodwill of the white power structure, and the black proprietor, a powerful man and a fast and shrewd one, had been close to the men on top for decades. So it was no use fighting that shit, even less feeling sorry or disappointed about it. I remembered that night, almost two years ago, we drove on to another spot. And I was trying to explain this to Case and the cat, how it wasn't much use my trying to get in here, and really I didn't want to try: at thought of the probable rebuff I felt more afraid than I ought to've. But Case replied, "Hey man, where you been? The civil rights bill been pass you know."

Well I knew that, yes how could I forget that? And it would apply here, to me at this door, yes it would. Wouldn't it? Did it work in reverse? What was it that was intimidating me, with the law on my side? But that was just it, the law was behind me, but the laws were not. Or if they were behind me, it was not with a desire to support my spirit. Damn, I glanced around, I did: I chuckled weakly at myself getting nervous. It was just . . . It was just I didn't enjoy being where I didn't really belong anymore. Once I had, once I prided myself on my capacity to float into unlikely rooms and situations. In this respect I was leading a rather sober and circumscribed life these days, with a little niche worked out for myself on the corner downtown, where I was recognized, remembered, accepted, and little remarked at, and rarely put through any changes, because every habitué had long ago absorbed the unlikelihood of my having drifted there, come to rest on those sidewalks, no different down deep from the others, though maybe with a different way to go.

Nevertheless, I hurried after them, Case hesitating at the door and looking back to see what might be keeping me before he disappeared inside. In a moment I was pushing my way through the door into the big bar and dancehall. It was the

largest nightclub I've ever been in in my life, and it was filled
with people in a leisurely, uncrowded motion toward the bar,
the dancing area, and the motel out in back. In the moments
after entering, I noticed this subtle motion, like currents in a
wide river, even before I'd located my friends, who'd made it
over to the bar, and were talking to three chicks. When I saw
this, the third chick, I forgot my speculations, I took my eyes
out of the stream of people, that'd been unconsciously searching for the manager or some sign that trouble was on its way. I
quit worrying and decided fate was playing my way. Soon we
were introduced; she was a bit shy, but with some liquor in my
gut I was able to cool that out. Seemed like these days I was
just getting tired of cooling out people about me, like I was this
other color cat who had to come on strong at all the right times
and places, or mellow just now, or then, because I had this
mark against me already. And I had always to anticipate just
what degree of hang-up the person might have and try to say
something appropriate — which is why I liked to stay downtown where I could be silent all day if I felt that way, and not
have to explain a thing, because people knew me. And once
there was a time when it all came natural, and I was working
for the movement, and people came out to me and wanted to
get to know me, and didn't start, or eye me with a selfish reflex
or suspicion.

Yeah, all this was running through my head, as I got a little
high, and sought to put a good spirit in the girl. Maybe I was
succeeding, I don't know, in a minute we were dancing. I think
she was just going to feel good anyway, and I met her there, in
the middle. Because if a chick is shying away from this white
boy that's me, then I got such a long uphill chase ahead of me,
that I can forget about anything for tonight, and as far as danc-

ing goes — no dance. I can feel that vibration so fast, and I might just fall off with it, and be that off color, and not try to dance a change through it. But here we were, out under the lights, and Willie Mitchell was up, on the jukebox, "Percolatin." I won't forget that funky instrumental. I'll always dig it, even though I kind of feel like it was my undoing too. Because somebody around here resented my presence, I don't know who: later I'd hear vaguely that the broad was somebody's wife, and wonder, so who ain't? I was so young, and such a kid! Five minute after I come in here where I know there's a complex of hostility like a hornets' nest of minds and powers that I do not really understand, no I can't picture it — but I could sense it: I almost didn't walk in here, but now, immediately the warmth of the booze begins to unwrap my mind that hasn't itself ever let me down and is sending me some signals tonight, and I considered the ignominy of just waiting in the car or calling to Case to bring me a beer outside, yes I did. But five minutes later I'm in the center of the floor, the center of the crowd's drifting attention, in forgetfulness of the dance, with the sleek, soft curves of a good-looking woman's body filling my eyes, my nose: I slouched as I danced, letting my gaze rest on nothing but her. I couldn't wait for the next slow number. In moments I was spaced out, and I didn't know how badly until, the music stopped, we turned slightly toward the bar, waiting for the next sound to decide for us whether we would dance to it, or return for a spell to our friends and the liquor. At this moment I saw the man, crooking his finger at me, and I glanced beyond myself and then didn't return my eyes to him, as if not suspecting he meant me at all, and I took her arm and guided her at an angle away from him toward Case and the people drinking. But he intercepted us, and lightly took *my* arm, which he let go immediately, saying, "I want to talk to you, step out here with me a minute." And I found myself following him, with only one terrified backward glance to see if Case noticed what was happening, and he had, he had risen from his stool and there was a look on his face that told me one thing only: I'd been right — danger . . .

Outside, he said, "Look here, I ain got nothin against you, but I can't have you aroun. Somebody be juiced up an . . ." he trailed off, and I never got a chance to protest his lame shit, right out of the book of white fears, where the cops pointed him to read it, because here came a patrol car. This is the street of no color, Power Alley. And out of the car, slowly, inexorably, got the deputies, as if by a supreme effort of my useless will I was only postponing the moment of the pinch, slow-motion of the cops approaching and the black man beside me grown silent, deep and cool.

"This boy causin trouble, Bo?"

"He ain did nothin, but I rather not have him aroun cause could be trouble . . ."

Having made these little speeches to each other, the sheriff's man, having already received his orders, took my arm, said, "Let's go, boy." I didn't resist, but I didn't comply. I knew where I was going. Like a sudden noose, the image of the gates of the jail was swallowing up my mind, and I felt cold dread replace the cool I might have summoned. He flicked the handcuffs off his belt, and I couldn't stifle a long whistle like a sigh as I began to walk. Everybody around me was cold. A few people had come out to watch curiously. Before I got into the ugly car, I turned around and saw Suitcase standing in the doorway, looking sorry, pitiful as a man can look, I guess, friend who just can't help. How do you peel the law off a friend, unless you're all ready to go under too? You going to enhance the catch? I shot him a look, the baddest I could manage, to include him, and justify him. Because they definitely got me for some days — Christ I hope no more! I'll just sign off a few in my mind right away and hope no more . . .

Into the role of dignified victim, my anger was rising, and I did not fling insults at the uniformed jokers in front as fast as they could think them up for me. I kept myself cool. I just let my anger be informed by my wisdom, that I'd gained a little of since the last time this happened to me. I knew where I was going — irritating the deputies further wouldn't change that — I saved my strength for the dungeon. However, the cops were not appeased by my silence.

It was the county jail, and this was my first time to see it. It was newer and cleaner than the city jail, but nothing nice like the picnic cage in Weary. Well it's a new experience, something new in jails for you, buddy, a light voice was saying inside me, some not quite successful comic sense that was trying to work out despite everything. Through a series of doors that had to be unlocked and then locked again before the next one was opened, the deputy brought me to the pen. There was a walkway around it, and after the cop locked me in, saying, "Comin up, another niggerlover —" he moved around to the side and stared through the bars, to see how I'd be received I guess. Over the pit of dread and fear, the unbelief in my gut that this had really happened to me, though I was looking around me in the bullpen, at the men playing cards on the floor, a few lying on their bunks and relaxed back on a sofa at the end of the pen fixed up from a couple unused mattresses, on top of my confusion and reluctance to really accept this as my present lot, reality was being dealt with by the front of my head, and ideas were being examined and rejected that hardly seemed mine. Ludicrously, I felt like apologizing for adding to the crowd. To lighten things up, I thought of joking, I hoped a new man wouldn't have to sleep on the sofa. Then I thought of try-ing to explain what had actually led to my arrest, maybe these guys could understand. But I kept my head, and I kept my peace. Everything in its time, and you got a good chance. I went over and sat on a bunk that seemed to be unoccupied.

"Hey, that's my bunk!" cried a small man coming out of the little cell in the corner that contained a toilet and a shower. He had white hair, and a finely chiseled face. He was clean-shaven, with a little bit of lather still clinging to his sideburns and his razor in his hand, and I wondered what he was doing shaving at ten o'clock in the evening. You going out tonight? I almost asked him. A night on the town? Let me recommend a place to stay clear of . . . There's not much space in jail, but there's a lot of time, I thought. And suddenly I was falling through the sad timelessness of the locked room, where life's little chores are reduced to an absolute minimum, and so may be prized, something to do on an evening. I rose from the bunk that belonged to the old man, and embarrassedly looked for an-other.

"Here, ain nobody got this'n," he pointed to one that I could have, and I glanced warmly at his kindness, but his face was closed and gray, he was turning away. He was back at the washbasin, and the sound of running water clattered through the place, before I could sink down on the thin pallet that cov-ered the steel painted gray.

All the walls, all the metal fixtures of the pen were painted a bright gray. I was aware of this inevitable grayness and of the total silence of the men close by, almost as if they were a single impression, a single empty smell. The cop was still standing outside, meanly gazing in at us in the cage. Only moments had passed, I suppose. I could hear him breathing through his nose, and was there a little of disappointed rage in the harsh puffs? None of the other prisoners were so much as noticing me, or looking at anything else but the faces of their cards, which they played silently . . . whiff, whiff of the cards touching the concrete, c-clink of pennies and dimes shifting each round.

"Where you live boy, tell us that!"

The guard shouted like the place was ten times its crummy size, but nobody looked up, not a flaw or flick in any motion betrayed a listener. I knew he was talking to me, but with this sort of solid ignorance of the man walling me in almost farther than his loud voice could penetrate, I took my time about responding.

"You boy! I'm talkin to you!" He slapped the bars with his keys, and one of the men on the floor groaned tiredly.

"Where you live, Yank?"

Christ that's a backass way of getting to the point, ain't it! I thought, but I damn sure didn't have the nerve to say so either, because I was very uncertain just when and how these boys inside here were going to start reacting, and I wanted to tell my story in my own way. And why couldn't the sonofabitch leave me alone? I'm the one was going to have to live here, wasn't I? And for how long . . .

"By the river," I mumbled.

"Where?" screamed the cop.

He had heard me but he wanted to make sure the others had too, and I told him again, and he shouted, *"Where by the river?"*

I lay back on the bunk, my heart beating way too fast, "In a *tree,*" I mumbled so softly I doubt he could've heard, but near-est me in the card game, a young kid, almost too young it seemed to be locked in here, this kid laughed aloud. He laid the side of his head on his knee and squinted over at me, titter-ing out the corner of his mouth, and then he wiped away the laugh with the back of his hand.

Strangely the cop was shook. I dug that. I checked that out so carefully I almost rose off the bed after my eyes. He was walking away down the walkway toward the first of the locked doors that would take him out to the office. He turned once, "You live with the niggers don't you, boy?" He walked further. Just before going out, after he'd unlocked the door with a great smashing of keys against steel, he said, "If I was you boys I'd kick the livin shit outa that niggerlover, cause that's what he needs. You ask him what he doin in this county, you ask him what kinda shit he doin over Meansville, you boys good white men an you got to stay in there with *him!* Annnh!" He coughed violently, and on his way out, added, "Shit, I'm sorry!" and coughed again like he had hot sand down his throat.

I was laid back on the bunk. I was almost at ease, because they were going to react to that one way or another, but I'd have to be cool. I couldn't fight that shit directly, I'd just have to wait for something to happen and find my way.

"Me, I wouldn't even talk to that rabbit-ear shithead," said the young boy, looking over my way. "I wouldn't give him one *word* to get me *outa* here!" he said with slow venom, and I real-ized abruptly that no matter who I was or what I did, I could never be unpopular as the cop who'd just walked out of here, and I wondered why.

"You with that nigger mess?" sounded a barrel-chested man with the deck in his hand. All he had on were his underpants and a continuous tattoo over his shoulders, back, chest, and arms, women, big cats, snakes, religious turns in the network of blue-black lines, lot of names of women and places. Some tattoos are hip, but I never did dig them on the back. I was noticing his pictures, but my mind was angling around to answer, for here was my time, things would get better or worse from this moment on, I knew that.

"Hey you got some nice shit on your back," I said. No I didn't either, but I couldn't shut up my humorous voice in my head that was threatening to make my rough situation worse, and strangely I was smiling, but I tried to bring some meanness into my voice when I said, "Who, you mean that man who runs the Playground?"

"The who?"

"The club, you never heard of it? Listen, I like to drink an I like to fuck, don't you? So whata you think I was doin when they busted me? I was drinkin an happy an dancin . . ."

There was a moment of silence. Most everybody seemed indifferent to me and my story. A few, however, were staring hostilely at me, and I wasn't out of it. I didn't know if I was deeper in it. I was oppressed by this desire to laugh — later I'd wish I could — like a devil plaguing me to laugh at a scene that was so bad it was almost funny. Only a few minutes had passed of what might be long days or weeks in the joint, and that was so exasperatingly painful I almost chuckled. Sheer exhaustion of the horrible foreview of time time time to kill had me by the funny bone, and I wanted to laugh, scream, curse, vomit up the weird dream, this reality that was dawning on me more strongly every moment. Involuntarily, I glanced at the locked door, like turning my face to a slap in the eyes; no, uh uh, no nice person, no friendly force will appear to spring that latch. They

got you man, and you could've stayed on the corner. I hated
my fortune, I hated the man. Case never believed he'd do
something like that. I sent my friend a good wish through the
walls, that he shouldn't feel too bad. But if he wanted to get up
some bail, that'd be okay. But I knew how impossible that
would be. I wondered what my crime might have been, I wondered what amount they'd set for my freedom . . .

"You young I see," the dealer was saying, "you must be dumb
for your age. You in the *South,* buddy — you cain't get away
with no shit like that!"

The boy who'd first spoken to me quit the game and began to
wander about the place abstractedly. But his face was not abstract, it wore an angry sneer that erupted when he stopped
near where I sat. "That sonofabitch! That low, sneaky, yellow,
fat-ass law! You know he came in here to search for a spoon las
week," he glanced away once for confirmation of this, "a fuckin
spoon! An he bring a shotgun! And the other one with him got
a shotgun. For us! Ha-ha-ha-ha!" He looked around the room
at some drunks, fat cons, and variously wasted dudes, who
looked kind of bad to me, I got to admit. But to the kid it was
laughable. "He was so scared while he check for that goddam
spoon! Ha-ha-ha! I could smell him tremblin, an shit he foun it
too! Under the commode!" He fell across the room laughing,
he tossed around against the bars under force of his satire. "I
wouldn talk to that yellow little cop, naw I wouldn look at him
to curse him! Why — look here —"

"Hey, Dognapper, keep it down will ya?" called the dealer.

He was winding up all right, he was flipping out. He must've
been in here a long time to build up a wild rage like this. When
he was spoken to, he shut up. He cursed, spat, sighed roughly,
and continued to walk up and down the little space of the pen,

but he calmed down and didn't shout any more. I found out he was called Dognapper because that was what he was in here for, stealing some dogs. He claimed they just followed him home but the owner claimed different. He'd been in here six weeks, he said, waiting for his trial. He was barely eighteen.

I was not acceptable, but I was accepted. I was a poor Yank without knowledge, morals, or sense. Nobody wanted to pay me any mind now, and I was so thankful of that. My numbed mind easily sank away, I lay on the edge of sleep. It was pleasant not to think of my misfortune anymore, I had almost found that special place where I really didn't care, I was almost feeling good —

Somebody nudged me. It was the old man, who had taken a seat on the bunk opposite. His name was Meeks. "You ain't asleep, are you?"

No, no I wasn't. I sat up. I had a few cigarettes, and he accepted one, and I lit his and then mine.

"You don know it, but you on the outskirts a hell in here," he said, with a confidential squint of his eye. "From here bout half a these boys goin to the chain gang. Me too I guess." He shook his head sadly. "Checks," he said. "I cain't stop writin em. I drink a little, I start awritin — here I am again. You know how long I been here? Seven months next week. I don know what they gonna do with me this time, an I don think they do either. Hell, I didn write no checks," he looked bitter and angry abruptly. "Anytime they's a bad check floatin, they pick me up. It's got so they don bother to let me loose no more," he chuckled ironically. His changes of expression and apparent mood were terrific. Now he looked mean and sullen. He pulled up his pants' leg and bared a ragged scar. "I was on the rock quarry in fifty-two when they bust they legs to protest the con-

ditions. I was one of em. That the las time they put men on
them rock piles, I was one of Mad Dog's boys that did that."
He dropped his trouser leg down over his calf again with a
flourish, like a curtain over a famous painting. "Listen, I've
wrote to the governor about the situation. He's studyin my
report, but that shit takes time. You in that nigger movement,
ain't you! Y'all think you uncovered some dirt in the South, but
you ain even got near to it. Cause what's gone on in the Georgia prison system an never seen the light a day would make yo
blood curdle, boy. I wish I could put it in a magazine, I wish I
could get it to the president, ah God! Listen, we were on a
hunger strike to protest conditions, I ain't gonna tell you where
till I know ya better. They let us starve a couple weeks, an then
they brought us in the messroom, all us leaders, they was about
a dozen of us you could call the ringleaders. They sat us down
in chairs around a table an put some slop in front of us. They
was a guard behind each one of us, an up on the walkway, like
this balcony up above they was another bunch of em with rifles.
Now we was spose to eat an we was told we gonna sit there till
we do. An meantime they jus whup us. Eat! Each guard behind a man clubs him, left side, right side, left an right. An
every man is bleedin down in his food. An up on that walkway,
next to the armed guards is all they little boys, they sons. They
brought em to get a look how some stubborn ol boys is handled.
Cause they breed them guards, an they train em an they breed
a taste in em for the sadism, an they start when they ain no
more'n six or seven years old. An so next to each one a them
double ugly sonofabitches upstairs, he's got his little kids, to
learn the ropes. Oh, an we eat finally. The men's heads jus
fallen in the slop, an you might say we et . . ."

The cigarette I'd given him was nothing but a tiny ember but he was still smoking on it, between trembling fingertips. Indeed he was all atremble, and if I thought he was a touch crazy, I was beginning to be affected by it. Yeah, I was finding out about this little jail, this waiting room or antechamber for a deeper horror, a dungeon for real. The Georgia chain gang? That's a grade B movie from the thirties, isn't it? Oh yeah, and this old man is a lost and broken actor playing bit parts for strangers in the county jail . . . Whatever else was happening, he had drawn away my self-pity like a mild pus.

thirty

IN THE MORNING, soon's I woke, I made a quick decision. Perhaps I made it in the last moment's unconsciousness. I remembered Feelgood's idea about getting high on nothing, and I took some good deep breaths, and let my mind rise up to a few inches off the ceiling. Thus floating — and it was nothing but jail air too — when I was certain I was above the patterns of the locked pen, and ready for them, I rose and washed up and even ran my comb through my hair. I had an altogether different attitude toward being incarcerated than I had the last time it had happened. A year and a summer had passed. Those days — the time of the CME march — seemed the sultry, contrary days of my very youth, when I would starve myself to punish a sheriff. Oh Christ, no wonder he'd thought me oddly ornery! This time I was going to do anything I could to make myself more comfortable.

When breakfast was served, I was damn hungry and ate every crumb of the cold biscuits and syrup. I was the first one up, but everybody jumped when the man with the tin plates clanked his way in and began shoving plates under the bars.

Before long the card game got started. Reasoning that I couldn't stay aloof from the main activity if I wanted to maintain my tolerable status on the scene, I stooped down and said, "Deal me in." I told them I had money out front where they'd taken it off me last night, and the dealer staked me twenty-five pennies. Well, it was a way to pass the time. Mostly they played twenty-one. I didn't really care, but maybe I'd come out of this hole a few dollars richer.

There were six of us in the game. Besides myself, Dognapper, and the big man he called Turk or Turk-hash, something like that, there was the house painter, who was named Strickland, and a wasted hang-jowl wino with the once-moist-and-now-dried-out look of a desert with fading red hair. They called him Eubanks. Lastly, a man I never did hear speak, a sly-looking little devil. I noticed a hole in one earlobe where he'd once worn a ring. He winced and grinned at his cards, and formed his mouth every which way as he played, but he never spoke. He laughed in his throat, a kind of deep giggle fluidly reaching a crescendo, and sliding away. At its peak, it seemed to envelope the lot of us, as if he were thinking of sucking the game in, like a lizard. Everybody stared at him when he did this, aggravated at more than the loss of a round. But I began to wonder if he had a tongue.

The game went on all day, and well into the evening. Penny by penny, I was winning something, not that I cared about it. I forgot about the phone call I was going to make. About four o'clock in the afternoon, I remembered, and in an offhand kind of way, I decided not to make it. Maybe I didn't want to trouble myself to beg the guards for half an hour for my rights. I felt kind of high, I don't know why. The idea slipped out of my mind, which was contentedly following the dull circle of the betting. Imagine a small game, tireless players, a kind of Monopoly played by small boys over the entire holidays. That's the tone of those days in there. Nothing happened.

On the fourth or fifth day, an exceptionally tall and very drunk dude was brought into the bullpen. I guess I've watched some basketball, and I got to say this cat was close to seven feet. His other distinction was the snakes tattooed up and down his arms. I don't remember his face any better than I do the face of some bowling pins. It was kind of bland and smooth in comparison to his height and girth. When he let him in, the turnkey said, "That the one right there — *Negro* lover!" He pointed at me. He gave the word *Negro* a real fine voice, like he was finally learning how to pronounce it for the first time, just as it was going out of style. The giant looked me over as he reeled by. He scuffed and scattered his way through the game that barely got out of his way in time to remember whose pennies were whose and fell out on somebody's bunk.

It turned out to be Meek's bunk. The old man shut his eyes and began to pick his nose. The game closed ranks, and continued, under a light in Turk's eye that might've been a shade jealous, and definitely was a color of calculating. He was thinking so hard about what to do about this man who was bigger than he was that he lost a few pennies in the hour that Snake Man rested. That's what I call him, this newcomer. And for some reason, I wasn't worried. Because the snake isn't all bad: he's misrepresented that way in the history of Christian consciousness. But he's got more than one side, ol snake. I'm thinking of having a few inked onto my forearm one day. Colors, patterns, diamonds, scales, fangs, forked tongue — the works.

Pretty soon this big joker woke up. Was anybody jittery? Inside I was laughing nervously because the goddam cop had pointed me. *Me!* I was playing cards rationally but I wanted to shake the iron bars. Listen, five thousand folks could shake this mother iron till they were blue in the elbows and what would they get? A headache . . . Nah, I wouldn't touch those bars anymore. Like I used to waste my time shoving at them the last time I was in jail. I wouldn't bother even if they were half sawed through. I knew I wouldn't climb out the window of this place if these boys had it open and were signaling all clear! I could look around and figure the ones who would try to make it. And would slip on a sleeping dog right outside the fence, or stop in the first old-homey and familiar bar they ran across for a short beer.

I watched the big man get up and step out in the pen. I didn't seem to be in my right mind because I wasn't afraid. In other words, attention was centering on me, and my attention wasn't even bothering with the pretty colored cards. I was checking out this hired assassin; if ever I had my cool together I did this time. Because by the little comment the turnkey'd made, I had no doubt that the man in front had offered him something for my scalp. I don't know, nothing much — ten bucks, a fifth of liquor — for a few bruises, a few pretty painful but not so serious blows that'd mostly heal before I got out of here. This sort of thing: this sort of county jug provocation by timorous hopeful sadists called sheriff's deputies.

"Black Jack!" I said, noticing that this was what my cards announced. I raked in about fifty cents worth of pennies.

The Snake Man, approaching, looked at me curiously. As I juggled the pennies back and forth and began to sing to them, he stopped in his motion, he hesitated, the better to check up on this civil rights worker whom he was supposed to demolish, and noticed that it wasn't quite like it was made out to be. That is, he wasn't whiffing the righteous and fearful vibrations that might have belonged to such a one, but instead was shocked with something quite different. In mid-cell he waited like a bear, sniffing the wind, and here I was giving forth incantation to the coins. Oh Christ, in the Boy Scouts, I was making up wordless poetry to those pennies and dimes. Listen to me winnings! Wooooooooooooo! Waaaaaaaaaaaaa! Ahhhhhhhhhhhh! Luckily in gym class back in high school I had learned a little about proper gymnastic juggling, and I began to do some things with those pennies. Well, I can handle three rings or oranges, that sort of thing. I did my best with three coins. Slowly the rest dribbled out my hands until I had but three left, and I made a star in the air and a copper galaxy of these meager three while I sang and whistled. I quite forgot about my assailant. (Though he hadn't announced himself as such, I'm not deaf and dumb, I heard the cop and I knew.) This is what he could not have foreseen, this wave of forgetfulness that confronted his snakes and his simple strength. He waited, and no doubt he was confused.

Out of the corner of my eye, I saw Turk-hash signal him, and the two of them went into his cell together for a little conference. The Turk had it nicely furnished, as this had been his home for quite a while. He had a chair in there between the bunks, and some shelves made of boxes. He had a coffee heater wired from the light socket. All the comforts: writing material, a stack of magazines, an array of toilet articles, a checkers set, and an extra deck of cards. This was all I could see from glances through the doorway on my way to the shitcell or to sit on the "sofa" at the far end of the pen. Old Turk must've been here a long time; but he claimed he was expecting to go on up any day now. He might have to rent a U-Haul for the trip to Reedsville. Now the two men were in there mumbling and discussing. Occasionally their voices would rise, in debate of the issue I was sure was my fate.

I sort of felt like walking in on them with a suggestion, since it was my funeral. Instead I got up off the floor and went to my bunk and sat down on it, and tried to get myself ready for whatever was coming. Cut the humor, I told myself, and get yourself together. Get serious, because when these dudes come out of there, they won't be playing. Instead of bickering and ultimately differing as I'd hoped they would, I could tell by the tone of the voices over there in the number one corner cell that they were nearing a resolution of the matter. My matter! Well I wondered what the Doctor would say right now. It was one thing to feel good and deal with some happenings from that level, no doubt you brought things up to you that might've brought you down; or you let them pass below unnoticed. But this business at hand was something else. This being directly threatened in a locked place. You just couldn't glide off back of the bus, with a nice smoke and a round laugh . . . I might have to fight, I knew that. I didn't have a prayer — but I had a hope. I hoped to hurt somebody.

I did?

Yeah, I was going to grab those snakes and peel em right off the dude's arm! I'd wrap one round his neck and hang him from the shower pipe . . .

"Yank!"

I looked around over in that direction. Turk had his head out the door of his cell and was beckoning to me. I took my time, but I walked on over.

"Court's jus finished up session, an the verdict is guilty," he said, and tilted his head to squint at me.

Well I knew what that meant, but not in particulars. I stared back, hooked my thumbs in my pockets, and leaned closer to him, unblinking.

"Uh the sentence is death," he said. And the weird part of it was, he didn't seem to be joking in any way or fashion. With an effort I kept from gasping or laughing, or taking my eyes off him. A cold sweat was taking on my neck and I was rocking back and forth on my heels so my legs wouldn't start shaking.

"Well fuck that shit," I managed to say.

"Yeah the judge is going to take that under consideration," he said, "whether a degree of clemency is in order. You can go back to your bunk now."

So I did, scowling to prevent any panic showing in my face. I don't imagine I was successful. I glanced at the doors that were locked of course and blank of any hope of intervention. What the hell was going to happen? On my bunk I didn't think, because, really, I didn't have anything to think about. I took out some tobacco I'd bought from the sheriff's store and rolled myself a cigarette. A Negro trusty took orders in the morning and brought you your tobacco or newspaper or soda or whatever in the afternoon. He wasn't trusted with any keys though. He opened a small latched door in the big steel one to the walkway. Then he placed your item on a broom which he extended through the little square hole across the space to the bars of the pen, and you grabbed it. He was very deft at it, and could pass a drink that way. Everything cost at least three times its normal price at the sheriff's store.

I was sitting on my bunk, thinking, someday I'll write about it. As if affirming life and the future, 1 thought to myself, there were a lot of things I'd write about. For the first time since I'd done it, I regretted destroying those notes I'd made at Cara Lee's and in Jones' apartment. Facing this trouble, locked up in the pen, I realized that the writing must have celebrated the life I'd led — life itself. I could easily recall it; I'd set it down yet. I'd celebrate again. Yeah — remembering the business that was so pressing it had almost slipped my mind — I'll write about this kangaroo court in the county jail. I knew I was going to live; I hadn't really lost my sense of humor. I looked around at everyone sitting in slouched attitudes of waiting. I couldn't see Meeks; he must be on his bed. Yeah, I'll write about you bastards! It was my last defense.

"Yank!"

I started.

Turk was calling once more. On legs that were half-dead already, I walked over.

"The sentence been reduced to a fine. You're a very lucky man. How much money you got?"

Quickly I figured it out. Christ, I didn't mind. I guess I was really kind of scared. I was almost a dollar ahead in the game, and that gave me about four dollars and a half. I told him that. He went back into conference with Snakes. A moment later he walked out of his cell and over to the main door and began hollering for a deputy.

Business was soon transacted. I gave Turk my winnings, and out front they subtracted all my money from the paper bag into which it had been placed when I'd been booked. The total was enough for a pint of whiskey, which was brought in by the deputy himself in a large Dixie cup. The two big men settled back in Turk's cell to drink it up.

"Hey, look here," I called to the snake judge, and ventured

into the entrance of the cell to catch his eye. "I know you ain't gonna deny a man a sip a that there that he's bought you!" I was giving him a sly but humble look around Turk who was rising to chase me away.

"Sure kid," said the biggest man, and handed me the cup once. Yeah, I thought, I knew a snake. I got me a few swallows of the whiskey, my share, and went back to my bunk to lie down and let it take a hold. Pretty soon I was feeling almost mellow.

Maybe the hours of getting stoned and listening to the grasses with Yellow and the Doctor had set me up for this. I can't deny I've always been a drifter, finding his way without forepurpose to places where he doesn't much belong, although the spots where I've lingered — this jail for instance, or the movement office — may correspond to something in the subconscious. My friends had shown me how to be happy without anything and without anywhere. Their river I had sat by with reflections and smoky images rolling through my brain so many, many hours, I wondered if the place could have been dreamt. Life will grow sad but it won't stop. In jail, after a time, freedom itself and the free world begin to dim and waver. Visible through a crack or little window only, or more likely only remembered, it is replaced by what is immediate and tangible. And for the imprisoned man, a new figure is begun, and all the dear values begin turning inside out. He may weep a lot at first, silently or very loud, waking us all with a scream as he remembers in the night that he's going to do without the comforts now, like his wife. And none of the men tries to quiet him, though if he goes on too long, they'll be moaning and groaning too and cursing their lot that he's reminded them of. But if anything's sacred in jail, it's these moments of realization and new terror. Because the men are a little superstitious and not all the way dead, nobody mess with him then. But inside the locks nothing is sacred for too long.

I remembered the weeks of waiting around in Cambridge, after I'd dropped my studies at Harvard, so long ago. In some odd way, on the planes of my present mood, I was carried back to that anguished yet delicious time of indecision, when I knew I was going but nothing else. I guess I'd enjoyed the ease or detachment, the lack of any demands on me. If I'd been allowed to leave this jail when I wanted, taking only my meals, sleep, and various relaxation here, it would've been exactly the same.

"Red clay, pot liquor, an dirty faces," sang one of the men, "In Dixieland Ah take mah stand — *Hello, Sheriff!*"

Everyone was looking toward the door. There were other respectful and friendly greetings called, and some of the men got to their feet and began making requests as none other than the sheriff unlocked the pen door. I could tell it was the man himself by his big hat and his big star.

"I hope it's a drunk," I heard Turk mumble. He was peeping past the man to see who might be coming in, and whether he might be worth anything.

In a corner, Eubanks the wino was saying, "If it ain't a lunacy warrant, then it's a wife warrant; if it ain't a peace warrant, it's a —"

The sheriff called my name, my first name. Stupidly I just sat there staring at him.

"Get up boy!" the sheriff demanded. "You belong to stay in here, but we can't afford ya no more!"

In a strange daze I got to my feet. My heart was leaping.

Ironically, on my tongue were the words, "Could I make a phone call please?" but I had no voice. Was I being freed?

I glanced back once at the broken rank of men. Eyes flickered and narrowed in farewell. Take care of yourselves, I thought to say, and I had the feeling, misplaced as it was. But there was nothing to say.

We made our way in silence through the series of gates. The sheriff's hatred of me was coming through the air like some kind of grease or butterfat; maybe he was frying me in his mind. But I was on my way out, and I didn't know what to make of it, because I had never come to deal with being imprisoned these many days. All in all, I was way behind in my response to life's surprises. My head was so strange, full of memories that didn't belong to me, lives that had no relation to mine, the rolling fog. When we got to the desk, the sheriff let go my arm and I stopped. But he kept going. He never glanced around again, but walked right out of the place. The desk sergeant extended a paper to me and a pen, and the envelope that contained my valuables. I was supposed to put down my signature that I was receiving everything I had entrusted to them.

"Somebody made bond for me?" I asked.

"How do I know?" asked the cop. "Sign that."

I opened the envelope. All my money was gone of course, taken out for the whiskey. The only thing left would be my green stone ring. I poured it out. It was broken up in pieces. I stood there looking at the smashed remnants of my beautiful ring in my palm.

"I ain't signin *nothin*," I mumbled bitterly.

"You gotta sign to get outa here," he insisted. "You wanna go back inside?"

This cop didn't know where my mind was. I turned and

looked at the gate I'd come out of. Sure I'd hate to go back in there, but I didn't care, I'd go to sleep. I was mad about my ring for which I'd paid ten dollars, and liked even better than that.

"Look officer, it says here, 'One Ring.' It says, '*Received!*' I'm not gonna sign that, because look at this shit!" I spilled the fragments on the desk in front of him, and he swept them off and jumped around his desk, and aimed a kick at me that I backed off from like lightning.

"Look, write down here, 'Some broken pieces,' or something, I'll sign," I conceded.

"Get outa here!" he yelled. He started for me, and there was no place to go but out the front door, and I ran.

And I ran! And then I stopped and walked, and tried desperately to assemble my thoughts, because why was this happening to me? I had to get to Angel's. I wasn't as happy to be free as I should've been because it had happened too fast, and with a weird aspect to it, like the sheriff coming to get me and suddenly vanishing. Why had they just let me go? I remembered what had happened in Mississippi, that Mississippi summer and the murders that I'd read about in the Georgia papers. They had arrested them and then suddenly, arbitrarily, let them go. Now I couldn't avoid the bitter remembrance, and it was blending with the memory of the cop trying to kick me minutes ago: and a chill of fear and a cold brittle hate were soon all I felt, though the afternoon had been warm for a moment, the sun was shining, and at the instant of escape there was a balmy breeze blowing. With Angel I'd feel myself again. For a second I had a taste like a milk shake I might buy myself, for a pleasure on the way, and then the lightheartedness was burned away, turned dry and acrid in the fears. It was so strange to be free — yes I almost wished I was back inside. The sky, the countryside, the court buildings, and even the stone steps behind me were glassy, as under an intense heat. I walked down a paved sidewalk through a gate in the barbed-wire fence that was open, and out onto the shining asphalt highway to town. The complex of institutions was out a few miles in the country, in a picturesque setting. I took one last glance at the joint, and I didn't see one guard or any person, and I started walking fast down the shoulder of the road. I was glad to be out of the hard trapped balance of pennies and prides that'd been life in there — but this! I was entering a new stage of confinement — the fears.

thirty-one

I STRODE FAST, trying to get a jump on it, whatever it was. How ironic that the expansive discipline of Feelgood, which had enabled me to get high even off the bad air of the enclosure, had shattered like my ring on the moment of freedom, and was not to be had again for the wishing, or willing. Maybe if I had *tried* to get out, I would now understand the release, and be strolling free and easy down the autumn afternoon. Had my drift and long silence given them the impression that here was a sympathizer who could safely be disposed of? Could my hate for them, alone, produce such fear? For a moment I considered the possibility that I was only inventing the danger that I sensed, and that I should enjoy, and take my leisure on the road, realizing that I was no longer of interest to the authorities.

I wished I could see it that way. The faster I walked, the more scared I got, but when I eased up and tried to amble, my fright tripled. The air was conveying a message of the danger to me, the probability was in the air, and I had no business to tarry. Now I could wish, suggest, pretend, or deny, but if I did

I would have to ignore my sixth sense which dwelt in the air and was finding there a murderous being, a danger, a likelihood of some disaster. And, ah damn, when I think on it now, I wasn't wrong.

The pastureland was giving way to hamburger heaven, and I'd reached the outskirts of Meansville. The windows of motels reflected the empty road. Hundreds of cars were parked everywhere, like coin collections, but few were in motion in my view. This in itself was eerie, like why was everything and everybody and all the vehicles all stopped for lunch or something. What mad coincidence, to further convince me that I'm going to be ambushed!

Dogged, said Mrs. Chaney.

And I'll see a few cops' or crackers' lives go down the sink for the three lives of those cats in Mississippi! I thought, enraged, forgetting my own dire exposure of the moment in a gladness even to think of revenge.

A corner of an industrial area came next along the road. The Swift's meat-packing plant assaulted my eye, and reminded me of past indignities that me and Knight had inflicted on the cracker princes. Not much we had! Ha-ha! A joyousness of past successes relieved my paranoia and, knowing what had already been accomplished, I didn't fear. I guess I was getting kind of stoned on my own motion, plus the big silver view of Swift's dominating the roadway as in the old bad days around here. Yes I was a stone's throw away from where a fire had raged one sweet night seemed not so long ago. Christ! — and for a fine moment I reveled in the deeds we'd done. And I revered the memory of my friend who was in New York or fell on elsewhere with his incendiary laughing spirit! Angel and I would soon be laughing. My walk had spring to it all of a sudden, out

of the well of my mind which was taking stock of reality and
the past for a change and not possible whiplash of the powers'
fancy in the future . . .

The automobiles began revving up in the parking lots around
the hamburger stands. A terrific din of engines under the feet
of nervous boys began to siren in the air. I was swearing at my
luck, that had these jokers jumping into their machines all at
the same time after early evening coffee break, to blow my
mind on the coincidence of it. — Nah, nah, no coincidence!
Stop evading mind that wants to blame this evil that is looming
now on a haphazard luck in time-space, and face up, get ready
motherfucker, get ready! Because here come some crackers —
the road was filling with cars, accelerating. They don't care —
they began to buzz past me, too close. I was on the shoulder
but so were they. If they can, they run your soul in that ditch
an cover it with Klan dung and a new freeway! So how about
that, Jones, so how about stop meandering along this highway
and cut off in the bush! Go around that gas station, and step in
behind that Pecan House, get off this open road, Jim —

Boy, I was talking to myself, and looking for a good side
street to duck down. But they all looked hostile as this highway, and the shiny Chevys driven by crackers were pouring
down every one. *Bleeeeeaaay!* — I glanced back. Here came
some honky, down the damn shoulder of the road, headed right
at me. He was just laying on his horn: *Bleeeee-B-bleeeaaaaay!*
At the last moment I dived into the ditch, and he swerved half
in the ditch right after me. I didn't quite get up. I knelt there
and watched the car careen away, with heads leaning out for a
back look at me, arms waving some damn message. Was that a
little gun I noticed in one hand?

Ahead, up the road, was a stand of small trees, a little dwarf woods it looked like, colors green and yellow. With all my heart I wanted to make it up there and enter its cover, but I couldn't get my legs together for the move. I was afraid the car would circle around for another shot at me. I waited, on my knee, and watched it disappear out of sight. And then I took off — I sprinted — keeping down, ludicrously, I thought, but I was that frightened. When I hit the fresh little woods, earth smells greeted me like old friends. The countryside impinged on the town at this point, it hadn't yet been uprooted and cleaned out for new developments. I ran back in the trees until I couldn't hear or see anything of the road or town anymore. The air had been filled with the possibility of police sounds to confirm my dread. The abrupt and inexplicable origin of this trip away from jail had resounded in my ear like a single drumbeat of the enemy's thousand drums. I was extremely tired. The silence of the little wood was kind; the earth was covered with fallen leaves that gently puffed around me and cushioned me when I fell down to rest. Now I could let time pass like the river, I felt safe from pursuit. I slept.

I awoke gradually. I noticed the sky through the leafy tips of the trees. I was in a new place — my mood reflected the still forest; perhaps it deepened the stillness. I was terrifically refreshed by perhaps an hour of sleep. The sun had moved no farther than that in the sky. I did not think of the recent fear, but only of where I was going. My confidence in freedom would be restored by a little smoke over at the motel with Angel.

The danger seemed not to have vanished. But I felt confident of avoiding it. I rose to my feet and continued in the direction away from the highway, through the forest. If I wasn't mistaken, this would be the way to the road that would take me to the center of town. This woods was really no more than a green slip at the edge of town. Straight out, it probably connected with a woodlands of the county, but I was cutting across it. In minutes I was on the other side of it, and standing in a dirt road that was not the exact one I was seeking, but it was familiar. This was the road on which Deacon and Mrs. Stock lived! On my way into town, I would have to pass right by their house. That made me feel good . . .

As I approached Mount Olive Church on the corner of the block, I heard a hymn. A service of some kind was in progress. And when I was crossing the street and nearing its front doorway, a movement song was surging up, and the air was electric with memory of our march, and all the marches . . .

> Ain gonna let nobody turn me roun,
> Turn me roun, turn me roun —
> Ain gonna let nobody turn me roun,
> Keep on a walkin,
> Keep on a talkin,
> Marchin up to freedom land!

I wanted to make it into town, but I was drawn up the steps by the sound. In the doorway I stood and gazed into the shady interior of the church; I stepped into the shade. A rainbow of colors passed over my eyes, and faded. A memory perhaps, or just a physical reaction to the change from the sunshine. A small group of people sat at the front of the church; they were making a big sound, with all their hearts. When it got low and soft and sad, it was still so vibrant and bighearted. Well, there was no safer place to be, even the cops were hesitant about entering a church to do some evil. I sat down in the last pew, just enjoying the sensations of the voices and the place. In a few minutes my eyes had got used to the lack of light, but I didn't think I could recognize anybody I knew. I saw a few faces, but nobody I knew well enough to go up and speak to. I was glad to be more or less hidden back here. I was self-conscious about being in church in my messed-up jail clothes. The people were radiant like after a long sing: a look of spent energy in their faces could have been grief turning to joy. All at once, out of the preacher's chambers, out the doorway behind the pulpit, walked the Director and Deacon Stock. That was a mighty surprise, and I wondered what was up. By the grave light in their faces as they came forward, the Director to take the stand, the deacon to sit beside him on the platform, I knew that something was wrong.

In a few moments I knew that somebody had been killed by the police, a young boy, who'd been playing down by the dump with some other kids, and been wantonly, unreasonably murdered. He'd been shot in the back, he was dead. The Director didn't mention his name, he described him as a "gentle child that was as little deserving of being hurt as any man on earth." I hoped it was none of the kids I knew. Not that it would change the sudden sad confirmation. The Director was more angry and more vocal than ever I'd seen him. He suggested no action, he did not refer to the nonviolent program. He offered the people only his rage. "The *law* murder the most innocent! An hide an succor them in the white race that commit these crimes. So that if a ordinary white man kill one of us . . . a *nigger* . . . he is as much as promoted to deputy an protected. It happens every year, the children and the weak among us are gunned *down* in cold blood, by the law, that is supposed to protect . . ." His anger was punctuated with long silences. He emphasized his feeling with his forefinger pointed down at the floor. His whole arm was shaking. In many synonymous statements he talked about the caprice of white power. The last was this: "Listen now, we were down at the station to pay a traffic ticket this *morning!* An who do they have on the desk, who they got? — That right, the *murderer*, the same cop! An while we had to put down the money an pay the fine, that foul . . . that filth . . . he *whistlin* . . ."

I wondered when he had been killed. The question in my mind was triggered by its own irrelevance, by a will to stave off deeper thought. I mean, if he'd been killed last week or last night, what difference? The attitude of the cop whistling was all the same. The Director left the pulpit with that bitter note ringing in the air. He walked right out of the place, for an effect, or because that's how bad he was feeling. On his way, he noticed me, kind of scrunched down under weights of sadness in the back row, and he extended his hand to me. I took it, though I was astounded, for at this time I would have been glad for a slim nod from the Director. Then out he went, leaving me a little more confused in my low bad mood.

I was familiar with the Meansville dump. Yeah, I knew the area where the shot rang out, and the kid fell . . . Christ, I could get lost and blank in mind thinking of the municipal wastelands with some poor people picking in it. As Deacon Stock rose to the pulpit, my imagination pictured the exact and far-reaching scene wherein the boy — who was it? — was murdered. On the farthest hill a mother and her babies are picking for raiment, or food or salables amid the refuse. The city men are burning piles of mostly paper and dried garbage close to the river at the north end, and the smoke is blowing under a mild wind across the river into the area known as East Meansville, where black citizens glance up and curse their luck, that this is the whim of the wind this day, and might be seen wiping ash off their cheek with a thoughtless finger. Do you know the feeling of an ash on your cheek; it's a teasing fleeting sensation that's demanding you to satisfy it, like your favorite appeasable image of death. In the river itself, as the shot is fired, all the little fish jump, and in this bad dream, the water moans, knowing a child, a friend, is lost.

Now the deacon was in the pulpit, my attention was returned to the altar by his mention of a name: the name of the kid. I didn't recognize it, so I don't remember it, but this did not relieve me, as I might have expected. It made the death seem more lonely. Like if I'd known him, I might share in the grief a little; and though I'd felt afraid I'd be familiar with the victim, the fact that I was not was a strange new sadness in itself. Why was I here then? These mourners didn't need any gratuitous extra pity from a passerby. I was on the verge of getting up and starting on my way again, out of respect for them all, the dead one, and myself, when the deacon extended his arm toward me, and called my name. I was already half standing. He said, "An he had many friends, and here is one of them . . . Come on an join us . . ."

Heads turned around, and if I hadn't been in the last row in the place, mine would've turned too . . . But it must be me! The deacon wants me to come forward, he says . . . I was talking to myself, like I wasn't sure what I understood, and if I repeated it mentally it might take a clearer shape for me. I took a few steps forward in the aisle. But I didn't know the dead one, I'd never heard his name before! Of course, I might've been his friend, had I had the chance . . . In the front the people were buzzing softly. Words were appearing out of the warm stream of their talk like butterflies out of the sky, a meta-morphosis to my ear, now a winged name: *Yellow* . . .

Yellow?

And now the deacon was saying, "He wasn't more'n a boy in mind, but he had heart of a great man, oh yes; he was a special one . . . An he was cursed in his lot, but blest in his soul, an may his soul find good rest with its maker . . ."

Now I was resisting that with all the heart *I* had, standing there in the aisle, hearing these words that told me it was so. And if I could've kept the knowledge away for another moment, I might've gone forward, and become one with the people grieving, whose grief must have had much in common with my own that was beginning to pour through me with the quickening flow of my blood that I believed had something in it of his. And as I stood there, dumbfounded, I knew that if ever I'd had a friend, the lighthearted man Yellow had been my friend, and had the cops known he was my friend? Whatever the constellation of circumstances that had led to the shooting, it could've been me, because he was my brother, my spirit man, cat who was teaching me, and I was learning when I'd gone to jail . . . Or was I? What was I doing that night out at the Pines other than thoughtlessly drifting into trouble with the powers that are a law to themselves, in their own time? Angling for a woman, a high, in what waters? I should've stayed downtown where I belonged. And they let me out when they got ready to, didn't they (by what logic I would've given an eye to know), only to discover that Yellow was gone . . . *dead?* Yes, the people gazing at me with some concern were telling me that. His name was echoing from their lips and filling the church like a light drone that has been building for centuries. And now that their faces were turned around toward me, I began to recognize acquaintances. There was Mae; there were others from CME. Cara Lee was not there, she'd never gone in much for church. I saw the barber who'd been the recipient of Jones' stolen barber's chair that day when Yellow had enabled me not just to feel but to act in accurate generosity. When it seemed I had so little to give. The good connection Yellow; and how many of his friends were here, friends to each other. And over on the right, smiling at me, and inviting me away from the terror that was paralyzing me, to a kinder grief, was Mrs. Boket. Oh I wanted to talk with her! But the Doctor was not in here, and somehow I felt that only he could tell me what had happened. I had learned more than I wanted to in the church that had seemed like a sanctuary at first — I'd stumbled in here to find out that the air had not lied to me, a horror had occurred, my unreasonable fears were confirmed. But I wouldn't sit down with them, to let it sink in. I was free from jail; a dear friend was dead, but in grief I did not enter the ranks of the mourners. The mystery turned me around. I wasn't ready to give him up yet. I sped from the church and into the street, and ran for the river road.

I must've run for a mile before I had to slow down to a walk. I passed the dump at a dead run, burning: here it was, here it was. An emotion that was anger, hate, grief, and wonder released the adrenaline and alchemized the strength. I was glad I'd done some pacing inside, I wasn't as weakened by the confinement as I might've been, but it was the near madness of the moment that drove my legs down the clay road. The considerable release of energy seemed to bathe my senses. Soon I was out of town again, on the other side. The countryside was startling in its beauty. Nobody knows the beauty of the outdoors like a man just out of jail, and the run cleared up even memory of the place and blanked my mind for the new sight. I got glimpses of the river, while I burned away my power, and with it my anticipation of seeing the Doctor soared up, like a bird flying along the winding course, above the trees that rooted always near its blue succor. When I'd weakened, as I walked, I tried to think. But my mind moved slowly, although maybe more deeply than usual. Perhaps because I felt I'd lost a brother, the thought came to me that Feelgood was more than a friend, I'd found him a way to a place in my life that was something like a father. And this might not be fair to him, and it was probably nothing that he wanted, but to myself it seemed it was too true. I was on my way to him to beg his explanation of the tragedy. I would also seek rest, in his house, and wisdom perhaps, because, if it's possible, I had less idea of the future than at any time in my life. I had no sense of anything but my feet following each other deeper into the river forest. Every few moments the terrible news I'd just received popped in my mind like the bursting of a molten bubble in hot glass, and strange rivulets of rage and confused unbelief flowed in seams of red dye through my brain, behind my eyes that lost sight of everything until — snap — the cycle had temporarily passed. Then a clear moment, when I'd know where I was going, right now, through the country, and that's all . . .

(And perhaps he was running toward the river when they got him. The Director had said they shot him in the back. Perhaps, in the moments of panic, he had turned all his hope and belief to the water, and run toward it, somehow depending on her to receive and conceal him when this was no longer possible because of the speed of the hunter. And maybe his soul had not stopped, when he was stopped. His soul was so fast, to the river . . .)

They *dogged* him, I thought, and began to cry, and tears as full of hate as bullets sped down my face. And I guess if I'd've had a gun, and the road had had some cops on it, or *any* crackers, I'd've fired and fired. As usual I was full of the emotion when there was not a chance of getting it expressed. Thinking that, I hated myself for it. As I walked I dreamed my way into the head of a man whose experience has made him hate cops, who is afraid of them anytime they come around, but one day gets his timing right — and kills three or four. Inside my head I heard Yellow chuckle: "Whew! Good thing dreams ain't crimes!" I smiled now at myself, and thought, God, the cat's good spirit still helps me out, maybe his soul does linger here . . . And then I got sad again. I wondered bitterly, What did he ever do to them? And I wondered, was there any anwer to that question . . .

It seemed I was nothing but a walking question, and it was a long walk, and the question that I would ask Feelgood kept forming and re-forming in my mind like the face of life itself. Essentially, I guess, I wanted to know what to make of the past, that was suddenly so terrible, and what attitude to take into the future; don't we all? Yes. But the thing of it was I kept meeting people around here who seemed to me to offer a vision that'd be more than helpful. But Feelgood's was the best, though he was in exile. Down by the river, he had shown me how to float, and I had him to thank for a stint in jail that could've been worse, but I found a height and a warmth that made it something passable. And no sooner did I get my freedom, which was unbearable, than I found out Yellow had been killed, and I understood why I'd felt the murderous vibration in the air, because my friend had been murdered! The train of thought that set off included all my recent wisdom, and was possibly nowhere. I couldn't be sure of that until I got where I was going, the house with the orange bus in front of it. I was walking and dreaming . . .

I had no recourse but to dream, because the damage that had been done my life by one whistling bullet off a cop that was playing judge to niggers like he thought this was the nineteenth century, that loss would never be recovered, not if Abraham Lincoln were to be born again in the form of Marcus Garvey. Because me and Yellow, we went by the underways of the nation, and snuck under some tree-lined rivers, where the clay washes away in the water, and a new hipster playing a Jew's harp might meet up with an old bum eating beans out of a can, or a dropout from the New African State might give a few moments of his time to a college coed concerned about saving some unheard-of species of near-extinct waterfowl on the marshes of now Black America, and if I were to die right now by a whim of some little sheriff, for anything, I don't know what (trust the powers to come up with a reason small enough), there might be no one to mourn me at all, since Yellow was shot. So I dreamed, picturing the dread town I walked through as a mysterious city whose heart I was approaching. And on the river that divided the city into an East and a West side, at a spot not notable for anything at all that the town could name, and the fishing was not so good there either, so the water itself did not mark it particularly, there lived my friend, to whose homestead I was determinedly stepping. Jesus, it was a long ways! Especially when I had to walk five miles or so through the county and that long mile across town to get at the beginning of the river road, where it took off near the dump, and started through the lost and ancient areas of this postwar-booming Meansville . . .

I was miles away yet, but I had a picture of him in the house, maybe out on the back stoop getting high, eyes closed, but he looks up when I come up, lets his eyes alight just a little, saying hello, after a long time — ·

"Where you been?" he asks after a moment.

"In jail, till this afternoon —" I stop, but try to add something to that, and don't have anything else to say, because what I've already said reminds me of all that's unsayable, which's been drifting all around me while I've walked, but when I try to speak of it, no different than the red sun up on the horizon that people have often called to my attention, there are no words, I hardly have a sociable word in my mouth and I just can't find a handle for an awful subject . . . "Man everything's happened since this afternoon, Yellow — and I'm out but there seems like a jail in the air . . ."

"Y'always get outa jail too sudden," he mumbles.

"Yeah, all of a sudden I'm out on the street . . . What happened, Doctor?"

In response he hands me the pipe. Pulling on the smoke, I look up in the sky, so it'll be my impression. I notice a flame in the sky. It isn't an offshoot of the sun, perhaps it reflects a fire that is burning somewhere on the land. It's pale, and the paleness of it persuades me that the fire is dying down. Perhaps downtown Meansville has been burning since Yellow had been killed, and whole blocks are smoldering now. It was pleasant to imagine so . . . My anger was easing up on me, having an image outside to attach itself to. I went on rehearsing the meeting that would take place when my strength and patience had finally overcome all these miles: the image of Dr. Feelgood giving me words and feelgood kept appearing in my head with the stubborn insistence of my desire for an answer, and I should have been content for it all to unfold but I couldn't help anticipating it.

"Boy, I ain gon rehearse it no more," he says abruptly, fixing me with a look that demands I accept what is and not pester him about it. "You been livin in the South, you an American, you spent your little time in jail, you ain got to ask me nothin . . . It might jus start to echo . . ."

So I don't say anything more, just draw on the smoke, and the garden burns a brilliant green, and the cabbages bulge, and the turnip greens wave in the air. "Naw, I don't understand it," I have to mumble on the crest of a stony acceptance of it.

"See me? I'm high, Jones!" he says, in a tone that seems to close the subject with a slam, almost as though I've been trying to steal something from him. But immediately he turns back to me and says, "What right you got to feel so sad?"

"Right!" At first the question offends me. "I was his friend too," I say, defensively, I realize.

"You a movemen all right," he smiles sadly. "I allow all my thoughts. I don grieve long, so I ain much afraid. You wanna picture when he was killed an give em that too? If you sorry, you don love Yellow . . ."

For a moment I feel so glad . . . I thought I loved Yellow. I know that if I was strong I would not let the feeling be interrupted . . . But immediately the knowledge he is dead crosses my mind with an enormous frightening weight . . . Can I ever be that strong? While I doubt it, somewhere in my mind Feelgood goes on talking:

"When did you hear, boy? I bet not till you got out, they keep all the news from you in a jail, I know . . . Well it was a shock to me too, cause can you believe it could hit you any other way? I took it in, yes, I knew what happened, an then I turn aroun, I watch it shoot on by. You see? I let the shock of it pass on through me an continue on its way, yeah. That bullet missed *me*, you understan? Now I'm gon tell you somethin you might know an that is Yellow was my son. So you see why I love him like I do . . ."

What? His son! It must be I feel pity for myself, that there will be no more afternoons by the river fishing with Cousin Yellow. I don't know what I'm going to do, because it seemed I was learning something, I thought I was about to break on through to a kind of easy permanent joy, and then when I hardly expected such shit, I was thrown in jail, and Yellow was murdered. And this circle of thought will not leave me alone. Was I only tormenting myself, or was this the message from the sun and stars for which I guess I'd been waiting. My God, I couldn't stop here, I knew that. How to go on, I wondered — how? As if fear followed grief, and the deepest gloom chased my loss like the dog I might have been, its tail, I almost prayed to the Doctor, they dogged him man! How will I ever care about folks again, or know any joy?

And I ask him, I form the most paranoid thought that I have: "Doctor, why was it they shot him and then let me go?" As if there is a connection there, in the past or the future. As if I'd caused it — or there was more trouble on its way.

And he says without the slightest hesitation, "You alive, son, cause it ain your time yet. Like everybody . . . Yellow was your good frien wasn he . . ."

. . . And yet I was only still walking the road, in the windless green air, and night was coming on, the sun had gone. The river trees and underbrush were cast in gloom of shadow, in the sky a nearly full moon was gleaming. I admired the mindless life around me, I felt the forms of the air imperceptibly changing, and between Yellow and me, as if in a river or a fire, the elemental distance was flowing and raging, and I might have understood how it was drawing us together, would make us one.

And then I flashed I might have got it wrong: it might not have been Yellow! And in the church a voice of fear might have sounded a bad image, to frighten me. The picture of the Doctor glancing at me, surprised, shaking his head, no. And I see Yellow walking out of the forest, into the garden, with his light smile that says I've been wrong about him as I'd been in the past. He isn't dead! And a tragedy of an unknown boy's death is distant, and even it can't stop my bounding spirit. I began to run again, and a fragrance in the air through which I dived kept shouting to me: this might be so! I was closing in on the last mile, and I evened my pace, I slowed, I let the second wind rise, and carry me easily, I coasted on my hope . . .

But in a parenthesis within the good wish, fear appeared once more, that all that lay ahead of me was stranger bitterness, and in my mind's eye the Doctor has walked out in his garden, he is stooping along a row, pulling weeds. When I arrive, he looks up at me with a steamy, deranged eye that speaks of places way, way off from my memory of him. I feel that we hate the same thing, and are separated by that hate. And when I try to speak of it, he cuts me off with an almost furious word. "Why live there!" he cries, and dismisses something with a violent wave of both hands. Where? I think, lost. "Look here, don just stan there flappin your mouth, gimme a hand! Help me with this garden, get your mind off your troubles . . ." I get down too, and begin to tear up weeds from between the cabbages. "Been neglectin this garden," he mutters, and doesn't speak for a while, gives his whole attention to the work.

He does it *well,* his motions are continual, his face reflects his hands' effort. There is a feverish glint in his eye. I see the subtleties or rhythms to his way of doing it, and I try to get into it like him. But there is so much I want to ask him — and I don't have a question. Occasionally he mumbles things like, "I'm an old man, an I plan to live! I'm gon eat these crops next winter." I keep studying him out of the corner of my eye for better signs, but he seems totally absorbed in his task . . .

The visions of hope and fear were competing in my head, as I ran, or floated, down the road. They alternated with a dialectical rapidity that must've kept releasing adrenaline, else from where did this long last spurt of energy come? I was past tired. It was night now, and my feet knew the road better than my eyes. They knew when I'd rounded the final bend, they knew the house was just ahead — and then I saw it, I saw the orange bus gleaming in the moonlight, and I laughed; it was a happy sight. Relieved, I walked, I gasped in air and found that new relationship to the earth, after the run. On the back stoop, would sit the Doctor, or in the garden, or perhaps he'd be in the kitchen — was that a light I saw back there? I walked around. He wasn't on the stoop. So — but no there was no light inside. And at a glance I knew there was nobody in the garden. I went inside, I lit the lamp — but all surfaces were bare! A chill touched me — sense of an unexpected emptiness in the house, and I grabbed a breath, and checked through the house, and saw all his clothes were gone. No, it didn't look like he was out for an hour, or the evening. His things were not here, that he never even bothered to lock. A terrible disappointment was bringing me low. Yeah, here was an answer for my hope and sorrow, but what could I make of it? Suddenly my fear was back. Remembering something he'd told me once about the heat, signs, and leaving, I stepped onto the porch and studied the beautiful garden. Did I think it'd tell me why he'd disappeared? For a moment I thought of waiting here the night. It was as good a place as any to take some rest — but so damn lonely, in an abandoned house where once a happy sage had lived! This was my picture, and the longer I stood and thought, the sadder I got. I imagined the process of this slight establishment of Feelgood's sinking into the earth. The house would rot, the bus rust to the clay, the forest would ease away the garden. The Doctor had never taken anything like that seriously, I was noticing the weeds with affection. I walked out into the garden. There were weeds, but they didn't crowd the vegetables. I could live here for some time, I reckoned, on all the good greens growing here, and with the river nearby. It was an idea, and momentarily it dissipated my strangeness. It was a possibility to think about, once I'd found out why my friend had left and what that meant for me. There was something evil and sad in the air, but even a word from him might have cleared that up. Only nothing was cleared, and my confusion confounded. What the hell had happened here in the good out areas of Meansville while I'd been in the jail? I remembered the night I met the fine old man, with Jones introducing me, which was confusing at first, because Jones didn't know who the fuck he was! Jones thought the Doctor was a con man! I spat, remembering this. In my mind was the image of him gliding away to the movies, an inexorable and fast motion away that stung me with the present. That night I thought I'd never find him again, I saw he was a country person by his bearing and clothes, and I knew only Meansville then. But now I was at his house, and his house was empty of his belongings, and all signs said he was gone, and the sad feeling that, just when I'd hoped to ask him something or other, he'd vanished, was my reality — a vanishing reality as it were. Empty-headed, I meandered through the winding garden. Now if ever I was lost and didn't know where I was going, I guess this was the time. Though I'd been afraid, I'd never doubted the Doctor would be out here to greet me with life's explanation, and so I'd dreamed and riffed and anticipated all the way — for nothing. Right now I felt like I was through with dreaming. Because I was so tired and drained — and through my second wind I'd guessed the most exhausted sleep was going to bless me after I got to Feelgood's house; and now I was strange slides beyond that. I'd arrived and found not even some good ghost of the man, no sign or remnant that might show me where I might look for him, and as I wandered through the garden, I thought I was going to drop from fatigue. My head was swimming, and I could hardly remember a thing and even my sorrow was no more than a dull lump under the strained confusion . . . But the curves were delighting me, the garden was so peaceful and it gave me pleasure. The curves of the garden were gently and greenly enlivening my drift, and I didn't fall to the earth or stumble back to the house for some sleep, but kept walking through the plants, not knowing. I was near the woods. I thought of the hill — *the hill of the senses* — and with a sudden joy I decided to walk there.

thirty-two

ON THE HILL I rested maybe an hour. I seemed to be past sleep, in another realm. The night was so deep, there was no way to be afraid out here. The emptiness and immensity of space was a terrific *nothing* that was deepening the absence of friend and answer at which I'd arrived with such a shock. I had no ideas, I just wanted to go on resting here . . . In the distance, over the horizon where the town should be, orange lights appeared and lasted. Something was happening over in town; I wondered what trouble in the aftermath of the murder. That light I had seen in the sky this afternoon, that had been no lie of the vapors, it must be fire. Revenge of some kind in motion for the killing, and I wished it well. But when I thought of the town, I thought only of Angel. If dreams were true, she'd be here beside me on the hill, or I would suddenly find myself near the motel in town, about to find her. I stood up, thinking to start walking. But I didn't think I had strength for the walk . . . Then it occurred to me Mrs. Boket might be at home by now, and that maybe I could borrow her car. There was a chance. I made it to the road and started on to her house, which was not far at all from the hill. The closer I got, the more closely I thought of her. I couldn't deny my desire for her which I'd felt since I'd first met her, so I indulged it. I quickened my steps. My desire — that I wasn't certain I approved of — put a little new strength into my sore feet . . . I saw her Cadillac, she was home. But when I knocked on the door, she was a long time coming. A lamp flared. Finally I could hear her. The door opened. Her face was weary. She was wearing a robe; maybe she had been asleep. She was surprised to see me, but she welcomed me warmly, in a far quieter voice than I'd ever heard her use before. As I watched her pull the door all the way open, I thought I saw a kind of interest develop in her eyes, as if she were watching me watch her. I rather lamely asked her how she was. When I was inside, I asked her, "Mrs. Boket, what happened?"

"I guess you know it," she said, and took a breath and didn't let it out. She hadn't yet asked me to sit down, nor had she sat down.

"Why?" I asked. "*How* did it happen?"

"Why?" she said, frowning at me. She sighed. "You know *why*, boy. These people . . ." she mumbled sadly. "Yellow never did know how to act toward no cop. He stay way away from em, but if one call him, he might jus start runnin — he be runnin an laughin . . . which he did many times before . . . an you know that kinda cop don't you?" She snorted lightly. She looked like she might start to weep. I hadn't pictured it, nor did I want to. It wasn't part of my idea about Yellow, that he might draw a bullet. But I was ever imposing my ideas on the people that I knew and I'd projected a mellow invulnerability on Yellow. Had I ever really known anybody in Meansville? Had I understood anyone in his own terms, or any relationship in the terms of those related? Had I been living in my head all this time? The doubts were assailing me, but I had to answer: yes and no, no and yes. I'd seen and been. I'd been, and seen. Surely Yellow was the one who'd known *me* longest, and I believed in him firmly. I believed in him, and yet I knew he was kind of crazy sometimes. I thought I could imagine him running in headlong fear from a cop. And yes I knew the southern cops. And I didn't know if this made the picture or not; it was one way to understand. He might have just been standing there smiling weirdly, or fast walking backward, or turning in circles to try and jump out of the fears . . . He'd marched with us in CME. Later, against my thief's credo, I'd covered him with what was at hand, sleeping there on the street bench on the corner. And that may have meant nothing to him, but it meant something to me. Yellow had brought me to the Doctor when I'd lost even the idea of trying to find that gentleman again. Knowing him as Feelgood's friend, I'd known Yellow was my brother. Though I knew the cops, I could not have anticipated this cruelty. I could not have warned him even if I'd been free outside. Looking at Mrs. Boket, I understood truly that my having been his friend had not put him in danger. She was regarding me with only her own sorrow. I asked after the Doctor.

"He back in the swamp for a while . . ."

At once I was heartened.

"He gon stay out there, cause he got to do somethin, what can he do? Be in the swamp — he know how to live out there. But he be back . . ."

The news was like a glow that lighted the room. The face of Mrs. Boket was good and easy like the first day I'd met her. The Doctor was needed here around Meansville, and knowing

he'd be back was lifting my mood almost to a high. I was starting to feel good again. I could tell by her expression she had no
doubt. And now an idea came into my head, and it gave me
ease, and I let it grow: soon I would leave this town, I knew it.
By what inner logic I felt it was time, I didn't know. Nor did I
have any idea when or by what means I would go, or where, or
what I'd do with the future. This freedom I couldn't have accepted a few hours ago, because I'd wanted to know everything. I could not even accept the limited freedom of being out
of jail. But this spirit was now mine, and held no fear, it sor-
rowed no longer for my friend whose existence had been broken
in our lives like a golden thread; it did not command and it did
not demand, and it didn't try to tell me anything. I remembered that I was going to ask Mrs. Boket for the loan of her car,
and I said so. She studied that a moment, and said all right, if
I'd bring it back tomorrow morning. I promised her of course I
would do that.

Well I knew I wouldn't make it with her tonight. I could tell
that by looking at her. She was very beautiful. But to her I
was just a kid she liked. And she was ready to go back to sleep.
She got me the key, and I left. I opened all the windows of the
Cadillac and rolled away down the road. The night was soft
and the air was purple and fresh. The sky was lightened by the
stars that had gotten bright. Once the hoot of an owl studied
my trip. I was feeling mellow, and I leaned back in the seat
and drove leisurely with my fingertips. I thought about the
Doctor, out in the swamp, leaving the evil, knowing and forgetting . . . Maybe I *had* made him into a father; if so I was leaving the house. My head was back to the good place it had been
before my release from jail. Perhaps the Doctor would return
before I left, and if so I'd see him, but I wouldn't be waiting.

Why should I say goodbye? I thought, He always wanted you to know that where he's at, you can't follow, you can only go and be there, on your way. I was enjoying the road and drive so much. Now this was some style to return to town after a spell in the jug! Maybe tomorrow I'd drive around awhile, I'd find Case and we'd ride and get high . . .

As I neared the motel I hit the torn-up area whose bright firelights I'd seen from the hill. The damage of the riot seemed to be confined to the black area. I remembered the movement's idea about the self-destructiveness of rioting. My emotions were mixed, because I remembered a time when I hoped for one in Meansville. I'd had hopes it would fling itself over the white boundary, and do some damage where it was deserved. Naturally my dreams had included bombs in the police station and one does not forget his dreams; but I'd changed. I had another relation to this here. I could hear Feelgood saying, "Revenge? Oh revenge been took, don worry. I know of some times. An in the future too . . . That circle till you break it. Let it run, I jump back to before . . ." And so I knew how to love Cousin Yellow in my soul. I didn't drum on the anger, so I didn't loose any fear, and I drove on to the motel. The look of the street got worse as I got nearer, but my pleasure in anticipation rose.

Ahead of me, on the sidewalk, I saw Knight Collins. It didn't surprise me to see him, almost as if it would have surprised me *not* to see him down here in the riot zone. I pulled over next to him, and called his name. He was holding something in his hands. He greeted me without a smile. "You ridin in style, ain't ya," he said, glancing into the car. "I'd ride with ya, but *this*." He held up a jar filled with a viscous substance. "Nitroglycerine," he said. "I jus want some police to mess with me!" He rubbed the jar. His fingers, like his eyes, seemed bitter and grieved. Without another word, he walked away. I didn't move for a while. I watched him walk down the street. I had seen no cops in the neighborhood, thank God. I wanted to follow him till I saw him heading safely home to CME. He turned the corner, and I drove slowly on till I could see him again. He was moving past the Paradise — no, he was entering the Paradise! with his jar of nitro. I waited. Moments later, out he came again, walking faster, with a paper sack from the take-out service. And right behind him came the owner. He was waving his hands with strong emotion. As Knight sauntered off near the curb, he kept emphasizing with his arms and even his shoulders. It must have been a shock to see somebody come in his place with an explosive. At least Knight was moving away from the center of the danger area. When I couldn't see him anymore, I drove around to the motel.

Angel welcomed me with a yawn and a grin. She said Case had told her I was in jail. She got back in bed, and I quickly joined her, and a finer place to be I knew of none. (And the longer you been in jail, the finer she gonna look, once said an inmate.) After a long time away, she kept welcoming me. She laughed, "You been over in the county too long, baby." Angel was an ample hostess and she loved to throw a party. Around the room were glasses and empty bottles and overflowing ashtrays, the evidence of good times had here tonight, but I didn't notice it when I came in. I was lying beside her, relaxed and staring at the ceiling that glowed in a homey way like the sky around the sun on an electric, misty morning. For the first time in weeks I was not looking at the steel ceiling of the jail with its routine punctures. I got up to turn off the light and I searched around to see if there was any undrunk alcohol. I called to

Angel, but she was half-asleep, and I gave it up. The dark glowed slightly from the neon motel sign outside. In the soft good night, I lay beside the woman and enjoyed the curves of her face and breasts with my eyes. I felt like I was looking at her for the first time. I wanted her again before I slept, and she didn't mind. It never seemed to me that she woke, but she smiled like the queen of hearts.

In the morning I slept late, and she went out and came back again before she gently shook me. I opened my eyes. I saw she'd brought coffee and doughnuts for breakfast. "Hey, time to get outa my bed," she laughed.

I loved Angel, I thought, but I wanted a woman all my own, yes; and a bed of my own too, for that matter. I sat on the edge of the bed and we shared the breakfast she'd brought. I told her I thought I was going to leave Meansville this day, and she looked at me quick, let down. I said, I had to travel sooner or later. It felt like the time. "So you puttin us down," she smiled.

"No, uh uh, you ask Suitcase about *his* mind, I'm not puttin nobody down either. It's a rhythm or something. I can't explain it, just like you don't explain yourself to me . . ."

"You ain even got a suitcase! I bet you gonna ask me for a couple dollars for the road! What you gonna do for yourself anyway?" She walked over to the window and opened it, and the slight current of air was nice in the cluttered room. For a time she stood there gazing out it and neither of us spoke. Finally I said, "I don't know, so I don't care."

Somebody's loud laughter on the corner carried through the window. Out there the streets were busted up, but people were walking, talking, and laughing. There were all kinds of times ahead, and I was going toward them. I got up and dressed. I didn't have a thing in my pockets, it was too bad. I would like to start out someplace with something, but I wasn't going to ask her either. But anything can happen when you don't have anything. I hummed a bar of a song I couldn't remember, and went in the bathroom to clean up.

"I remember when I first met you, over there with Jones," she was musing. "Ya'll use to come by the Paradise in his ol truck an not even wash up before you start in drinkin . . . Some woman gonna get you," she called to me in an almost threatening tone.

She didn't have a mirror in the place. It was something I could never quite figure out. I stood in the middle of the room and combed my hair inaccurately. "You're probably right," I said, wondering.

"Sure, an she'll settle you down, you'll get fat!" she threatened.

"Well that's all right," I told her. "I'm skinny as a string bean right now. I wanna get some a that happy fat on me." That set her laughing.

I drifted in and out of things. I wanted to make this a right departure, which was so rare for me. But I felt so good! Even the sadness that I wouldn't see Angel anymore was a kind of mellow thing. I kissed her and started for the door. She went over to the bed, and sighed the littlest sigh, and looked up with a smile. "Don't blow your cool," she smiled.

Driving the Cadillac, I knew I wasn't cool. And things had never been right when I was. I was warmly afloat of light, the streets, the sights, my past, and the absence of the future. I drove past the corner, but I didn't see Case. I didn't stop. There were a whole lot of cops down the way where the white neighborhood began, and I cut off for the river. But immediately I pulled over and parked. I had a thought: I was going to hitch out of here today and I knew I looked pretty ragged. I ought to at least get a haircut, because out on the road, with it all growing down my neck, I'd soon be looking bad and unlucky, and that discourages the people from giving you lifts. I got out of the car and walked the block back to the barbershop of Yellow's friend who still owed me a trim. In the morning, he was doing no business and he acted happy to see me; he gave me a good cut and talked evil of the law all the time. I agreed with him and still didn't fall into the sadness of last night. Before I left, I asked him how the chair was holding up, and he pointed at it and said, hell, it was his best chair. I confided in him I was in a desperate financial condition, and said if he would let me have a five, I'd call it fair and square between us. To my slight surprise, he was glad to let me have it. With a generous grin, he handed me ten! All the way back to the car I was blessing the sweet luck of my impulse to clean up a little for the road. I sped away on the river road.

In front of Mrs. Boket's I thought, well it was fun to drive, from here on it starts to get rough; and then the pleasure of the luck road touched my heart. As I walked toward the house, I was thinking, my goodbye to Mrs. Boket will be my goodbye to this town that I've loved . . . The door was open, and when I called hello, I heard her call from the kitchen. I walked in, and found her standing by her stove with a cheery look on her face. Right away I started to thank her for the use of her car, and tell her that I'd had a good time, I was in a good place — I wanted her to know that. She nodded her head and smiled. "Want some breakfast?"

"Well I've had some," I said, nevertheless sitting down at the table. I told her I was going to leave this town, and the state, and she nodded, like that was interesting and maybe very good.

She didn't ask me where I was going, or anything like that. She was Feelgood's woman, she knew well that it didn't matter. She was taking some loaves of bread out of the oven. "Here have some while it's hot," she said, and I did. I walked the length of the kitchen, I was eager to be on my way. — Where? — I thought of asking her for a ride to the highway, but I was full of energy, I was ready for the walk . . . When I glanced at the table again, I saw some lines on it — fishing lines with hooks. I hadn't seen them. I stared at them for a long moment, like slowly an idea was appearing to me, and then I saw it. "Mrs. Boket, where does the river go?" I heard myself asking her.

"Where? I don really know . . . a long ways . . . to the sea," she was looking at me mildly.

"It must cross some roads, highways, sometime," I mumbled, more to myself. I looked to her. "You think I could sort of borrow one of these lines, Mrs. Boket? I think I'm going to spend some time on the river before anything else. Whose are they?"

"Whose? They all of ours. Sure, take some, we got plenty. You got to have some lines on the river."

I took one, and another for a spare. Well, I was going. We shook hands and she walked me out the kitchen to the green land over which it was a few steps to the river. She said the Doctor would be glad she'd seen me. She said, take care! and smiled, looking away to the distance concealing the river.

I made my way along it a few miles to the spot where we'd often fished. I was going to rest and fish awhile. Then I figured I'd walk along it past Meansville, getting a last look at the town from the point of view of the river. Up above it someplace, I'd stop for the night, and if the fishing hadn't been enough down here, try again. Then I'd cook dinner — I was relishing the day and evening . . . I wished I had my thumb piano that was stored away up North. I thought of Mrs. Boket again, and I'd always wished I had it with me to show her. One of these days, I'd hit a road I liked, and one day I'd be playing it. I had an image of the future, the streams of the piano sounding and blending into unthought space. I guessed I'd stay on the river until I got tired of eating "sunnies," and I hoped it'd be mellow.